SOLUTE UPTAKE BY INTACT PLANTS

Arthur Wallace
Professor of Plant Nutrition
UCLA

Arthur Wallace
2278 Parnell Avenue
Los Angeles 64, California
July 1963

Lithographed in U.S.A. by
EDWARDS BROTHERS, INC.
Ann Arbor, Michigan

PREFACE

The various papers comprising this progress report were prepared over a period of three years. Some of them were in cooperation with different graduate students. This will explain certain style differences found throughout as well as some duplication and differences in thinking. This report is partly a summary of several student dissertations.

Many problems are raised in the various discussions of this report. Several peculiar observations are described. It is very unlikely that this report contains final answers to any of the urgent problems in plant nutrition. Studies are being continued here in some of the areas discussed.

Some of the research was supported by the United States Atomic Energy Commission (Contract AT(11-1)-34, Project 51). The paper on page 147 particularly was part of that project. Other of the studies are being supported by a grant from the National Science Foundation. The progress reports on pages 62 and 106 are part of this project.

A summary has been provided for most of the articles. These are on pages 18, 26, 29, 32, 38, 41, 59, 61, 74, 82, 86, 89, 92, 97, 101, 104, 106, 118, 123, 127, 129, 131, 133, 135, 138, 142, 146, 155, 158.

CONTENTS

CONTENTS

INTRODUCTION

The purpose of this report is to summarize results obtained in this laboratory and some views on some aspects of the very complicated subject of solute uptake and translocation by intact plants. The information is not all new and much of it confirms and illustrates known principles. The report is not intended as a comprehensive review of any part of the broad subject. Major reasons for not preparing such a monograph are that such is beyond our competence, the subject is very complex, and much confusion exists on the subject. The author was impressed by a statement of Dainty (1962) in his recent review where he stated that he did not understand much of the written material on solute uptake and transport by intact plants. The same applies to the author. Much of the large amount of literature currently evolving concerning transport in cells is also equally difficult to understand.

The terminology of this subject is likewise complicated. The following quotations from recent monographs on the subject illustrate the terminology problem. The first is from Mineral Salts Absorption in Plants, J. F. Sutcliffe, Pergamon Press, 1962, page 27.

"Uptake, intake and absorption are used synonymously, and do not imply any particular method of entry of salts. When these expressions are used, net movement is implied unless otherwise indicated in the text. Gross uptake is sometimes referred to as influx and the difference between gross and net uptake as efflux (syn. outflux). Efflux, like influx, may occur by purely physical processes such as diffusion and exchange, or depend upon metabolism (active transport). In the former case, it is called leakage and in the latter, excretion or extrusion. Active transport into vacuoles, or into the cavities of non-living cells in the stele of roots, is sometimes called secretion by analogy with similar processes in animals.

"Accumulation implies movement of ions against a concentration gradient generally as a result of active transport. It can also occur passively, e. g., by the establishment of Donnan equilibria or by adsorption. When ions are absorbed and at once incorporated irreversibly into organic constituents of a cell, an element may be accumulating in the organism, but the process is not referred to as salt accumulation. "

The second quotation is from Electrolytes and Plant Cells, G. E. Briggs, A. B. Hope and R. N. Robertson, Botanical Monographs, edited by W. O. James, Vol. 1, pages 130-131, 1961.

"We propose to define accumulation as follows: briefly, accumulation is the process whereby substances are moved into a cell or system through the metabolic activity of that system. We exclude instances where the concentration of an ion is greater inside than out in consequence of an exchange with ions of like charge which are acting as counterions to a restrained ion, even if this is a product of metabolic activity, but include the situation where the inside concentration of the diffusible ion exceeds that calculated on the Donnan equilibrium, even if the concentration may be lower on the inside than on the outside. This definition also includes the passage into a vacuole during the time when the internal concentration is less than the external concentration, provided that as a consequence of metabolic activity the rate of passage is higher than it would be during passive diffusion. We also use the term accumulation for both ions in the situation where ions of one charge are moved (for instance into a vacuole) against an electrochemical potential gradient and are followed by ions of opposite charge moving along the electrochemical potential gradient.

1

"Active transport - a widely used term - was defined by Ussing (1949, 1957) as the process whereby an ion is moved against the electrochemical potential gradient and is therefore dependent on decrease in free energy in some metabolic process."

The terminology used by us in the present report itself must be a little peculiar. In all studies attempts were made to either remove the solutes under study from the free space - both from water-free space and from the Donnan-free space - or else to minimize their presence in the free space. According to both of the above definitions then we may not be dealing with "accumulated" solutes. Since metabolism may not be involved in uptake of some of the materials under study, the term, accumulation, may not be correct. The correct terminology may be "uptake or absorption less the free space constituents in roots". In specific experiments described in the pages that follow the terms accumulation, uptake, or absorption, may not all be precise. It should be born in mind, however, that free-space components were removed from roots in the present studies before roots were assayed.

An enormous amount of work has been done on ion transport in animal cells such as erythrocytes, muscle cells, and nerve cells. Much less has been done with plant cells and these are much more complicated than animal cells. Animal cells have an external membrane but plant cells supposedly have two membranes in addition to a cell wall. The compartmentalization which results is exceedingly complex. Much more, moreover, is known about solute uptake and transport in single plant cells, in excised roots of plants, or in tissues of storage organs from plants than for whole plants. The problems are much more complex for the whole plant. Some noble efforts, however, have been made to solve these problems for whole plants but the whole has been hindered because of insufficient knowledge of the parts.

Those concerned with the mineral nutrition of plants must also reckon with the complexities of the soil environment. Even though experimental material can be separated from soil, the problems imposed by soil must eventually be encountered, if not solved.

In recent years several reviews, monographs, and other important writings have appeared on this general subject for animal and/or plant materials. Some of these with an indication of their subject matter are listed.

Arisz, W. H. (1956) Protoplasma 46:5-62. --- Role of a symplasm in salt transport.

Bange, G. G. J. (1962) Acta Bot. Neer. 11:139-146. --- Competition by different metal carriers for an enzymatic metal carrier breakdown reaction. If true, this greatly revises concepts of ion transport.

Briggs, G. E. , Hope, A. B. , and Robertson, R. N. (1961) Electrolytes and Plant Cells, Botanical Monographs, edited by W. O. James, Inorganic plant nutrition. Absorption of electrolytes by plant cells.

Brouwer, R. (1954) Acta Bot. Neer. 3:264-312. --- Transpiration and salt uptake.

Dainty, J. (1962) Ann. Rev. Plant Physiol. 13:379-402. --- Electrical potentials and ion transport.

Epstein, E. (1956a) Ann. Rev. Plant Physiol. 7:1-24. --- Carriers and free space in salt uptake and transport.

Fried, M. and Shapiro, R. E. (1961) Ann. Rev. Plant Physiol. 12:91-112. --- Accumulation in root vs. accumulation in shoot.

Harris, E. J. (1960) Transport and Accumulation in Biological Systems. Academic Press, New York, New York. --- Described by title.

Kleinzeller, A. and Kotyk, A. E. (1960) <u>Membrane Transport and Metabo-</u><u>lism.</u> Academic Press, London and New York. --- Reports from the 1960 Prague symposium of the subject.

Laties, G. G. (1959) Ann. Rev. Plant Physiol. 10:87-112. --- Relation-ship of respiration rather than cation exchange to salt accumulation.

Lundegardh, H. (1955) Ann. Rev. Plant Physiol. 6:1-24. --- Mechanisms of absorption, transport, accumulation, and secretion of ions.

Overstreet, R. and Jacobson, L. (1952) Ann. Rev. Plant Physiol. 3:189-206. --- Models for ion absorption by roots.

Russell, R. S. and Barber, D. A. (1960) Ann. Rev. Plant Physiol. 11:127-140. --- Effect of transpiration on salt uptake.

Steward, F. C. and Sutcliffe, J. F. (1959) Plants in relation to inorganic salts. In: <u>Plant Physiology II. Plants in Relation to Water and</u> <u>Solutes.</u> Ed. by F. C. Steward, Academic Press, New York. --- Salt relations in intact plants.

Sutcliffe, J. F. (1959) Biol. Rev. 34:159-220. --- Salt uptake in plants.

Sutcliffe, J. F. (1962) <u>Mineral Salts Absorption in Plants,</u> Pergamon Press. --- A review of the subject with the author's ideas on salt uptake vs. protein synthesis.

Wilbrandt, W. and Rosenberg, T. (1961) Pharmacol. Rev. 13:109-183. --- The concepts of carrier transport.

There are many important questions concerning solute uptake and trans-port in intact plants for which unambiguous answers would be welcome. Some of these questions relate to single cells as well as to intact plants. Following is a brief listing of some of these questions:

(a) Do electrochemical gradients explain ion movements in whole plants as they may do for individual cells (Dainty, 1962)?

(b) Are there separate mechanisms for accumulation of solutes in roots and for accumulation that leads to transport to shoots (Fried and Shapiro, 1961; Briggs, Hope, and Robertson, 1961, pp. 194-195)?

(c) Is there a continuous free space from the cell walls of roots to the leaves of plants? Bernstein and Gardner (1961) say no. Likewise, are there con-tinuous protoplasmic connections or symplasm (Arisz, 1956) from root surfaces to leaves?

(d) Is the phenomenon of pinocytosis of importance in uptake of materials by plants? Pinocytosis is defined by Wilbrandt and Rosenberg (1961) as up-take of external solution (with or without suspended material) by vesicles formed at the cell surface.

(e) How can the transpiration stream influence the active transport of salts if water movement is passive in nature? If the answer seems so obvious, why do so many investigators quarrel about it? (Bernstein and Nieman, 1960, have proposed one mechanism.)

(f) Why are cation relationships in plants from an agronomic point of view somewhat different from those elucidated by plant physiologists at the cellular and tissue level? Is the root cation exchange capacity which bears no direct relationship to metabolic processes in roots a regulator of either the Ca-K ratios in plants or of the total cation content of plants? (Drake, Vengri, and Colby, 1951; Crooke and Knight, 1962.)

(g) What are the reasons how some plant species or varieties within species are more susceptible to mineral element deficiencies or to toxicities than other varieties or species? (Brown, 1962; Wallace et al. , 1952; Wallace, 1962, pp. 28,36.)

(h) Can the stem exudate be used as a criterion of mineral element availa-bility to plants? (Bollard, 1960.) In this connection, how does it happen that substances that can be transported to leaves cannot be transported in the stem exudate? (Wallace, Sufi, Jeffreys, 1962.)

(i) Can the salts that are accumulated in the vacuoles of roots be mobilized for transport to shoots?

(j) Is there a circulation system for salts in higher plants? (Biddulph, 1959; Biddulph and Biddulph, 1959.)

(k) How are plants able to obtain metals from extremely insoluble minerals in soils? (Jenny and Grossenbacher, 1962; Chaberek and Martell, 1959; Jamison, 1942; Peech, 1941; Smith, Rasmussen, and Hrnciar, 1962; Wallace, 1962a, p. 14.)

(l) How are plants able to take specific ions from balanced nutrient solutions when the ability of other ions to bind or chelate with carriers is much greater; i.e., what is the nature of selectivity?

(m) If some ions, viz., Ca perhaps, are passively moved into plants, how can such ions antagonize the uptake of other ions which are metabolically taken up?

(n) Why do some of the metabolic inhibitors decrease the uptake of ions which are supposed to be non-metabolically accumulated?

(o) How do some metabolic inhibitors increase transport of some ions to shoots and at the same time decrease uptake by roots? (Arisz, 1956; Briggs et al., 1961; Pearson, 1962; Bhan et al., 1960.)

(p) If electrical potential gradients are of great importance in the accumulation of cations (Dainty, 1962), should the work be ignored of Breazeale et al. (1951, 1953) who reported that specific voltages greatly increased the uptake of specific cations by plants?

(q) How does ringing (girdling) of woody plants suppress solute transport which supposedly occurs in the xylem (Wallace and Mueller, 1958)?

(r) Are mineral elements that are transported to the shoots of plants taken up (accumulated) at specific zones in the roots and do these zones have a peculiar metabolism (parenchymatic vs. meristematic)? (Wiebe and Kramer, 1954; Sutcliffe, 1962, p. 111.)

(s) Do decorticated roots provide a means of learning of transport of ions from roots to shoots? (Branton and Jacobson, 1962.)

The classical approach to studies of solute uptake by cells has been considerably modified in recent years. Since much of the information reported in this book relates to the classical approach but adapted to whole plants, a brief discussion of the new approach in relationship to the old is in order.

The following is summarized from the recent review of Dainty (1962). He has pointed out, as has been done by many animal physiologists, that ions move under the influence of electrochemical potential gradients and that concentration gradients alone do not drive the movements of ions like they do with non-electrolytes. The electrochemical potential is the criterion according to whether an ion is actively or passively transported. The existence of an ion at a higher concentration inside a cell than outside is not evidence of active transport of that ion. Only the existence of that ion at a higher electrochemical potential inside the cell than out proves that work might have been done on that ion.

In some cells, particularly some animal cells, it appears that sodium ions constantly move into the cells "down" their electrochemical potential gradient and are pumped out of the cell "up" the electrochemical potential gradient by some unknown active transport mechanism. This outward sodium pump appears to be coupled to an inwardly directed potassium pump.

Plant cells have complex structures. The potential difference between the vacuole of a plant cell and the external solution bathing the cell can be expected to be the algebraic sum of the potentials across the tonoplast and plasmalemma, also perhaps one across the cell wall and sometimes across an unstirred layer of external solution near the cell wall. The potential difference can be measured with microelectrodes. The electropotential difference between the vacuole and external medium of some Nitellopsis cells was measured at about -120 mv. Calculations were made for equilibrium potentials from the internal and external concentrations (inside vacuoles; Na 54 mM, K 113 mM, and Cl 206 mM, outside; Na 30 mM, K 0.65 mM, and Cl 35 mM). For Na it was -15 mv, for K it was -130 mv, and for Cl it was +45 mv. K, therefore, was almost in electrochemical equilibrium and would be expected to move passively. The calculated potentials, when compared with the existing potential, indicated that the influx of Na should be greater than the efflux and that the efflux of Cl should be much greater than the influx. Since this did not occur, Na efflux and Cl influx must be due to operation of forces other than of the electrochemical potential gradient. A reasonable hypothesis, Dainty says, is an outwardly directed Na pump and an inwardly directed Cl pump. This, he says, is excellent evidence of active transport. Since the concentrations of K and Na in the cytoplasm were similar to those in the vacuole, it was concluded that the Na pump was located at the plasmalemma. The site of potential drop also indicates plasmalemma. It is believed that the inwardly directed Cl pump is at the tonoplast —partly because of the accumulation of organic acids in vacuoles of cells of higher plants. The outwardly directed Na pump may or may not be connected with an inwardly directed K pump.

In conventional studies of salt uptake in which salts are accumulated against concentration gradients, there is no indication of which ion of the pair is actively pumped. No studies of ion competition or of uptake vs. time, or of temperature, or of metabolic inhibitors, can give an unambiguous answer to the question as to which ion is pumped.

In some studies at Washington State University (Etherton, 1961; Etherton and Higginbotham, 1960) the approach described above by Dainty (as interpreted by the author) has been applied to cells of higher plants with the same general conclusions. This group found an effect of concentration on the functioning of a K-Na pump. The interaction was roughly as follows:

(1) At high external concentration, K and Na were both extruded;
(2) At medium external concentrations, Na was extruded and K was in electrochemical equilibrium;
(3) At low external concentration, Na approached electrochemical equilibrium and K was actively accumulated.

Dainty, therefore, concludes that measurements of electropotential differences for each ion are necessary in any investigation of ion uptake and that an inwardly directed anion pump at the tonoplast is of primary importance in the physiology of plant cells.

CATION AND ANION INTERRELATIONSHIPS IN PLANTS

Even though plant physiologists have proposed that considerably different mechanisms obtain for uptake by plants of K, Ca, Mg, or Na, the concentrations of each in plants often appears to be very much related to the concentration of the others (Van Itallie, 1938; Hoagland, 1944; Bear and Prince, 1945; Wallace, Toth, and Bear, 1948a, 1949). In many but not all plant species and under certain conditions the me. sum of the cations per unit of dry weight appears to be constant. This implies that a decrease in the concentration of one is equivalently compensated for by an equivalent increase in another. This is illustrated in figure 1, particularly for alfalfa. The increases or decreases which do occur in the total cation contents of plants may be because of decreased availability of one where the uptake of another is increased. Hoagland (1944) reported that the decrease in uptake of one cation was not always compensated for by an increase in another.

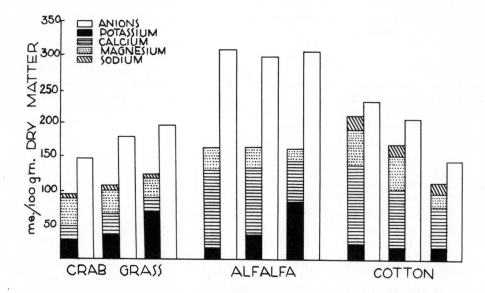

Figure 1.   Cation and anion me. sum of 3 plant species grown under different levels of cations.

In figure 1 the total concentration of cations with crab grass increased with increasing K and with cotton it increased with increasing Ca and Mg. This implies that cation constancy is not a general phenomenon and it has been possible to vary the total cation content of alfalfa by increasing the total cations supplied in nutrient solution (Wallace, 1952).

The anion sum of the plants in figure 1 was either constant or it varied as did the cation sum. The anions measured were N, P, and S only and the total content of each was calculated as NO_3^-, $H_2PO_4^-$, or $SO_4^=$ to correspond with the forms most likely taken up by plants. The results in figure 1, therefore, imply that at least in some species a decrease in one of NO_3^-, $H_2PO_4^-$, or $SO_4^=$ or an excess of one may influence the concentration of each of the others in the plant. Moreover, it would be expected that such things as Cl^- and HCO_3^- would have the same effect. To a limited extent this type of observation has been made. Figure 1, of course, implies that it may not be observed for some plant species. The results obtained when varying the K and Ca supply with alfalfa (Wallace and Bear, 1949) which caused a variation in most every other inorganic nutrient in the plant is at least partially explained by figure 1. Shear et al. (1946, 1948) reported somewhat similar results. Some aspects of these data may mean the following:

(a) A high total cation content of a plant is associated with a high N and probably high protein and P contents. Conversely, a low N or low protein content is associated with low mineral nutrient content of plants.

(b) N, if absorbed as the cationic form, may induce low absorption of K, Ca, and Mg depending somewhat on pH. Similtaneously, if little NO_3^--N is present, absorption of P, S, and Cl will be increased.

(c) Induced cation and anion deficiencies are possible from cation and anion competition. For example, Mg deficiency can be induced from the application of large amounts of K and, likewise, P deficiency should be possible from an excess of NO_3^- or other soluble anions.

(d) Unessential ions, such as Na^+, and an excess of Cl^- may often contribute a large share of the total cation and anion contents of plants and may be involved in ionic competitive effects. Some of the relationships that have been discussed are of special importance in connection with the seasonal variation in the mineral content of alfalfa (Wallace et al. , 1949).

A relatively large number of relationships have been reported among the plant nutrients (Beeson, 1946). Examples of these are — (a) N fertilizers increased, or did not influence, or decreased P concentrations in plants, (b) K fertilizers decreased or did not change P concentrations in plants, (c) Mg fertilizers increased or did not change P concentrations, (d) NaCl applied to K-deficient plants resulted in higher P concentrations, (e) N fertilizers reduced the Ca concentrations of plants, and NH_4-N was very effective in this respect, (f) K fertilizers generally reduced Ca concentrations, and (g) Mg applications often decreased Ca concentrations. These factors are, of course, complicated by soil reactions and environmental conditions.

Many of these interactions can be explained by the overall cation-anion relationships referred to above. This is very evident when NO_3^- is replaced by NH_4^+ as a nitrogen source. With no competition from NO_3^-, the amounts of $H_2PO_4^-$, $SO_4^=$, Cl^-, and other anions are increased in plants. Simultaneously, there is competition of NH_4^+ with K, Ca, and Mg. Some physiological problems that arise from these observations relate to the differences in the biochemical types of inhibition of NH_4^+ on K vs. Ca on K, or vs. that for NO_3^- on $H_2PO_4^-$. The results are not easily explained by known biochemistry at the cellular level and true competition may not always be involved. For example, a certain amount of Ca is essential to the mechanism for K accumulation (Viets, 1944) and for the selectivity of K accumulation relative to Na (Epstein, 1961) while other levels of Ca inhibit K uptake.

Indeed there are many responses in plant nutrition that at least on the surface do not correspond with findings of cellular physiologists. Another of these relates to the influence of root cation-exchange capacity (CEC) on the Ca-K ratio in the plant. Figure 2 illustrates how a plant with a low root CEC (crab grass) can absorb much more K than can alfalfa from a soil low in available K and thrive, while in the same soil alfalfa dies of potassium deficiency. Those species that tend to take up large amounts of Ca tend to accumulate smaller amounts of K while those that tend to take up small amounts of Ca easily obtain sufficient K.

This phenomenon seems to be explainable on the basis of Donnan distribution differences caused by differences in root CEC (Smith and Wallace, 1956a). This is in spite of the observations of cellular physiologists that root CEC has nothing to do with ion accumulation mechanisms (Laties, 1959).

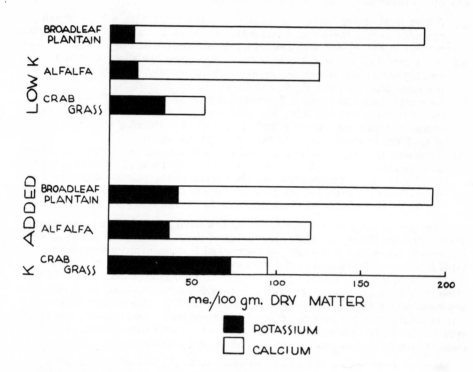

Figure 2.   K and Ca contents of 3 plant species when grown in a soil low in K and also in the same soil with K added to the soil.   The crab grass was not deficient in the low K soil, but alfalfa had deficiency symptoms.

The following discussion from Huffaker et al. (1958) and Wallace (1960) summarizes the work of this laboratory on root CEC to that time:

The Donnan relation has been expressed as follows (Mattson, 1948), where X is the activity of an ion in the outside solution, Y is its activity in an inside solution, and Z is the concentration of the ion in combination with a non-diffusible anion.

At equilibrium with KCl:

$$X_{Cl} \cdot X_K = Y_{Cl} \ (Y_K + Z_K) \text{ or}$$

$$\frac{X_{Cl}}{Y_{Cl}} = \frac{Y_K + Z_K}{X_K}$$

At equilibrium with $CaCl_2$:

$$X^2_{Cl} \cdot X_{Ca} = Y^2_{Cl} \ (Y_{Ca} + Z_{Ca}) \text{ or}$$

$$\frac{X_{Cl}}{Y_{Cl}} = \left(\frac{Y_{Ca} + Z_{Ca}}{X_{Ca}}\right)^{\frac{1}{2}}$$

Combining

$$\frac{Y_K + Z_K}{X_K} = \left(\frac{Y_{Ca} + Z_{Ca}}{X_{Ca}}\right)^{\frac{1}{2}} \qquad (1).$$

If two separate systems indicated by subscripts 1 and 2 and in which the Z terms differ have the same amounts of cations in the outside solutions at any given time (X_K and X_{Ca} the same in each system), then the following relationship obtained by dividing equal quantities by equal quantities will hold:

$$\frac{Y_{K_1} + Z_{K_1}}{Y_{K_2} + Z_{K_2}} = \left| \frac{Y_{Ca_1} + Z_{Ca_1}}{Y_{Ca_2} + Z_{Ca_2}} \right|^{\frac{1}{2}}$$

This equation is valid only if the outside solutions have constant activities. The Y values of this equation can be used, by making two assumptions, to compare the respective K and Ca contents of two different plants represented by subscripts 1 and 2 and having different root CEC and grown in nutrient substrates of constant activities. The first assumption is that the Z term is equivalent to the root CEC. The other is that the CEC is assumed to be very small in relation to the amount of K or Ca accumulated in a plant over a period of time so that the Z terms cancel out. Under these conditions an equation for plants reduces to the following where k and k' are constants which appear to be unity (the CEC term comes from definition of the conditions):

$$\frac{CEC_1}{CEC_2} = k\left(\frac{K_1}{K_2}\right) = k'\left(\frac{Ca_1}{Ca_2}\right)^{\frac{1}{2}} \qquad (2).$$

The works of Mattson (1948), Elgabaly and Wiklander (1949), and Lundegardh (1951) have established that plants with high CEC of roots favor adsorption of divalent cations relative to monovalent cations, while those with low CEC favor adsorption of monovalent cations relative to divalent cations. Qualitatively this means that Ca_1/Ca_2 and K_2/K_1 are functions of CEC_1/CEC_2. For K this does not correspond with equation (2). It is apparent that the K form in equation (2) will hold for single salt solutions, but when both monovalent and divalent cations are in the same nutrient solutions or soils the ideas of Mattson and others should hold. Under such conditions, if a quantitative relationship exists, the generalized equation becomes as follows (k and k' are constants which at least sometimes are equal to unity):

$$\frac{CEC_1}{CEC_2} = k\left(\frac{K_2}{K_1}\right) = k'\left(\frac{Ca_1 + Mg_1}{Ca_2 + Mg_2}\right)^{\frac{1}{2}} \qquad (3).$$

Since McLean (1957) and Dunham et al. (1956) have reported a large number of plant analyses together with root CEC, some of their data were calculated for comparison with equations (2) and (3) (table 1). Ca + Mg was used because both are the macrodivalent cations absorbed by plants. The data from Dunham et al. are means of 4 sets of plants from each of 6 different nutrient solutions. For all those values except one (there may have been an error in the determination of CEC), there was very close correspondence between CEC_1/CEC_2 and $(Ca_1 + Mg_1/Ca_2 + Mg_2)^{\frac{1}{2}}$. In the majority of cases the ratio of CEC was closely related to K_2/K_1, although there were cases where the relation was K_1/K_2. In general these values do indicate that equation (3) is a possible quantitative form. Objections to it will be discussed on page 127.

The K, Ca, and Mg contents of different plant species grown under similar conditions could be related in a majority of cases by $CEC_1/CEC_2 = K_2/K_1 = (Ca_1 + Mg_1/Ca_2 + Mg_2)^{\frac{1}{2}}$, where the subscripts 1 and 2 represent different species. Data on root CEC and plant contents of K, Ca, and Mg obtained from a large number of citrus, corn, and soybeans grown in soil gave correlation coefficients as follows (Huffaker and Wallace, 1958):

$$CEC_1/CEC_2 \times K_2/K_1 = +0.88^{**},$$

$$CEC_1/CEC_2 \times (Ca_1 + Mg_1/Ca_2 + Mg_2)^{\frac{1}{2}} = +0.64^{*},$$

and

$$K_2/K_1 \times (Ca_1 + Mg_1/Ca_2 + Mg_2)^{\frac{1}{2}} = +0.75^{**}$$

Even though the correlations were significant, the relations appeared to be far from simple and in some cases did not hold. For example, plants grown in sand corresponded less in the divalent ratios because of high Mg contents in corn. In some cases CEC ratios corresponded well with K_1/K_2 rather than with K_2/K_1.

Table 1. Ratios calculated from data found in the literature.

Species	Source of data	$\dfrac{CEC_1}{CEC_2}$	$\dfrac{K_1}{K_2}$	$\dfrac{K_2}{K_1}$	$\left(\dfrac{Ca_1 + Mg_1}{Ca_2 + Mg_1}\right)^{\frac{1}{2}}$
Corn/snapdragon	*	0.73	1.45	0.69	0.71
Chrysanthemum/corn	*	1.48	0.97	1.03	1.30
Stocks/corn	*	1.53	0.89	1.13	1.63
Larkspur/snapdragon	*	2.09(?)	1.45	0.69	0.83
Corn (high N/low N)	**	1.27	0.74	1.34	1.20
Soybean (high N/low N)	**	1.11	1.18	0.85	1.12

* Dunham et al., 1956
** McLean, 1957

These effects can explain several observations in plant nutrition as follows (Wallace, 1960):

(a) Competition exists among mixed plantings like legume and grass mixtures (Gray et al., 1953). Alfalfa with a high root CEC competes poorly for K with grasses and weeds that have a low root CEC.

(b) Rootstock influences on mineral composition of foliage in trees (Wallace,

Naude, Mueller, and Zidan, 1952). For example, rough lemon rootstock in citrus has a higher root CEC than does grapefruit. For a given scion the leaves and fruits on rough lemon rootstock have less K and more Mg than those on grapefruit rootstock. This has been found to be of practical importance.

(c) Nitrogen has many effects on cation contents of plants (Wallace, Kimball, Mueller, and Welch, 1952) and also on root CEC. There is now some evidence that both could be in part related. When plants are deficient in N, increasing the N level increases the root CEC (McLean et al., 1956). At high N levels there may be decreases in root CEC (Huffaker and Wallace, 1959c). Ammonium N decreased root CEC relative to nitrate. Increasing N levels have been shown to be generally associated with more Ca and less K in plants, but not always (Wallace, Kimball, Mueller, and Welch, 1952). Ammonium N results in greater depression in Ca and Mg contents in plants than for K, as would be expected for a low root CEC. Factors that increase organic acids in roots (Clark, 1936; Iljin, 1951; Jacobson and Ordin, 1954) appear to also increase root CEC.

(d) Root CEC influences susceptibility of certain crops to nutrient deficiencies. This is the type of thing involved in (a) and (b). An example of the effect is that plants with a high root CEC cannot grow well in soils low in available potassium (Gray et al., 1953).

The root CEC within plant species has been changed by nutritional variables (Huffaker and Wallace, 1959).

The mineral analyses of 34 different plant species were reported by Parker and Truog (1920) in an attempt to show that a relationship exists between the Ca and N contents of the plants. When calculated on the equivalent basis, the sum of the three cations was more closely related to the N content than was the Ca alone in all but 8 of the 34 samples reported (Wallace et al., 1949).

In recent years there has been considerable interest concerning the cation relationships in plants, but the interrelationships of the different anions among themselves and in relation to cations have generally been neglected. Relationships do exist between total cations and total anions in plants (Wallace et al., 1949). The data in table 2 which are from the same report indicate that there was no significant Ca-N relationship among the alfalfa plants studied. Significant negative correlations have also been reported between Ca and N.

An influence of N on the Ca-K ratio in many crop plants has been reported (Beeson, 1946; Olson, 1950; Wallace, 1952). Correlations calculated from data of Parker and Truog (1920) gave coefficients of +0.882 for Ca x N, +0.182 for K x N, +0.585 for Mg x N, and +0.844 for Ca + K + Mg (me.) x N. Only K x N was not significant. Ca was as much related to N as was the sum of all three cations. An inverse relationship between Ca and N taken up after fertilization of either is more common than a positive relationship (Beeson, 1946). In a more recent study both positive and negative influences of N on the Ca-K ratio were evident (Welch et al., 1954). The effect certainly can be different depending upon whether or not NO_3^- or NH_4^+ was the major source of N available to the roots. Much of the effect obtained can very likely be related to the influence of N in the particular situation on the root CEC which could be either increased or decreased (Huffaker and Wallace, 1959c). Wallace et al. (1952) reported that high nitrogen fertilization of orange trees decreased K and increased Ca concentration in the orange leaves which would fit with an increase in root CEC. The total cation concentration of a plant can be a function of the total cation concentration of a nutrient medium (Wallace, 1952).

The correlation coefficient of the sum of the exchangeable bases in the surface 6 inches of soil on which 31 field-grown alfalfa samples were obtained and the cation me. sum of the alfalfa from these soils was +0.64 and highly significant (Wallace, 1949). This means that there was a tendency for saturated soils having a high CEC to produce alfalfa with a high cation content. This phenomenon is similar to that observed for the alfalfa grown in the sand cultures with the different total nutrient concentrations.

Table 2.   Approximate rank correlation coefficients of cation and anion contents of alfalfa grown in Egypt.

Factors Correlated	r'	r' ÷ standard error*
Cation x Anion	0.84	2.62
Cation x N	0.77	2.31
Anion x K	0.78	2.34
N x K	0.77	2.31
Anion x Ca	-0.39	-1.17
Cation x K	0.41	1.23
Cation x Ca	-0.23	-0.69
Anion x N	0.94	2.84
Mg x P	0.70	2.10
Cation x P	0.52	1.56
Anion x P	0.48	1.44
Ca x N	-0.36	-1.08
N x P	0.72	2.16

*Any value above two considered significant.

There was a positive and significant correlation (r = +0.60) between the cation and the anion me. sums of these particular field-grown samples, even though the ratio of the measured cations to the measured anions varied from 0.38 to 0.73. It is generally believed that a low pH of the nutrient medium favors anion absorption (N, P, S), and that a high pH favors cation absorption (K, Ca, Mg, Na). This appeared to be a factor influencing the relative proportion of cations to anions both in sand and in the soil. The correlation coefficient of the pH of the surface 6 inches of soil and of the ratio of measured cations to measured anions of the 31 alfalfa samples was significant, but was only +0.44. The soil pH values ranged from 5.2 to 7.8.

The Ca-K ratio has been given much attention in plant nutrition. Some investigators consider the amounts of the individual elements of much greater importance than the ratio of the elements (Goodall and Gregory, 1947). Correlation coefficients were calculated for the relative proportion of each of the individual exchangeable soil cations and for the same cations within the plant for the 31 field-grown samples (Wallace, 1949). Soil K and soil Ca were correlated significantly with plant K and plant Ca respectively (r = +0.66 and +0.61), but soil Mg and plant Mg were not (r = +0.08). Application of soluble Mg did, however, increase considerably the Mg content of the alfalfa (Wallace, 1949). Soil K correlated negatively with plant Ca (r = -0.87) and was the highest coefficient obtained. Soil Ca correlated negatively with plant K (r = -0.52). The Ca-K ratio in the soil influenced the plant K (r = -0.80) and the plant Ca (r = +0.79) more than did the absolute value of either element on its own concentration within the plant. This means that a soil having a relatively low content of exchangeable K often resulted in alfalfa having a relatively high K content, provided the content of exchangeable Ca was very low. Similarly a high level of exchangeable K in the soil occasionally resulted in a low K content of the alfalfa because the Ca level was also high.

The Mg-P relationship has been looked at in this laboratory to a limited extent (Wallace and Ashcroft, 1956a). The technique was sand culture with the cations and anions supplied with ion-exchange resins. In studies of rough lemon, avocado, barley, and bush beans, little evidence was found to indicate that increasing Mg level resulted in increased content of P in plants, although this was indicated in some crops having a low Mg requirement, but only at a high P level.

In more elaborate studies with ion-exchange resins the problem of inter-action of high and low cation levels factorially with high and low anion levels was investigated (Welch et al. , 1954). The interaction of different levels of adsorbed cations and adsorbed NO_3^--N was studied in a pot experiment. A factorial design of three levels of cations and three of N was used. Ca, Mg, and K were supplied at the same ratio at all three levels and P and S were unvaried. Three successive plantings were made which were lemon cuttings, oats, and oats and radishes together. These two species were seeded together because their roots have different CEC. The adsorbed ions proved to be an excellent source of nutrients for the plants. A balance sheet was prepared for all nutrients removed by the crops. Yields were limited in the second and third crops by both N and cation levels. K proved to be the limiting cation. Ca and Mg absorption was depressed as the cation level was increased because of increased K uptake. The me. of cations per 100 grams dry plant weight increased with increasing cation levels for two oat crops, but was more con-stant for the lemon and the radish crop. Increasing N levels resulted in in-creased N and in an increased total anion uptake, but resulted in depressed P and S uptake. The level of adsorbed N did not appear to influence the total cation content in lemon and radish, but there was a slight effect on oats, par-ticularly in the first crop. The level of cations did not appear to influence the N or the me. sum of anions in the plants beyond the differences caused by yield variations. The cation-anion ratios in the plants were much narrower than those in the nutrient medium. Increases in N tended to result in increased K and Mg contents in the lemon cuttings and in oats when the supply of cations was high. When the cation level was low for oats and at all levels for radishes, increases in N tended to result in decreased K. The latter effect was partly related to K depletion at the low cation levels combined with yield increases due to N.

The conclusion can perhaps be made that there was less effect of cations on anions and vice versa in these studies with exchange resins than when the effects have been studied with salts.

An interesting K-N relationship was observed for field-grown alfalfa where the available K varied considerably (Wallace, 1951). Increasing K appeared to result in a decrease in the N concentration and hence, in the protein of the hay. Some of the salient data are reproduced in table 3.

The source of the Cl was the K fertilizer and Cl tended to compete slightly with the N. A correction can be made in the N percentage to account for Cl competition.

Leaves are high in nitrogen. The low K plants being small had a higher leaf percentage than did the high K plants. This meant that low K plants drew a much larger percentage of the N from the roots than did high K plants. A correction can be made for nitrogen in the hay for unequal distribution between roots and tops. If one considers that variation in cation sum for the four K levels represents the differences in carbohydrate dilution of minerals by the plants of different K status, a correction can be made for this factor. Table 4 summarizes the various corrections on N concentration that can be made in the data and the conclusion is that the factors mentioned do appear to account for the differences in N in the alfalfa.

Table 3. Influence of K fertilizer levels on alfalfa yield and composition.

| Parameter | lbs. K_2O per acre per year in fertilizer | | | |
	0	60	120	180
Yield hay, lb/acre	4930	7080	7890	8570
% of dry matter				
K in hay	.50	.76	1.11	1.41
N in hay	3.18	3.01	2.85	2.74
Cl in hay	.07	.21	.32	.50
N in roots	1.67	1.79	2.10	2.49
Cation sum of hay*, me./100 gm.	140	130	129	125
Leaf to leaf + stem**, %	58.1	52.0	48.7	45.6
Proportion of total anion milliequivalents*				
N (%)	85.8	83.6	82.2	79.8
Cl (%)	0.8	2.6	4.1	6.4
N + Cl (%)	86.6	86.2	86.3	86.2

*The cations usually absorbed by plants are potassium (K), calcium (Ca), magnesium (Mg), and sodium (Na). The anions commonly absorbed by plants are nitrate (NO_3), phosphate (H_2PO_4), sulfate (SO_4), and chloride (Cl). The use of chemical equivalents makes possible the evaluation of these elements on a uniform basis according to their combining powers. The sum of both cations and anions in alfalfa is usually constant as is the ratio between them. Ordinarily the cation and anion values are reported as milliequivalents (me.) per 100 grams of dry material.
**Leaf percentage.

In studies of the seasonal composition of orange leaves it was observed that leaves produced in different seasons of the year contained, as long as they remained on the tree, different but characteristic concentrations of K, Ca, and Mg (Cameron et al., 1952). Studies of varying soil temperatures with barley and soybean indicated the same trend in Ca + Mg/K ratios for warm soil as for citrus leaves initiated when the soil temperature was warm and vice versa for cold soil (Wallace, 1956). Some of the data are reproduced in table 5.

The interaction at 32°C for the two plant species in table 5 would not necessarily complicate the orange-leaf data because that temperature is higher than that of the orchard soil (North and Wallace, 1955). The results were believed to be independent of transpiration and soil moisture differences.

Some plant species definitely can obtain K easier than do others. An interesting question relates to whether or not such species need the extra K that they accumulate. In a small study of this point bush beans reached a maximum size when the external K concentration was 0.0001 $\underline{M}$ but corn did not reach maximal size until the external K supply was 0. 005 $\underline{M}$. The respective K concentrations of the two species at the two levels was, as per cent of dry weight, 1. 9 and 1. 4 at $10^{-4}\underline{M}$ and 3. 0 and 4. 9 at 5 x $10^{-3}\underline{M}$ for the beans and corn, respectively. It would appear from this study that corn needed the extra K.

Table 4. Summary of the calculations showing the changes caused by certain factors on the nitrogen content of alfalfa hay when grown at different potash levels.

Factor	Potash treatment lbs. K_2O/acre/year				Maximum deviation in total nitrogen
	0	60	120	180	%
Original per cent of nitrogen	3. 18	3. 01	2. 85	2. 74	0. 44
Calculated nitrogen percentages based on changes					
If carbohydrate production had been equal*	2. 75	2. 89	2. 76	2. 74	0. 15
If chloride absorption had been absent	3. 21	3. 09	2. 98	2. 94	0. 27
If the distribution of nitrogen between tops and roots had been equal**	3. 18	3. 32	3. 44	3. 55	0. 37
Means of probable values					
	3. 05	3. 10	3. 06	3. 08	0. 05

*Calculated by using differences in the cation me. sum as an index of carbohydrate dilution.
**This factor also compensates for the differences in leaf percentage.

The subject of critical levels is an elusive one. The wide range in critical level for K in field-grown alfalfa vs. that grown in sand culture and its ramification is a case in point as noted by Wallace (1952). Alfalfa, when grown in water and sand cultures, ordinarily contains much higher cation and anion values than does field-grown alfalfa of the same maturity. This suggested that a nutrient concentration factor is at least partly responsible for some of the variation in critical level. This was verified in a study with alfalfa grown in solutions of varying concentration but with constant ratios of salts (Wallace, 1952).

The mean cation me. sum of alfalfa from 31 field locations in New Jersey was 141, and the me. sum of the anions was 255 (Wallace, 1949). These values correspond to those of the alfalfa grown in the dilute nutrient solutions. The latter plants had less yield than those grown in concentrated solutions. The maximum size of the plants from the sand cultures was much in excess of that of average field-grown plants. For these reasons it is possible that most field-grown plants are deficient in total amounts of all nutrient elements. Plants grown in a solution containing 0. 01 total equivalents per liter produced 32. 5% less dry matter in the tops than did those from an optimum solution of 0. 02 equivalents per liter, and those in a 0. 0016 equivalent per liter solution, 63. 0% less. In line with this, the concentration of the soil solution of fertile soils has been reported to be higher than that of infertile soils (Scofield, 1927; Stewart, 1918).

Table 5. Cation contents and ratios of whole barley and soybean plants grown in different soils at different soil temperatures.

Soil Temper- ature	Potassium		Calcium		$\dfrac{Ca + Mg}{K}$	
	Barley	Soybeans	Barley	Soybeans	Barley	Soybeans
	me./100g. dry wt.		me./100g. dry wt.		me. ratios	
12°C	46	38	107	134	2.8	6.3
22°C	58	48	69	115	1.5	4.6
32°C	53	55	139	101	3.0	3.5

This "intensity" factor is possibly partly responsible for known variations that exist in the critical levels of the various nutrients. This is well illustrated by alfalfa grown in sand culture and that grown in the field. Alfalfa yields increased when grown in sand cultures up to 3% K in the plants (Wallace and Bear, 1949). Alfalfa grown in the field does not respond to K above plant contents varying from 1.0 to 1.5% (Bear and Prince, 1945). There are, of course, more factors limiting growth in the field than in sand culture.

In 1953 the author proposed a hypothetical yield curve for varying K, Ca, and Mg supplies to plants (Wallace, 1953a). This curve is reproduced in figure 3. Since that time attempts have been made here to verify it. Even more complex interactions have been indicated but definite shifts in critical levels have been obtained and the curve can be considered as at least partly correct. A. C. Schuffelen, private communication 1962, suggests that K inhibits the uptake of Mg much more than Mg inhibits the uptake of K. Such interactions must be considered.

Smith (1962) has adapted a critical level-yield curve from results of other workers. This curve has most of the essential characteristics to explain results except one. That one factor is the variability nearly always observed in the critical or optimum level and an accurate yield curve should have this concept included. Instead of a curved line without width, the plot should have area with the curve having width to indicate a range of levels through which each response may vary. These shifting critical levels are indicated by figure 4. Bould (1962) considers that a critical level is valid only when all other nutrients except the one under test are at optimum levels.

Studies have been made in this laboratory using N^{15} to compare NO_3^- vs. NH_4^+ absorption by rough lemon cuttings (Wallace and Mueller, 1957). The main effects of the experiment are in table 6. These indicate that there was a tendency for less total nitrogen absorption as the ratio of nitrate to ammonium was increased. This was the result of ammonia being absorbed to a greater extent than was nitrate. As an average for all treatments the ratio of ammonium to nitrate absorption was 1.84.

Pretreatment with ammonium nitrogen resulted in reduced uptake of both nitrogen sources. In contrast, pretreatment with nitrate resulted in an increased absorption of ammonium nitrogen but no change in nitrate absorption. To obtain an approximation of the effect of nitrogen contents of plants prior to the isotope treatments on the subsequent absorption of ammonium and nitrate, correlation coefficients were calculated for the 54 pairs of data in each case. The coefficient of correlation between nitrate absorption and original nitrogen content was -0. 35, which was significant at the . 01 level. The coefficient between original nitrogen content and ammonium absorption was -0. 11, and this was not significant.

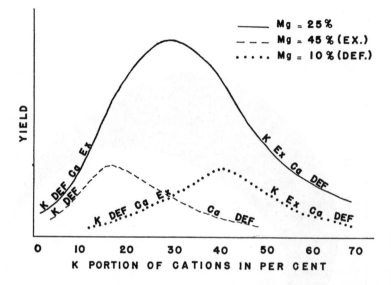

Figure 3.   The critical levels of any nutrient element are usually not constant.   An important reason is the interaction of that element with other elements.   These curves illustrate the possibility that the critical potassium level may be shifted either up or down, depending upon the levels of magnesium and calcium (reprinted from Wallace, 1953a).

There are some apparent discrepancies between the results of this experiment and previous concepts of nitrogen in plant nutrition.   One of these relates to the effect of the nitrogen content of a root on subsequent nitrogen absorption. Roots that are low in a particular nutrient supposedly absorb more of that nutrient than roots well supplied with it (Humphries, 1951; Humphries, 1952; Wallace, 1953b).   The present results, where pretreatment with nitrate resulted in increased ammonium absorption, are of interest.

In general the literature indicates that ammonium absorption is decreased at low pH and nitrate absorption at high pH (Goring, 1956; Hewitt, 1952; Miller, 1938; Nightingale, 1948; Weissman, 1950).   Present results indicate that this did not occur when the low level of either source was supplied.   The data indicated that pH effects on either ammonium or nitrate nitrogen absorption were absent at the concentration of 2 me. /liter for each.   At concentrations of 8 me. /liter nitrate absorption tended to decrease with increasing pH, while ammonium tended to increase.   The reports in the literature may be correct only for relatively high application rates.   The data also indicate that the findings of Weissman, that nitrate absorption was influenced by pH only if ammonium nitrogen was also present (Weissman, 1950), likewise may be subject to concentration effects.   That ammonium is generally absorbed almost twice as fast as nitrate had been previously observed for this type of plant material (Wallace, 1954).   When this did not occur it was a consequence of pH on the increased absorption of nitrate.   At low pH absorption of nitrate was sometimes increased and since H^+ tended to compete with NH_4^+ for uptake the 2:1 ratio for ammonium to nitrate uptake sometimes disappeared at low pH.

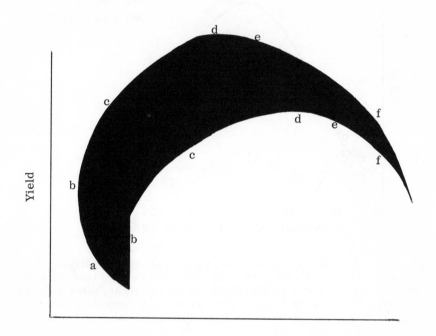

Figure 4.   Hypothetical yield curve.   a. Steenbjerg effect, b. minimum percentage, c. poverty adjustment, d. critical level, e. luxury consumption, and f. toxicity.

Summary

Interrelationships among cations and anions constitute an important aspect of mineral nutrition of plants.   Although balance between positively and negatively charged ions and simple competitive effects within the ions of like charges explain many of the effects, some of the effects are complex.   Relationships considered include cation equivalent constancy in plants, relative absorption of mineral cations and mineral anions, some effects of unessential ions, effect of root cation-exchange capacity on Ca-K ratios in plants, cation-nitrogen relationships, magnesium-phosphorus relationships, calcium and potassium levels in soil vs. those in plants, availability of mineral ions from ion-exchange resins, soil temperature effects on cation relationships, reasons for shifting critical levels, and ammonium and nitrate nitrogen relationships.

Table 6.   Main effects of the three different factors on nitrate and ammonium nitrogen absorption by rough lemon cuttings.

Factor	Nitrogen absorbed as per cent of dry weight		Total	Absorption Ratio $NO_3 : NH_4$
	nitrate-N	ammonium-N		
Source ratios $NO_3:NH_4$				
20:80	.025	.101	.126	20:80
50:50	.038	.077	.115	33:67
80:20	.059	.047	.106	56:44
F. value	33.4**		N. S.	
L. S. D. (.05)	.013		—	
Pretreatment				
No N	.052	.078	.130	40:60
NO_3-N	.046	.098	.144	32:68
NH_4-N	.024	.047	.071	33:67
F. value	31.6**		34.0**	
L. S. D. (.05)	.013		.019	
pH				
3.5	.040	.064	.104	38:62
5.5	.045	.075	.120	38:62
8.0	.036	.086	.122	30:70
F. value	18.0**		N. S.	
L. S. D. (.05)	.013		—	

(Reprinted from Wallace and Mueller, 1957).

EFFECT OF CONCENTRATION ON SOLUTE UPTAKE BY PLANTS

With S. M. Sufi

This report proposes to discuss nothing except the effect of concentration of solutes on their uptake or accumulation by plants.   The problem of salinity is not considered.   As in other reports of this series the term uptake means total solutes absorbed less that removed with washing and exchange of the free space.

Most of the earlier work on effects of concentration on solute uptake in plants concerned long-time effects with balanced salt solutions with which there was relatively little effect, although some.   One of the authors (Wallace, 1952) had some experience with such an experiment in which growth, water relations, and ratios of ions absorbed by the plants varied with salt concentration of the nutrient solution.   In the past 15 to 20 years an enormous number of experiments have been made all over the world in which ion or salt uptake at different concentrations have been measured.   Little attempt has been made to evaluate these results, partly because of their apparent complication.   If solutes enter cells (influx) and leave cells (efflux) simultaneously, effects of concentration on net flux are sure to be complicated.

Olsen (1950) stated that the rate of ion absorption for a given ion was

independent of the ion concentration lying below 0. 003 meq. /l. If the proportions of the different ions in the external solution are changed, the ratio of
these ions absorbed by plants is usually also changed. Olsen found that the
rate at which the individual ions were absorbed from a composite nutrient
solution is largely determined by the ratio between these ions in the nutrient
solution and not so much by their absolute concentration. Epstein (1956a)
demonstrated that the relation between concentration of ion and its rate of
absorption was that of a Langmuir isotherm. Upon plotting the reciprocals of
these variables, straight lines were obtained according to the technique of
Lineweaver and Burk (1934).

In a study with aged potato discs, Wallace and Jeffreys (1962) observed
that uptake of iron from a chelating agent, ethylenediamine di(o-hydroxyphenyl
acetate) (EDDHA), varied according to concentration (c) by the equation,

$$\text{Uptake} = c^{\ln 2} \tag{1}$$

When uptake was measured in μmoles per sample and c in moles per liter
the equation was

$$\text{Uptake} = 2.\,105 \times 10^4 \, c^{\ln 2} \tag{2}$$

The uptake plotted as a straight line against $c^{\ln 2}$ (which is $2^{\ln c}$ also) over
a concentration range of 10^{-3} to $10^{-6}\underline{M}$.

This expression was found empirically by trial and error of a number of
expressions that might have fit the data. Of some interest is the predicted
value from the expression of 4. 93 as the difference in uptake for a 10-fold
difference in external concentration. An average value of 4. 93 was obtained
from the regression line of the iron uptake by the discs. A value close to this
was obtained also for Mn uptake by bush beans (Hale and Wallace, 1962b).

In 1955 Higinbotham and Hanson reported that the equilibrium value for Rb
uptake fit an equation in the form of the Freundlich absorption isotherm as
follows:

$$Y = k \, c^n \tag{3}$$

where Y is the amount absorbed, c is the external concentration, and k and n
are constants. This equation is exactly in the form as those given in (1) and
(2) except that the constants were given in equation (2).

According to Epstein (1956a) it is very difficult to express in one single
equation the relationship between the external concentration of an ion and its
accumulation in the plant. Sutcliffe (1962) says that uptake and external concentration are often, but not always, related to one another in a hyperbolic
relationship. Departures from this hyperbolic relationship may be expected
and can be justified. Equations (1), (2), and (3) are hyperbolic.

In a recent report from this laboratory the uptake (less free-space components) of K and HCO_3^- by intact bush beans were reported for different concentrations of $K^{42}HC^{14}O_3$ (Huffaker et al. , 1960). These data are given in
table 1 as recalculated on the basis of equation (1). Equation (1) predicts that
a 10-fold decrease in external concentration will result in a 4. 93-fold decrease
in uptake. Using this value the theoretical values were calculated as percent-
ages of that of the highest external concentration which was set at 100%. The actual
values were also calculated as percent of the highest external concentration.
The data fit the theoretical values reasonably well for both K and HCO_3^-
especially at the higher concentrations.

Smith and Wallace (1956c) reported experiments with intact bush beans and barley in which K and Ca uptake (less free-space components) were measured. Concentration ratios in plants (defined for a 10-fold difference in external concentration) are given in table 2. The ratios were reasonably close to 4.9 for both K and Ca and appeared to be independent of the complimentary anion. The plants described in table 2 were low-salt plants for K. When plants were pretreated with K, the ratios were higher than 4.9.

Table 1. Expected and actual results of K and HCO_3^- uptake from different KHCO$_3$ concentrations based on an expected relationship between uptake and external concentration of $c^{\ln 2}$ (see equation (1)).

Concentration of KHCO$_3$ (c) M	$-c^{\ln 2}$ or $-2^{\ln c}$	Concentrations in plants				
		K	HCO_3^-	K or HCO_3^-	K	HCO_3^-
				(theoretical*)	(actual)	
		μe./g. dry wt.		Percent of highest		
1.0	1.00	1496.0	516.0	100	100	100
0.5	1.61	942.0	302.0	62.1	62.9	58.5
0.1	4.93	319.0	87.4	20.3	21.3	16.9
0.05	8.00	279.0	46.9	12.5	18.7	9.1
0.02	15.03	170.0	21.5	6.7	11.3	4.2
0.01	24.2	129.0	13.4	4.1	8.6	2.6
0.005	39.1	92.8	8.1	2.6	6.2	1.6
0.0005	192	50.0	1.9	0.52	3.3	0.36
0.0001	588	44.0	0.3	0.17	2.9	0.06

Assays were made with K^{42} and C^{14}.

*Each decrease of 10-fold in external concentration represents 4.93-fold drop in the percentage. The percentage values are the reciprocals of $-c^{\ln 2}$ expressed in percent.

In table 3 are some concentration ratios for NH_4^+ and NO_3^- nitrogen sources with rough lemon cuttings calculated from data of Wallace and Mueller (1957). The ratios were quite similar for both forms of nitrogen and in general they were just a little bit smaller than a predicted value of 4.9. They were more erratic than some of the other data considered.

Materials and Methods

The general materials and methods given here hold also for subsequent reports as will be pointed out at appropriate places.

Experiments were conducted on bush beans (Phaseolus vulgaris, variety Tendergreen). The plants were grown by germinating seeds in sterilized quartz sand in wooden flats in a glasshouse. The flats were watered regularly with distilled water. Five to 6 days from germination, sound uniform seedlings were transferred to 100-ml. culture tubes containing nutrient solution which was formed of the following salts in moles/liter: KNO_3, 0.00025; $NH_4H_2PO_4$, 0.0005; $MgSO_4$, 0.001; K_2SO_4, 0.0005; and $Ca(NO_3)_2$, 0.00125.

Micronutrient elements were added in the following concentrations: 0.1 ppm. Mn as $MnSO_4$, 0.1 ppm. B as H_3BO_3, 0.12 ppm. Zn as $ZnSO_4 \cdot 7 H_2O$

and 0. 03 ppm. Mo as sodium molybdate. Fe (5 ppm.) was supplied as Fe-EDDHA.

Table 2.　Concentration ratios for K and Ca uptake by bush bean plants*.

Concentrations of external solutions compared	Beans			Barley		
	Calcium					
	at K levels of			at K levels of		
	$\underline{M}$			$\underline{M}$		
$\underline{M}$	0	10^{-2}	1	0	10^{-2}	1
	Ratios					
$\dfrac{10^{-1}}{10^{-2}}$	7. 4	4. 2	8. 1	5. 6	4. 7	3. 5
$\dfrac{10^{-2}}{10^{-3}}$	4. 8	3. 6	4. 1	3. 6	4. 0	5. 8
Means	5. 3			4. 5		

	Potassium					
	at Ca levels of			at Ca levels of		
	$\underline{M}$			$\underline{M}$		
	0	10^{-3}	10^{-1}	0	10^{-3}	10^{-1}
	Ratios					
$\dfrac{10^{-2}}{10^{-3}}$	4. 0	5. 8	7. 6	4. 4	4. 8	4. 9
Means	5. 8			4. 7		

*Assays were made with K^{42} and Ca^{45}.

The nutrient media were continuously aerated during the entire growing period.   After 8 to 9 days, the nutrient solution was carefully poured out and the roots washed with distilled water before adding the experimental solutions. Experimental solutions contained $10^{-4}\underline{M}$ $CaSO_4$ to preserve the integrity of the roots.   The pH of the experimental solution was always adjusted to 7 and checked frequently.   The absorption period selected was 5 hours for the cation and anion uptake studies except for the time studies.   The absorption period for the non-ion mannitol was 24 hours.   Each of the nutrient solutions was a-erated during the experimental period.   At the end of the absorption periods, roots were rinsed with distilled water and the roots were washed to remove isotopes from the free space for 1 hour in 0. 01 $\underline{M}$ $CaCl_2$ or mannitol for the non-ionic mannitol.   After washing the free space, the plants were washed again in run-ning tap water for 2 or 3 minutes and separated into roots, stems, and leaves. The procedure used depended on the type of radiation emitted by the various isotopes used in this study.   The radioactive isotopes K^{42}, Rb^{86}, Sr^{85}, Br^{82} and C^{14}-mannitol were used as tracers in the various experiments.   After separating the plants into roots, stems, and leaves in the C^{14}-mannitol studies, these parts were put in paper bags and dried in a forced-draft oven at 70°C. The dried plant material was ground in a Wiley mill and weighed and then aliquots were spread evenly in metal planchets. These were then counted for C^{14} with a Q-gas thin window flow counter. Results were then expressed as μmoles according to the principles of Hendler (1959) and from specific activity relationships. Background was subtracted and corrections for self-absorption were made using self-absorption factors.

Table 3. Concentration ratios in rough lemon seedlings of NO_3^- and NH_4^+ nitrogen sources supplied at different concentrations*.

mM concentrations in external solutions compared	No pretreatments pH of external solution			All pH levels and all pretreatments Means
	3.5	5.5	8.0	
		Ratios		
Nitrate-nitrogen source				
8/2	6.4	5.2	3.5	4.3
5/2	1.3	7.2	2.1	3.1
8/5	12.0	1.5	3.5	4.4
Means	6.6	4.6	3.0	3.9
Ammonium-nitrogen source				
8/2	2.6	4.3	4.8	3.9
5/2	2.9	2.4	5.5	3.6
8/5	1.8	5.4	2.1	3.0
Means	2.4	4.0	4.1	3.5

*The ratios were calculated on the basis of 10-fold differences by the use of proper factors even though the actual concentrations were narrower than that. The assays were made with N^{15}.

In experiments with K^{42} and Br^{82} which are gamma emitters with a relatively short half-life, root, stem, or leaf sections were forced to the lowest one-centimeter portions of glass test tubes and counted before drying with a scintillation-well counter. Corrections for decay were made at different time intervals. The samples were then dried and weighed.

When other gamma emitters were used such as Rb^{86} and Sr^{85}, each of which has a relatively long half-life when compared to K^{42} and Br^{82}, the plant material was dried first and then counted with the scintillation-well counter.

The amount of different solutes absorbed or accumulated was calculated from specific activity relationships and expressed in micromoles per gram of dry weight.

Plants were kept for 5 hours in the tagged salt solutions. The salt concentrations ranged from $10^{-4}M$ to $10^{-1}M$. The ratios of the various solutes from different external concentrations when one is ten times the other is defined in this work as "concentration ratio".

Results and Discussion

Substances absorbed by plants over a certain range of external concentration are in some cases in direct proportion to the external concentration while others appear to be related to equations (1) and (3). Those taken up in direct proportion to the external concentration are supposedly taken up in accord with Fick's law of diffusion.

The uptake (less free-space components) of the bush bean plants in the various experiments are in table 4.

Table 4. Uptake (less free-space components) of several different solutes by intact bush bean plants when exposed for several hours to different concentrations of the solutes.

Solute	M Concentration			
	10^{-1}	10^{-2}	10^{-3}	10^{-4}
	μmoles per gram dry weight of whole plant			
K from KBr	50.9	14.5	3.9	0.5
K from KHCO$_3$	81.5	24.0	5.5	1.0
Rb from RbCl	21.1	4.6	1.1	0.2
Sr from Sr(NO$_3$)$_2$	53.5	6.6	2.3	0.8
Br from KBr	41.0	3.4	0.3	0.03
Mannitol	414.0	47.3	6.2	1.1

The means of concentration ratios reported in table 5 for the 3 cations were on the average close to 4.9. The values were somewhat erratic within treatments for a given cation. It is unknown at this time whether or not all the variation can be ascribed to experimental error. The type of curve which these data give is indicated in figure 1 where uptake is plotted against concentration. When uptake was plotted against $c^{\ln 2}$ a straight line is obtained (Wallace and Jeffreys, 1962). This obtains at least for some concentration ranges.

Table 5. Concentration ratios for various elements from different levels of external concentrations and for a period of 5 hours**.

Ion or solute	Concentrations compared									Means
	$10^{-1}/10^{-2}$			$10^{-2}/10^{-3}$			$10^{-3}/10^{-4}$			
	5°C	20°C	30°C	5°C	20°C	30°C	5°C	20°C	30°C	
	Concentration ratios in plants									
Cations										
K*Br	3.5	3.6	3.4	3.7	4.2	5.7	7.8	4.8	4.7	4.6
K*HCO$_3$	3.4	3.8	4.0	4.4	4.5	4.5	5.5	4.7	4.4	4.4
Rb*Cl	4.6	–	2.4	4.2	–	3.1	5.5	–	3.3	3.9
Sr*(NO3)2	8.1	–	6.9	2.9	–	2.5	2.8	–	4.1	4.7
Anion										
KBr*	12.1	10.9	12.0	11.3	5.8	5.8	10.1	11.0	12.8	9.1
Non-ion										
Mannitol	9.4	6.1	6.6	7.6	13.9	14.0	5.6	10.1	9.1	9.2

**The absorption period for mannitol was 24 hours.

The anion, bromide, and the non-ionizable compound, mannitol, however, departed from the hyperbolic relationship ($c^{\ln 2}$) and followed a linear relationship (figure 2). This means that a 10-fold increase in external concentration resulted in a 10-fold increase in bromine (Br^{82}) and mannitol (C^{14}) taken up by the plants (less free-space components). Similar results have been obtained for the chelating agent EDDHA (Hale and Wallace, 1962a). These, therefore, appear to follow Fick's law of diffusion.

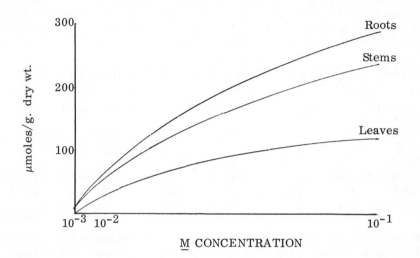

Figure 1. The effect of varying the concentration of K in the external solution on K accumulation from 10^{-3} molar to 10^{-1} molar $KHCO_3$.

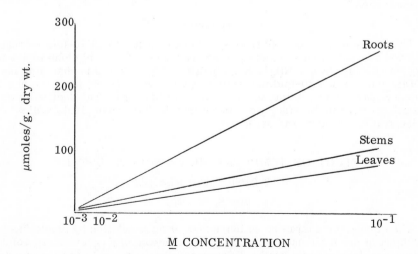

Figure 2. The effect of varying the concentration of Br in the external solution on Br accumulation from 10^{-3} molar to 10^{-1} molar KBr.

Knauss and Porter (1954) reported that absorption of the cations Ca, Sr, Fe, Mn, Zn, and Cu by <u>Chlorella pyrenoidosa</u> was directly proportional to the concentration of the ions in the nutrient solution over remarkably wide ranges of concentration. These correspond with the data here for bromine and mannitol and not with the data for cations. Knauss and Porter, however, reported that at low concentration the uptake of the anions phosphate and sulphate varied with the logarithm of the concentrations of each ion.

The existence of an ion at a higher concentration inside a cell than outside is not necessarily evidence of active transport of that ion (Dainty, 1962). Donnan equilibrium can result in uptake against a gradient. Evenso as a matter of interest the final concentration gradients for the solutes with bush beans used in the present study were estimated (table 6).

Table 6. Estimated concentration gradients for the plants grown in this study.

External Concentration M	In roots in 5 hours as % of external solution					
	K 5°C.	K 25°C.	Br 25°C.	Sr 25°C.	Rb 25°C.	Mannitol 30°C.
10^{-1}	13	31	32	10	11	67
10^{-2}	64	118	25	31	39	76
10^{-3}	177	219	44	164	200	38
10^{-4}	244	555	47	462	1260	59

Studies with different concentrations may be complicated by the existence of gradients in unstirred layers of the external solution adjacent to a cell wall. These unstirred layers may be up to 100μ thick (Dainty, 1962) and may give rise to electrical potentials. Additional complications of concentration on salt uptake were indicated by Kihlman-Falk (1961) who found 4 different phases of ion uptake and these were all differentially influenced by the external salt concentration.

Summary

The uptake by plants (less free-space components) for a 10-fold increase in external concentration seemed to be increased by a factor of close to 4.9 for Fe, Mn, Ca, K, NO_3^-, NH_4^+, Sr, Rb, and HCO_3^-. For Br, mannitol and EDDHA there was a 10-fold increase in uptake for a 10-fold increase in external concentration (according to Fick's law of diffusion). The degree by which the solutes used in the study were taken into the bush bean plants against the concentration gradient was estimated.

EFFECT OF TEMPERATURE ON SOLUTE UPTAKE
BY BUSH BEAN PLANTS
With S. M. Sufi

The effect of temperature on ion uptake or accumulation by plants has been a subject of much misunderstanding. The concepts of Q_{10} and energy of activation have been loosely used. Temperature has commonly been used as a criterion of whether or not a given ion is metabolically accumulated. Dainty (1962) has summarized current thinking on salt uptake in terms of an ion pair as follows: no studies of ion competition, or of the shape of uptake vs. time curve, or of concentration gradients, or of the effects of temperature, or of metabolic inhibitors can give unequivocal answers to the question of which ion is pumped. He has shown how a study of ion fluxes under well-defined electro-chemical potential differences can supply the necessary information.

The temperature coefficient or Q_{10} is the ratio of reaction rates at 2 temperatures 10^oC apart, that is, a ratio of reaction rate at $(T + 10)^oC$ to that at T^oC. It has long been known that many chemical reactions are approximately doubled or tripled in velocity for a 10° rise in temperature in the range of room temperatures. The rates of physical reactions are on the other hand usually only slightly changed by a corresponding rise in temperature.

The following expression relates the Q_{10} with temperature in ion uptake studies where T_1 and T_2 represent different temperatures:

$$Q_{10} = \frac{\text{uptake at } T_2}{\text{uptake at } T_1}^{\frac{1}{(T_2-T_1) \div 10}}$$

Hoagland and Broyer (1942) found a Q_{10} for potassium accumulation of nearly 3 between 0.5^o and 20^oC. Lundegardh (1958) reported a Q_{10} of 2.20 to 2.45 for K uptake by wheat roots from KCl solutions. Steward (1942) gave high but variable Q_{10} values for the accumulation of KBr by potato and artichoke tissue. Robertson (1944) investigated the accumulation of KCl by carrot tissues at 7°, 13°, 19°, and 25^oC. He demonstrated that the rates of accumulation increased with increasing temperature and the Q_{10} varied from 2.0 to 2.1. Sutcliffe (1954) showed that the uptake of K at 5^oC by red beet discs did not increase with an increase in the absorption time. The uptake of K at 25^oC on the other hand increased significantly with time, thus indicating that the Q_{10} will show higher values as the length of the absorption period is increased. Hylmo (1953) gave a Q_{10} of 0.9 for Ca uptake by peas in 24 hours between 0^oC and 10^oC, while from 10^oC to 20^oC he gave a Q_{10} of 2.0.

A main argument against the use of Q_{10} concerns variation in activation energies. Kinetic data over a range of temperature can be represented by an empirical equation proposed by Arrhenius:

$$K = Se^{-Ea/RT}$$

where K is the velocity, S is a constant, Ea is the activation energy, e is the base of natural logarithms, R is the gas constant, and T is the absolute temperature. If the above equation is put in a logarithmic form, differentiated with respect to temperature and integrated between limits, it becomes:

$$\text{Log}\frac{K_2}{K_1} = \frac{Ea}{2.303R}\frac{(T_2 - T_1)}{(T_1 T_2)}$$

where K_1 and K_2 are the rate constants for T_1 and T_2 respectively. The activation energy for many metabolic reactions is about 13,000 calories per mole. The activation energy for a diffusion process is usually much lower, but wide ranges do exist and it is not always possible to draw conclusions from the magnitude of the activation energy.

Materials and Methods

The same general materials and methods described in the preceding paper were used in this study. The results of this study as in the previous were reported as uptake less the free-space components in roots. The latter were removed at the conclusion of each experiment by exposing the roots for 1 hour to a 10^{-2} M aerated $CaCl_2$ solution. This would reasonably remove any radioisotopes from the water- and Donnan-free space.

Results and Discussion

As a result of investigations on the effect of various root temperatures on K accumulation the following observations were established or confirmed (table 1):

The Q_{10} for K accumulation varied with:

1. The duration of the absorption period.
2. The concentration of K in the external solution.
3. The range of temperature used.

While K^{42} accumulation showed temperature dependency after 24 hours of absorption time, the 5-hour periods exhibited little temperature dependency (figure 1). In other studies the Q_{10} consistently increased between 2 and 24 hours. Sutcliffe (1954) observed similar effects of temperature on K accumulation with time by red beet discs, but gave no explanation.

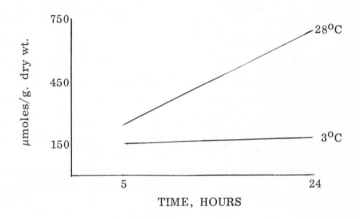

Figure 1. The effect of two time intervals on the uptake of K at $3^{o}C$ and 28°C from 10^{-1} molar KBr. Results were similar at 10^{-2} molar KBr.

Q_{10} values for K accumulation (uptake less free-space components) calculated between 20°C and 30°C were higher than Q_{10} values calculated between 5°C and 30°C. This is in accordance with Hylmo's (1953) observations where he obtained Q_{10} values as high as 2 for Ca between 20°C and 30°C, and Q_{10} values as low as 0.9 between 0°C and 10°C.

The accumulation of Rb^{86} behaved similarly to the accumulation of K^{42} with respect to temperature as illustrated in table 1. The Q_{10} for Rb^{86} accumulation also varied with the duration of the absorption period, the concentration of Rb in the external solution, and with the range of temperatures used. Higher Q_{10} values for Rb accumulation were obtained, however, for 5 hours of absorption time rather than for 24 hours.

Wanner (1948a, b) found a Q_{10} of 1.4 for the accumulation of K ions and a Q_{10} from 2 to 2.5 for the absorption of NO_3^- and Br anions. He proposed active uptake of anions but not of cations. Present studies give little indication of this. The Q_{10} calculated for Br^{82} was over 2 on the average indicating a dependency of Br^{82} uptake on temperature.

The uptake of Sr^{85} was independent of temperature. The Q_{10} values for Sr^{85} uptake were around 1 for different time intervals, for the various concentrations of Sr in the external solution, and for the low and high temperatures used. The uptake of C^{14} mannitol was also independent of temperature. The Q_{10} values calculated on a whole plant basis were on the average close to 1.2.

Table 1. Q_{10}'s calculated for the uptake less free space of K, Rb, Br, Sr, and mannitol between 5° C and 25° C.

Solute	Absorption Period	Concentrations in moles/liter				Means
		10^{-1}	10^{-2}	10^{-3}	10^{-4}	
K	5 hours	1.15	1.53	2.01	2.34	1.76
K	24 hours	1.75	1.99	2.41	3.04	2.40
Br	5 hours	1.83	1.34	3.05	3.42	2.41
Sr	1 hour	1.07	1.29	1.05	1.14	1.13
Sr	3 hours	1.19	1.19	1.31	1.18	1.22
Sr	5 hours	1.17	1.24	1.32	1.46	1.29
Sr	24 hours	1.21	1.18	1.38	1.28	1.26
Rb	5 hours	1.09	1.51	1.79	4.09	2.21
Rb	24 hours	1.18	1.35	1.59	1.67	1.44
Mannitol	24 hours	1.06	1.35	1.11	1.44	1.24

Some investigators because of the great similarity between Sr and Ca often use the isotopic form of Sr to tag the Ca ion. Some have indicated that Ca is passively taken up by tissues and cells, Smith (1955) and Moore et al. (1961). From the experimental results, the uptake of Sr and mannitol was independent of temperature and, hence, may correspond with Ca.

Summary

The effect of temperature on uptake of K^{42} varied considerably with time of exposure of plants to the K^{42}. The uptake less free-space components of K^{42}, Rb^{86}, and Br^{82} in general showed a temperature dependency at low external concentrations but not at high. Br^{82} uptake was most dependent on temperature. The uptake characteristics of K^{42} were somewhat different from those of Rb^{86}. The uptake of Sr^{85} and C^{14}-mannitol was independent of temperature.

SOME EFFECTS OF SOME METABOLIC INHIBITORS ON
SOLUTE UPTAKE BY BUSH BEAN PLANTS
With S. M. Sufi

The relationship between respiration and salt uptake by plants has been studied for many years. Representative reviews of this particular subject are by Robertson (1951), Lundegardh (1955), and Laties (1959). One of the general conclusions of all this literature is that even though there is a great dependence of salt uptake on metabolism, there is very little evidence to indicate a stoichiometric relationship between O_2 uptake and salt uptake.

The use of metabolic inhibitors has been an important tool for elucidating mechanisms of salt uptake. The ideal of a specific inhibitor acting upon a single enzyme, however, is at present essentially unrealized. One problem is that the inhibition of respiration is frequently incomplete, even when a fully differentiating dosage of inhibitor is applied. This has caused several including James (1953) to raise the question as to whether this can be taken to indi-cate that respiration, and hence salt uptake, is proceeding by more than one route. This does not necessarily have to occur.

According to James (1953) sodium azide resembles cyanide in its capacity for forming complexes with metals and like cyanide combines as undissociated (hydrazoic) acid with cytochrome oxidase and as N_3^- ion with cytochrome-c. Its complexes are slightly less stable than cyanide, but the degree of inhibition obtained is usually very similar.

Weeks and Robertson (1950) indicated that the inhibition of respiration and accumulation by azide and cyanide is reversible. The evidence is that inhibi-tion of cytochrome oxidase is accompanied by complete inhibition of the accumu-lation mechanism. This does not prove that the salt accumulation mechanism is directly connected with the oxidation at the cytochrome oxidase stage, since a block at the oxidase is probably accompanied by decrease in activity of many other processes.

Ordin and Jacobson (1955) conducted a study of the effects of inhibitors on respiration and the absorption of both the cation and anion of KBr by excised barley roots. Absorption of both ions was inhibited by substances which in-hibit glycolysis and the Krebs cycle. For most inhibitors tested, inhibition of subsequent K absorption was equal to or greater than that of Br. KCN at low levels inhibited bromide absorption more than potassium absorption. Foulkes (1956) studied the effect of azide on K uptake in baker's yeast. He suggested that azide inhibited K transport in yeast, not by reacting with cytochrome oxidase in mitochondria, but by combining with a carrier in the cell wall.

Case (1951) and Loomis and Lipman (1948) showed that 2,4-dinitrophenol (2,4-DNP) inhibited oxidative phosphorylation at concentrations between 10^{-3} and $10^{-5}M$. Robertson, Wilkins, and Weeks (1951) investigated the effect of 2,4-DNP on the respiration and salt accumulation in carrot tissue. This inhibition of oxidative phosphorylation increased the rate of cytochrome-medi-ated electron transport, but simultaneously depressed the accumulation of salts. This observation led Briggs (1961) to speculate that it is not simply the electron transport system in the cell that is associated with the accumulation mechanism, but that coupled phosphorylation is necessary. Chasson and Levitt (1956) reported that 2,4-DNP inhibited the uptake of ions by certain tissue and may even cause a leakage of ion from the tissue. Robertson, Wilkins, and Weeks (1951) indicated that 2,4-DNP, while increasing respira-tion, inhibited the accumulation of ions by carrot discs. These workers con-sidered whether the inhibition was due to a direct effect of 2,4-DNP on the mechanism, or whether 2,4-DNP indirectly prevented the mechanism from operating by causing some disorganization within the cell, possibly in the mitochondria. Whether 2,4-DNP prevents salt accumulation because it pre-vents net production of ATP, or whether 2,4-DNP prevents salt accumulation and energy production separately of each other, was investigated by Honda and Robertson (1956). They suggested that the degree of respiratory control by phosphorylative coupling reactions cannot be determined by only the 2,4-DNP effect on respiration rate. One of the 2,4-DNP effects in increasing respira-tion may result from rendering the mitochondria "leaky" (page 75).

The distinction between uptake into cytoplasm and vacuolar secretion was elucidated by experiments with respiratory inhibitors. Arisz (1956) working with Vallisneria spiralis found that KCN prevented uptake into cytoplasm but did not interfere with transport or vacuolar secretion; whereas 2,4-DNP inhibited only transference from cytoplasm into vacuoles.

Harris et al. (1960) indicated that methylene blue blocked cation transport at a concentration of 5×10^{-5} M.

Materials and Methods

The same general materials and methods described on page 21 were used in this study. As before the results are uptake less the free-space components in the roots. The uptake as reported here just as in the previous reports could be synonymous with accumulation.

Results and Discussion

In some inhibitor studies reported here, high inhibition was obtained (table 1). This suggests that the effect of an inhibitor may be on some mechanism other than respiration. For example, Honda and Robertson (1956) demonstrated that 2,4-DNP can affect both the rate of respiration and cell permeability.

Table 1. The effect of various inhibitors on the accumulation or uptake of K, Rb, Sr, Br, and mannitol by bush beans.

Solute	10^{-3} M NaCN				10^{-4} M 2,4-DNP				10^{-3} M Methylene blue			
	at M concentration of element in external solution											
	10^{-1}	10^{-2}	10^{-3}	10^{-4}	10^{-1}	10^{-2}	10^{-3}	10^{-4}	10^{-1}	10^{-2}	10^{-3}	10^{-4}
	% Inhibition (-) or % Increase (+)											
K^+	-16	-50	-71	-80	-49	-48	-83	-80	--	-53	--	-94
Br^-	-17	-85	-89	-83	-47	-81	-67	-91	--	-30	--	-80
Sr^{++}	+52	-65	-78	-57	+25	-50	-52	-59	--	--	--	--
Rb^+	+41	-32	-52	-90	-7	-39	-37	-83	-10	-67	-76	-94
Mannitol	--	+39	--	+53	--	+62	--	+37	--	+78	--	+85

Generally, the inhibitors used inhibited Br^{82} uptake to a greater extent than K^{42} or Rb^{86} uptake. This is in agreement with the findings of Ordin and Jacobson (1955) who indicated that for most of the inhibitors tested, the accumulation of Br was decreased to a greater extent than that of K.

With KBr this means that proportionately more organic acids would be produced in roots in presence of an inhibitor than without inhibitor to balance the excess of K. The various inhibitors used in this study tended to inhibit more at low than at high concentrations of the ion in the external solution. This generality is perhaps obvious but its exact meaning is subject to more than one interpretation.

According to Harris et al. (1960), 5×10^{-5} molar methylene blue blocked cation transport. The electron acceptors used here, methylene blue and potassium ferricyanide, both decreased the uptake of K and the anion Br as well. K uptake, however, was decreased slightly more than was Br uptake (table 1).

The uptake of Sr was not affected by the metal oxidase inhibitors, cyanide and azide. The uncoupler 2,4-DNP decreased Sr uptake but not to a great extent and this may be explained by 2,4-DNP affecting premeability as suggested by Honda and Robertson (1956).

None of these inhibitors used had any inhibitory effect on the uptake of mannitol. An increase was observed in uptake rather than a decrease (table 1). This will be discussed on page 90.

General similarities and differences in uptake (less free-space components) of the solutes used in these studies

There is really little need at this point to attempt an integrated picture of the results of this and the two preceding reports (table 2). Not much can be concluded as to mechanisms involved. Only in the case of mannitol was there a degree of consistency (no inhibition, no temperature dependency, uptake proportional to concentration). K and Rb are perhaps consistent even though inhibition was little or absent at 10^{-1}M salt concentration, and no temperature dependency was noted at that concentration. It could be that the energy barrier at 10^{-1}M K or Rb is not great. Sr and Br gave inconsistant patterns. If one makes the assumption that one ion, for example K, were metabolically accumulated, the problem exists that for some characteristics measured every other solute tested differs from K in one or more characteristic. Mannitol may be passively accumulated but similarities exist between some of the ions and mannitol. This all emphasizes the futility of making conclusions concerning metabolic uptake from such data.

Table 2.   Summary of similarities and differences in responses of the solutes to concentration, temperature, and inhibitors.

Solute	Concentration effect* (see page 19)	Temperature effect (Q_{10}) (see page 26) 10^{-1}M**	10^{-4}M**	Inhibition, % with CN$^-$ 10^{-1}M**	10^{-4}M**	with 2,4–DNP 10^{-1}M**	10^{-4}M**
K	4.9	1+	2+	-16	-80	-49	-80
Br	10	2	2+	-17	-88	-47	-91
Sr	4.9	1	1	+52	-57	+25	-59
Rb	4.9	1	2+	+41	-90	+ 7	-83
Mannitol	10	1	1	-	+53	-	+37

*Approximate values for uptake for 10-fold differences in concentration.
**Concentration of solute for which the uptake was studied.

Consideration of salt relations of intact vascular plants is a complex phenomenon arising from the anatomy of various tissues and organs (Sutcliffe, 1962). While some solutes are apparently carried passively with the transpiration stream via cell walls, others are actively transported using energy from metabolism (Russell and Shorrocks, 1955). It was not until investigations of the effect of such factors as temperature and metabolic inhibitors on salt uptake were made during the last few years that a dependence of absorption on metabolic energy became widely accepted (Sutcliffe, 1962). Even so the field is a mass of confusion.

Summary

The effect of some metabolic inhibitors on uptake of some solutes by bush beans was investigated. Uptake of K and Br was inhibited at each concentration of ion used. Sometimes at high concentrations uptake of Sr and Rb was increased with inhibitor. Uptake of mannitol was increased by all the inhibitors used. Effects of concentration, temperature, and inhibitors were summarized.

SOME INVESTIGATIONS OF FACTORS WHICH INFLUENCE
TRANSFER OF SOLUTES FROM ROOTS TO SHOOTS
With S. M. Sufi

Differences in behavior for the processes of accumulation into roots and of transfer to shoots are very apparent but little understood. There is considerable evidence that very different biochemical reactions are involved in the two processes. Some examples of reported differences are the following:

(a) Jackson and Evans (1962) reported that addition of Ca to Ca-deficient plants resulted in decreased Mg transfer to tops but not in decreased Mg accumulation by roots.

(b) Bhan et al. (1960) found that cyanide inhibited Na uptake by roots but increased that transferred to shoots. Similar results have been reported by Pearson (1962) and Kadman (unpublished work in Israel).

(c) Epstein (1956a and b) indicated that ions absorbed by the active transport mechanisms of the roots are largely unavailable for translocation to the shoots.

(d) Russell (1954) found that azide decreased P uptake by roots and simultaneously increased P transfer to shoots.

(e) Arisz (1953) reported that KCN prevented uptake into cytoplasm but did not interfere with secretion into the vascular system.

(f) Chloride ions were not stored in roots but were transferred to shoots, but, in contrast, sulfate ions were stored in the roots and later transferred to shoots of bean plants (Mitsui et al., 1961).

(g) Hale et al. (1962) reported that some metabolic inhibitors decreased iron uptake by roots but increased that transferred to leaves.

Fried and Shapiro (1961) have favored the concept of separate accumulation processes for roots and for shoots. They thought that this explanation was more useful than an interchangeable mechanism whereby one process leads wholly to root accumulation and another which leads mostly but not entirely to shoot accumulation. Perhaps the techniques from which their conclusions emerged were not sufficiently definitive to give unambiguous answers to the problems at hand. Multistep processes may obscure results.

Path and Mode of Movement to Stele and Shoot

Hypotheses are proposed for the transport of ions from the external solution across the cortex into the stele. One hypothesis starts with accumulation of salts in the outer cell layer, followed by transference from one vacuole to another vacuole across the cortex until movement into the xylem vessel occurs. The alternative view is that salt may move—at least as far as the endodermis—without passing through the vacuoles of the intervening cells. Scott and Priestly (1928) suggested that salts may move freely through the water-filled cell walls up to the endodermis which is the main barrier to diffusion. They suggested that ions are further transported through the endodermal protoplasts and plasmodesmata into the stele. Crafts and Broyer (1938) concluded that ions pass across the cortical tissues of roots mainly in the cytoplasm. They also regarded the endodermis as a barrier to free ionic movement. Arisz (1954) advanced the symplast theory where he considered that ions entered the cytoplasm by an active process and then moved through a continuous symplast (protoplasmic connection) until a final active process released them into the xylem.

A third approach was suggested by Steward (1959) in which salts are actively secreted from the living cells into the non-living elements by processes similar to those operating in salt glands. Such a secretory mechanism according to Steward (1959) may be located at the protoplasmic surfaces adjoining the conducting elements, or the endodermis may function as a cellular secretory membrane such as those which are familiar to animal physiologists (for example, frog skin and gastric mucosae). This is in contrast to those who believe that a low oxygen tension at the endodermis permits leakage of salts into the stele by reason of failure of enzymes to maintain the barrier.

The role of water intake and effects of transpiration on solute uptake by intact plants will be described on page 83.

Materials and Methods

Experiments were conducted on bush beans (Phaseolus vulgaris, variety Tendergreen). The plants were grown by germinating seeds in sterilized quartz sand in wooden flats in a glasshouse. The flats were watered regularly with distilled water. Five to 6 days from germination, sound uniform seedlings were transferred to 100-ml. culture tubes containing 1/4-strength nutrient solution with micronutrients as described earlier.

The nutrient media were continuously aerated during the entire growing period. After 8 to 9 days, the nutrient solutions were carefully poured out and the roots washed with distilled water before adding the experimental solutions. Experimental solutions contained 10^{-4}M $CaSO_4$ to preserve the integrity of the roots. The pH of the experimental solution was always adjusted to 7 and checked frequently. The absorption period selected was 5 hours for the cations and anions except for the time and temperature studies. The absorption period for the non-ion mannitol was 24 hours. Air was bubbled in the absorption media during the experimental period. At the end of the absorption periods, roots were rinsed with distilled water and the free space was washed for 1 hour in 0.01 M $CaCl_2$ for the cations, in 0.01 N KBr for the anion bromide, and in 0.01 M cold mannitol for the non-ionic mannitol. After washing the free space, the plants were washed again in running tap water for 2 or 3 minutes and separated into roots, stems, and leaves. K^{42}, Rb^{86}, Sr^{85}, Br^{82}, and C^{14}-mannitol were used as tracers in the various experiments. After separating the plants into roots, stems, and leaves in the C^{14}-mannitol studies, these parts were put in paper bags and dried in a forced-draft oven at 70°C. The dried plant material was ground in a Wiley mill, weighed and spread evenly in metal planchets. These were then counted for C^{14} with the thin window gas-flow counter. Background was subtracted and corrections for self-absorption were made.

In experiments with K^{42} and Br^{82} which are gamma emitters with a relatively short half-life, the plants were separated into roots, stems, and leaves; these plant sections were forced to the lowest 1 centimeter portion of glass test tubes and counted with a scintillation-well counter before drying. Corrections for decay were made at different time intervals. Samples were then dried and weighed. When Rb^{86} and Sr^{85} were used, each of which has a relatively long half-life when compared to K^{42} and Br^{82}, the plant material was dried first then counted and weighed.

The amount of different ions and mannitol absorbed was calculated from specific activity relationships and expressed in micromoles per gram of dry weight.

Results and Discussion

The distribution pattern for a 5-hour absorption period of K^{42}, Rb^{86}, Sr^{85}, and Br^{82} was in the following order: roots > stems > leaves. The non-ionizable compound mannitol, however, exhibited a different distribution pattern at 24 hours: leaves > roots > stems as illustrated in table 1.

Table 1.   The uptake and distribution of various solutes in roots, stems, and leaves of bush beans for an absorption period of 5 hours at room temperature (25° C).

Concentration in Moles/liter	Roots	Stems	Leaves
		μmoles/g. dry weight	
		K^{42} from KBr	
10^{-1}	189. 5	117. 1	62. 0
10^{-2}	88. 6	24. 6	4. 8
10^{-3}	17. 0	6. 2	1. 4
10^{-4}	3. 4	1. 2	0. 3
		Rb^{86} from RbCl	
10^{-1}	113. 6	22. 3	5. 9
10^{-2}	43. 8	5. 4	0. 5
10^{-3}	21. 4	1. 6	0. 14
10^{-4}	9. 9	0. 5	0. 09
		Sr^{85} from $Sr(NO_3)_2$	
10^{-1}	82. 8	144. 6	94. 1
10^{-2}	26. 0	26. 9	2. 8
10^{-3}	13. 9	9. 9	0. 4
10^{-4}	4. 6	0. 4	0. 03
		Br^{82} from KBr	
10^{-1}	182. 2	56. 0	62. 6
10^{-2}	12. 7	5. 7	4. 7
10^{-3}	2. 3	1. 6	1. 0
10^{-4}	0. 2	0. 1	0. 04
		C^{14}-mannitol	
10^{-1}	324	133	820
10^{-2}	55	28	159
10^{-3}	21. 0	15. 0	24. 0
10^{-4}	2. 3	1. 8	0. 18

Effect of Root Temperature on Solute Transfer to Shoots

The effect of root temperature on transfer of solute from external solutions to shoots is indicated in tables 1 to 3. It would appear that for K the transfer to shoots was temperature dependent at the low concentrations. The absence of this effect in roots may be due to the fact that they were subjected to a several-day pretreatment with K which might have saturated the vacuoles (Arisz, 1956). In contrast to K, Rb uptake showed a temperature dependence for both leaves and roots as the concentration decreased. Sr uptake was not temperature dependent in either case. Br perhaps was more temperature dependent for roots than for leaves. There was a tendency for the uptake of mannitol by roots to be temperature dependent but transfer to the shoots was not (see page 91).

In all the temperature studies in this report the roots of the plants were the only plant part subjected to various temperatures. The aerial portions were left at room temperatures. Before each experiment, the experimental solutions were poured into the culture tubes and the temperatures of these solutions were maintained as desired. Since the radioactive isotopes in the leaves must first enter the plant via the roots, any influence of root temperature on absorption and/or translocation will be expressed in the final amount present in both the roots and the leaves, or the leaf/root ratio. The data in table 4 tend to indicate that leaf/root ratios are somewhat higher at 25°C when compared with those at 5°C.

Table 2. The uptake and distribution of various solutes in roots, stems, and leaves of bush beans for an absorption period of 5 hours at a root temperature at 5°C.

Concentration in Moles/liter	Roots	Stems	Leaves
		μmoles/g. dry weight	
		K^{42} from KBr	
10^{-1}	113.7	54.7	27.3
10^{-2}	54.7	19.3	1.2
10^{-3}	15.1	3.7	0.3
10^{-4}	1.9	0.4	0.03
		Rb^{86} from RbCl	
10^{-1}	66.8	29.9	3.73
10^{-2}	25.7	1.89	0.10
10^{-3}	6.21	0.52	0.04
10^{-4}	0.97	0.08	0.01
		Sr^{85} from $Sr(NO_3)_2$	
10^{-1}	60.05	96.7	63.7
10^{-2}	20.20	17.9	2.9
10^{-3}	6.09	4.27	0.41
10^{-4}	3.32	0.01	0.03
		Br^{82} from KBr	
10^{-1}	73.2	33.8	35.7
10^{-2}	4.6	3.20	3.1
10^{-3}	0.4	0.40	0.30
10^{-4}	0.06	0.05	0.03
		C^{14}-mannitol	
10^{-1}	114	116	779
10^{-2}	15.0	21.0	115
10^{-3}	3.9	7.7	14.0
10^{-4}	0.50	0.70	1.6

A previous study in this laboratory indicated that by just cooling a segment of a stem with a cold-water jacket, a large decrease in N^{15} transport from root to shoot of citrus was obtained (Wallace and Mueller, 1958).

Effect of the External Solute Concentration on Solute Transfer to Shoots

The fraction of the absorbed solute which was transported to the leaves increased progressively as the external concentration of the solute was increased. The amount of a solute transported to the leaves divided by the amount absorbed by the whole plant is referred to in the literature as the transport index. In this study, a more sensitive index of solute transport is the leaf/root ratio. The leaf/root ratio is used as the ratio of the micromoles dry weight of a solute in the leaves divided by that in the roots.

Table 3. $Q_{10's}$ for leaves and roots calculated from tables 1 and 2.

Concentration Moles/liter	Roots	Leaves
	K from KBr	
10^{-1}	1.3	1.5
10^{-2}	1.5	2.0
10^{-3}	1.1	2.2
10^{-4}	1.3	3.1
	Rb from RbCl	
10^{-1}	1.3	1.2
10^{-2}	1.3	2.2
10^{-3}	1.8	1.9
10^{-4}	3.1	3.0
	Sr from $Sr(NO_3)_2$	
10^{-1}	1.2	1.2
10^{-2}	1.2	1.2
10^{-3}	1.5	1.1
10^{-4}	1.2	1.0
	Br from KBr	
10^{-1}	1.6	1.3
10^{-2}	1.7	1.2
10^{-3}	2.4	1.8
10^{-4}	1.8	1.1
	mannitol	
10^{-1}	1.7	1.0
10^{-2}	1.9	1.2
10^{-3}	2.3	1.3
10^{-4}	2.2	0.3

Leaf/root ratios were somewhat inconsistent but tended to increase with a corresponding increase in the concentration of solute in the external solution, table 4.

Effect of Metabolic Inhibitors on Transfer of Solutes to Bush Bean Leaves

As reported in table 5 cyanide at a concentration of 10^{-3} M decreased absorption of K, Sr, and Br in the roots and actually increased transport to the leaves. Azide increased transfer of Br to leaves while decreasing the uptake into roots. Similarly, Russell (1954) working with barley plants, found that 10^{-3} M azide decreased phosphate absorption by the roots and increased its transport to shoots.

The work of Arisz (1953) with Vallisneria spiralis leaf segments indicated that KCN prevented uptake into cytoplasm but did not interfere with transport

or vascular secretions. If the transport within the <u>Vallisneria</u> leaf with its
well-developed phloem is analogous to phloem transport in plants, then the
cyanide effect can be explained in terms of two processes: Process I: the
formation at or near the root cell surface of a complex between the entering
ion and a product of respiration; this process is sensitive to cyanide.
Process II: which results in the ultimate transport of the ion to the shoot and
is insensitive to cyanide.

Table 4.   Leaf/root ratios calculated for various solutes.

Temperature	10^{-1}	Concentrations, M 10^{-2}	10^{-3}	10^{-4}	Means
		K^{42} from KBr			
5°C	.24	.02	.02	.02	.08
25°C	.40	.16	.09	.08	.18
		Br^{82} from KBr			
5°C	.20	.39	.33	.25	.29
25°C	1.04	.18	.20	.10	.38
		Rb^{86} from RbCl			
2°C	.05	.004	.006	.01	.02
25°C	.05	.01	.01	.005	.02
		Sr^{85} from $Sr(NO_3)_2$			
3°C	1.06	.11	.07	.009	.31
25°C	1.13	.11	.03	.006	.32
		C^{14}-mannitol			
5°C	6.83	7.66	3.59	3.20	5.11
30°C	1.65	2.58	4.19	.35	2.10

Whether or not these results with metabolic inhibitors indicate that there
are separate mechanism for uptake of solutes into roots or into shoots is unknown at this time. The moderate inhibition, if significant, of Sr^{85} uptake by
cyanide confuses the picture somewhat in that Sr uptake and transfer to shoots
showed no temperature dependency. The metabolic inhibitors do have an
effect on water flow through the plant—they tend to cause wilting. Some
indirect effects resulting from decreased water movement may cause the
results obtained here and elsewhere. A hypothesis of differential effects of
inhibitors on salt uptake into roots vs. salt movement to shoots, however, is
tempting.

Summary

The distribution pattern in bush beans for K^{42}, Rb^{86}, Sr^{85}, and Br^{82} in
5-hour studies was in the following order: roots > stems > leaves. Mannitol
exhibited a different distribution pattern. Transfer of K^{42} and Rb^{86} to leaves
was dependent upon root temperature but that of Sr^{85}, Br^{82}, and C^{14}-mannitol
was not. Leaf/root ratios tended to increase with external concentration.
Some metabolic inhibitors increased transfer of solutes to shoots even though
they inhibited uptake by roots.

Table 5. Effect of metabolic inhibitors on solute movement into leaves and roots of bush beans*.

% Inhibition (−) or % Increase (+)

Salt Conc. M	$K^{42}Br$ 10^{-3} NaCN	$K^{42}Br$ 2×10^{-3} NaN$_3$	$K^{42}Br$ 10^{-4} 2,4-DNP	KBr^{82} 10^{-3} NaCN	KBr^{82} 2×10^{-3} NaN$_3$	KBr^{82} 10^{-4} 2,4-DNP	$Sr^{85}(NO_3)_2$ 10^{-3} NaCN	$Sr^{85}(NO_3)_2$ 10^{-4} 2,4-DNP	$Rb^{86}Cl$ 10^{-3} NaCN	$Rb^{86}Cl$ 10^{-4} 2,4-DNP	$Rb^{86}Cl$ 10^{-3} MB	Mannitol 10^{-3} NaCN	Mannitol 10^{-4} 2,4-DNP	Mannitol 10^{-3} MB
Roots														
10^{-1}	−41	−50	−68	−17	−30	−47	+123	−19	−26	−31	−48	—	−2	−22
10^{-2}	−67	−68	−64	−85	−85	−81	+53	−58	−38	−37	−59	+101	+1	—
10^{-3}	−70	−60	−77	−89	−80	−67	−46	+34	−51	−63	−76	—	—	—
10^{-4}	−84	−78	−83	−83	−83	−91	−26	−20	−95	−92	−98	+32	+56	+385
Leaves														
10^{-1}	+69	−63	−69	+33	+155	−21	+14	+52	−78	−72	−77	—	—	—
10^{-2}	+53	−67	−64	+12	+310	−75	+288	−42	−73	−28	−90	+29	+76	+74
10^{-3}	+23	−64	−76	+1	+136	−84	+47	−64	−56	−60	−92	—	—	—
10^{-4}	+22	−64	−83	+73	+61	−80	+87	−37	−93	−20	−96	+113	+6	—

*The concentration of each inhibitor is given in $\underline{M}$ at the head of each column. MB is methylene blue.

SOME EFFECTS OF TEMPERATURE AND CONCENTRATION ON P^{32} UPTAKE BY BUSH BEAN PLANTS

With C. R. Carmack

Since the effects of concentration and temperature on uptake of solutes described in earlier sections of this report were rather interesting, similar studies were made with P^{32} in preliminary experiments. Very elegant studies have been reported concerning P uptake by plant materials (Hopkins, 1956; Hagen et al., 1957; Jackson and Hagen, 1960; Leggett, 1961; Jackson et al., 1962). Their studies in part were patterned after those of Chance et al. (1955) on oxidative phosphorylation.

Two separate experiments were made and they both gave almost identical results. Only one, therefore, will be described. Bush bean seedlings germinated in sand as usual were transferred after 9 days to 100 ml. portions of 1/10-strength nutrient solution for 4 days. The solutions were then changed to 4 different concentrations of KH$_2$PO$_4$ in quadruplicate. Two of each were maintained at 23°C for 5 hours and the other two at 3°C. Only the roots were maintained at the different temperatures. The pH was not maintained but varied between 4 and 5. At the end of the 5 hours the roots were washed in running water and leaves, stems, and roots were separated and dried. These samples were wet-ashed and aliquots dried for counting at infinite thinness on glass planchets. Counting was with a thin window Q-gas counter. The results were calculated as μmoles/g. dry weight from the specific activity relationships.

The post treatments may not have been long enough to remove all the P^{32} from the free space and so this may have caused a little error in the results.

Table 1. Uptake of P^{32} from different KH$_2$P^{32}O$_4$ concentrations at two different temperatures.

KH$_2$PO$_4$ $\underline{M}$	Leaf	Stem	Root	Whole Plant
		μmoles/g. dry weight		
		23°C		
10^{-1}	48.7	9.5	280.1	57.6
10^{-2}	9.1	3.9	48.1	10.7
10^{-3}	3.0	0.8	18.3	3.8
10^{-4}	1.6	0.4	10.4	2.10
		3°C		
10^{-1}	3.1	15.4	121.2	24.4
10^{-2}	0.57	1.5	7.0	1.9
10^{-3}	0.04	0.08	0.7	0.14
10^{-4}	0.00	0.01	0.21	0.03

The uptake values are given in table 1. At 23°C there appeared to be no effect of concentration on distribution of P^{32} among plant parts but at 3°C there was. The Q$_{10}$ values were 1.5, 2.4, 5.2, and 8.4 respectively for 10^{-1}, 10^{-2}, 10^{-3}, and 10^{-4} $\underline{M}$ KH$_2$PO$_4$. One may conclude that some diffusion obtained at the high concentration and that a metabolic accumulation process was essentially inoperative at the low temperature. A discussion of the meaning of Q$_{10}$ was given on page 27.

The concentration ratios for ten-fold differences in concentration are given in table 2. Only at the higher concentrations and at 23°C was the value near that of 4.93 (see page 20). The free-space problem may have obscured the ratio at the low concentrations. At the low temperatures two of the concentration ratios were around the value of 10. This also may be indicative of a mechanism breakdown at low temperatures.

Table 2. Concentration ratios for the data of table 1.

M	3°C	23°C
	Ratios	
$\dfrac{10^{-1}}{10^{-2}}$	12.8	5.4
$\dfrac{10^{-2}}{10^{-3}}$	13.6	2.8
$\dfrac{10^{-3}}{10^{-4}}$	4.7	1.8
Means	10.4	3.3

Summary

In 5-hour studies with bush bean the Q_{10} of P^{32} uptake between 3 and 23°C was 1.5, 2.4, 5.2, and 8.4 for 10^{-1}, 10^{-2}, 10^{-3}, and 10^{-4}M KH$_2$PO$_4$ respectively. The concentration ratios for ten-fold differences in external concentration was near 5 for the two high concentrations compared at 23°C and near 2 for the two lowest. At 3°C they were about 10. It was speculated that an accumulation mechanism was nearly inoperative at 3°C.

UPTAKE OF C^{14} FROM UREA AND BICARBONATE
BY BUSH BEAN PLANTS
With J. C. Procopiou

Urea is of interest because of its extensive use as a plant fertilizer, especially in foliar sprays. Much work has been done concerning metabolism of urea after its uptake by plant tissues. Relatively little work has been done concerning the mode of entrance of urea into the roots of intact plants.

The main purpose of this work was to learn something of the nature of absorption of urea by plant roots and its subsequent translocation to other plant parts. This is a rather difficult problem and the complications involved make progress extremely slow. The major problems are (a) the complexity of a whole plant, (b) possible metabolism of the urea molecule in the first cell that

---

The following special abbreviations are used throughout this report: 2,4-DNP, 2,4-dinitrophenol; PEP, phosphoenolpyruvic acid; and p-OHMBA, p-hydroxymercuribenzoic acid.

it encounters, and (c) the use of urea in which only one part of it is labeled with an isotope. Studies with single cells or with tissues having uniform cells are much more likely to be meaningful than studies with intact plants. Studies with plant parts, however, cannot provide all the answers for the intact plant, and these problems are just as important as those for single cells.

If C^{14}-urea passively enters root cells and in part is metabolized, the non-metabolized molecules would be subject to efflux but the metabolized molecules may be fixed in the cell in various reactions or would be transported to leaves as different compounds. The metabolic fixation, if extensive, may mask any effects of environmental factors on uptake. In the studies made here the urea molecules were labeled with C^{14}. The hydrolysis of urea (urea + $H_2O \rightarrow 2NH_3$ + CO_2) results in C^{14}-carbon dioxide. After initial cell penetration the label may become C^{14}-carbon dioxide instead of urea. This makes interpretation in terms of urea difficult.

C^{14}-bicarbonate was used because it also releases $C^{14}O_2$. If the urea label behaves as CO_2, then C^{14}-bicarbonate could be expected to behave similarly. Comparisons were made between urea and bicarbonate in most of the studies. Ammonia was not used with the bicarbonate but perhaps should have been.

C^{14}-urea and C^{14}-bicarbonate have been subjected in these studies to usual tests for separating passive uptake from metabolic accumulation by plant tissues. The present studies were made mostly with intact plants even though the usual procedure is to use single cells, excised roots, or discs of storage tissues.

Absorption of Urea by Plants

There is good evidence that plants can absorb intact urea molecules. When maize seedlings were grown in sterile culture with urea as the only source of nitrogen, urea could be detected in the shoots and even in guttation drops (Bollard, 1959). Bollard (1959) also detected urea in the xylem sap extracted from young apple trees growing in sand to which urea solution had been applied. Collander (1954) found that the permeation velocity of ethylurea, methylurea and urea for Nitella cells was 6.6×10^{-7} cm./sec., 3.2×10^{-7} cm./sec., 1.3×10^{-7} cm./sec. respectively when the cells were living, and 4.4×10^{-4} cm./sec., 5.0×10^{-4} cm./sec. and 5.7×10^{-4} cm./sec. when the cells were dead. Wallace and Ashcroft (1956b) compared urea, nitrate, ammonium, and ammonium nitrate on ion uptake by rough lemon cuttings and bush beans. The effect of urea was in many respects different from that of ammonium nitrogen and they concluded that the urea was absorbed before its hydrolysis.

Urea absorbed by the roots soon resulted in increased leaf urea content (Reifer and Melville, 1949). These workers report that a rye grass plant contained 1 mg. urea nitrogen per 100 g. fresh weight. One hour after fertilization with 5-10 g. urea per plant watered into the soil, the leaves showed 4 mg. urea N per 100 g. and 35 mg. per 100 g. in less than 24 hours. Webster et al. (1955) working with excised bean leaves suggested that urea is absorbed as an intact molecule and forms a pool of free urea in the cells before it is metabolized. Horie (1957) reported that in radish leaves immersed in a urea solution, total absorption increased with concentration and time and that 2,4-DNP had no effect on absorption. By comparing, on the basis of leaf nitrogen and shoot growth, apple seedlings sprayed with urea on either the upper or lower leaf surface, Rodney (1952) showed that nitrogen compounds entered through the leaf cuticle since there were no stomates in the upper leaf surface. Kuykendall and Wallace (1954) working with detached Eureka lemon leaves immersed in urea solution found a Q_{10} value of 1.19 between 4 and 24°C. By increasing the external urea concentration from 2 to 4 per cent the uptake was roughly doubled and both results were interpreted by them as indicating passive uptake rather than metabolic accumulation.

Mitsui and Kurihara (1957) studying C^{14} uptake from C^{14}-urea by rice and wheat plants from soils reported that plant roots can absorb urea as well as ammonium carbonate. In their 10-day experiments, and because of the rapidly occuring decomposition of urea in the soil to give ammonium carbonate, they thought that carbonate might have been the dominating form by which C^{14} was taken up. The same workers (1959) studying C^{14} uptake from C^{14}-urea and NaHC^{14}O$_3$ from nonaerated water cultures found the same distribution pattern but twice as much C^{14} uptake from NaHCO$_3$ as from urea. In soil cultures, however, more C^{14} was taken up from urea. In their water cultures C^{14} was accumulated more in the roots when urea was the carbon source. They could not conclude but they suggested that a considerable amount of C^{14} was taken up as urea with urease being the factor limiting net uptake. Urea hydrolysis in the nutrient solutions used occurred since only 74% of the added N that was not taken up by plants was found as urea in the external solution after 48 hours.

Utilization of Urea by Plants Containing Urease

Webster et al. (1955) supplied bean leaves with either C^{14}-urea or a mixture of C^{14}-bicarbonate and ammonium chloride and found the same pattern of C^{14} incorporation into the free amino acids and amides. They concluded that the first step in metabolism of the urea molecule is its hydrolysis to ammonia and carbon dioxide. Similarly, Boynton et al. (1953) studied the metabolism of nitrogen by apple leaves sprayed with N^{15}-urea. They found the pattern of incorporation of N^{15} into amino and amide nitrogen to be comparable with the pattern given when ammonia was used instead of urea. Webster (1959) indicated that some urea may be metabolized without being hydrolyzed. Dilley and Walker (1961) obtained evidence that this cannot be the case in excised apple and peach leaves. Bollard (1959) concluded that in the plants containing urease, any urea will be hydrolyzed to carbon dioxide and ammonia. Ammonia will be further used according to how each plant uses ammonia.

Utilization of Urea by Plants Lacking Urease

Walker (1952) pointed out that Chlorella can grow with urea as the sole source of nitrogen although attempts to find urease in Chlorella cells have so far failed. In agreement with Walker, Bollard (1959) stated that there are plants capable of utilizing urea in which urease has not been found. Such plants may produce urease as an adaptive enzyme when urea is added. In bacteria, as in higher plants, urease appears to be a constitutive enzyme, being present in organisms grown in media without urea (Lister, 1956), but in Pseudomonas aeruginosa it was formed only if urea was added to the medium (De Turk, 1955).

The method by which urea is assimilated in urease-free plants is not known. Freiberg et al. (1957) found radioactivity in allantoic acid in banana leaves supplied with C^{14}-urea. Walker (1952) suggested that in Chlorella, urea may be able to combine with ornithine to produce arginine. Hattori (1958) found that the increase in arginine content occurred without delay, in line with Walker's suggestion. Arginine in urease-free plants and plants lacking arginase could be metabolized by a reversal of the ornithine cycle as was suggested by Walker (1952).

Following urea application, increases in glutamine levels have been reported in apple leaves (Boynton et al. , 1953), in potato discs (Steward and Pollard, 1956), in citrus (Impey, 1959). Increases in arginine have been found by Walker (1952) in Chlorella pyrenoidosa and in Scenedesmus obliquus by Thomas and Krauss (1955). Nandi, quoted by Bollard (1959), reported that seeds of 4 leguminous species, none of which contained urease, germinated in contact with urea contained 4-8 times as much arginine as seeds germinating in water.

Bicarbonate Uptake by Plants

The amount of HCO_3^- present in a solution in equilibrium with the CO_2 in air depends on pH. The amount of these species present in a nutrient solution containing HCO_3^- at any given pH can be calculated from the Henderson—Hasselbalch equation

$$pH = pKa + \log \frac{(HCO_3^-)}{(CO_2)} .$$

At pH 8 and 0^{0}C over 95 per cent of the CO_2 present in the solution will be as HCO_3^- and about 70 per cent at pH 7 (Bhan et al. , 1960).

The relative importance of HCO_3^- vs. CO_2 in biochemical reactions was discussed by Huffaker et al. (1960). They pointed out that the CO_2-fixing enzyme system requiring ribose-5-phosphate as a substrate used the CO_2 form rather than the HCO_3^- form. They were less sure about the system using PEP but Maruyama and Lane (1962) have shown it to be HCO_3^-. Huffaker et al. (1960) showed that the HCO_3^- form was taken up by plant roots. It was further demonstrated by Huffaker et al. (1960) that for concentrations of $10^{-3}M$ HCO_3^- or lower appropriate corrections should be made to account for the HCO_3^- derived from atmospheric CO_2. At pH 8 the concentration of any solution of bicarbonate or water in equilibrium with the air should be increased by $6 \times 10^{-4}M$. For pH 6. 5 Hurd (1958) gave the value of $17 \times 10^{-6}M$ for the bicarbonate derived from the air. Further, the amount of C^{14} measured in the plant material may not indicate the amount of carbon taken up since some of the bicarbonate in the external solution might have been diluted with the respiratory CO_2 and some might have been lost through respiration of the products of the assimilated carbon (Bhan et al. , 1960).

CO_2 Fixation by Plant Roots

Until about 1940 it was believed that roots did not fix CO_2 or HCO_3^- appreciably (Overstreet et al. , 1940). Bonner and Bonner (1948) demonstrated dark CO_2 fixation by Bryophyllum leaves after which the organic acid content increased, especially of malate. CO_2 fixation was demonstrated to occur in barley roots by Overstreet et al. (1940) using C^{11}, in parsley roots by Vennesland et al. (1947), in barley roots by Laties (1949), Jacobson (1955), and Poel (1953). The last of these investigators showed that this dark CO_2 fixation was oxygen dependent. Malic, citric (or isocitric), aspartic and glutamic acids, asparagine and glutamine contained most of the C^{14} from the $C^{14}O_2$ fixed. Subsequently it was demonstrated that other plants can fix CO_2 in the dark and differences in the ability for CO_2 fixation were found between species and even varieties (Brown, 1956; Stolwijk and Thimann, 1957; Bedri et al. , 1960). Several mechanisms are known by which CO_2 fixation may occur. The reaction of PEP and CO_2, activated by magnesium, to give oxalacetate irreversibly, described by Bandurski (1955), occurs in bean roots and seems to be of prime physiological importance (Jackson, 1957). As yet it is very uncertain whether or not the carboxykinase system is present in roots of higher plants.

Although accumulation of bicarbonate-derived carbon in plants has been clearly demonstrated, the direct absorption of bicarbonate has been doubted (Miller, 1960). Hoagland (1944, p. 123) stated that bicarbonate ions do not appreciably accumulate in the cells. This does not mean that they are not absorbed. Lundegardh, quoted by Hurd (1958), reported that HCO_3^- was not accumulated by plant roots. Jacobs (1924) showed that carbonic acid, H_2CO_3, or its anhydride, CO_2, has a unique power to permeate the cell including the tonoplast. Voznesenskii (1959) concluded that roots can absorb gaseous CO_2 as well as small amounts of carbon dioxide from solutions. Huffaker et al. (1960) presented evidence that HCO_3^- and not necessarily CO_2 alone was taken up by plant roots. Hurd (1958) also stated that bicarbonate was taken up. Geisler (1963) found that $CO_2 + HCO_3^-$ in small quantities stimulated root growth.

Materials and Methods

Solution cultures with C^{14} labeled urea or HCO_3^- were used in the studies. Bush beans (Phaseolus vulgaris L. var. Tendergreen) were grown by germinating seeds in sterilized quartz sand, No. 16, in wooden flats in the glasshouse. They were watered regularly with distilled water. In a few experiments the plants were grown there for 14 days and then uniform, vigorous ones were carefully removed after the whole flat was immersed in water to facilitate removal. The plants were then washed in tap and distilled water and used in the experiments. In the description of each experiment such plants are described as plants grown in sand. In most of the experiments, however, the plants used were grown as follows: six days after the sowing of the seeds as described above, vigorous, uniform seedlings were selected and transferred to 100 ml. culture tubes with one-fourth strength of the following nutrient solution, in mole/liter: $Ca(NO_3)_2$, 0.005; KNO_3, 0.001; $MgSO_4$, 0.004; K_2SO_4, 0.002; $NH_4H_2PO_4$, 0.002. Micronutrient elements were supplied as follows: 1.0 ppm. Mn as $MnSO_4$, 0.1 ppm. B as H_3BO_3, 0.12 ppm. Zn as $ZnSO_4 \cdot 7H_2O$, and 0.03 ppm. Mo as H_2MoO_4. Iron, 5 ppm., was supplied as FeEDDHA (the iron form of ethylenediamine di(o-hydroxyphenylacetic acid)). CO_2-free air was used to aerate the solutions. The seedlings were handled with care so that no roots were broken. When the plants were 14 days old the nutrient solutions were discarded, the roots rinsed with distilled water and the experimental solutions added to the culture tubes. Experimental solutions were labeled with either C^{14}-urea or C^{14}-bicarbonate. All experimental solutions were made up to $10^{-4}M$ $CaSO_4$ to preserve the integrity of the roots.

The pH of the urea solutions was adjusted to 7.5. The pH of the low concentrations, $10^{-3}M$ and $10^{-4}M$, had a tendency to drop to as low as 6.8 and the high ones, $10^{-2}M$ and $10^{-1}M$, tended to rise to 8.0 during the tests. The pH of the bicarbonate, always from $KHCO_3$, was adjusted to 8.0, unless otherwise indicated, with NaOH or HCl and not allowed to drop below 7.5 to avoid losses of CO_2. In high bicarbonate concentrations, $10^{-1}M$ and $10^{-2}M$, the pH tended to rise to 9.0 and 8.8 and at low, $10^{-4}M$, tended to drop to 7.7 during the tests. Unless otherwise indicated the experiments started at 11:00 a.m. The concentrations of the bicarbonate solutions were corrected for the CO_2 derived from the air as described by Huffaker et al. (1960).

In a few experiments roots only were used which were prepared as follows: roots of 14-day-old bush beans grown in sand were washed with tap and distilled water and cut in sections 1-2 cm. long. These are called excised roots in contrast to the excised whole roots. The latter means the whole root system (not cut in sections) of 14-day-old plants grown in nutrient solutions as were described above. These roots were incubated in the experimental solutions and further treated as were the roots of the intact plants. Usually there were 4 or more replications and most experiments were repeated several times.

At the end of each experiment the experimental solutions were removed, the roots rinsed with distilled water and then the roots were bathed for one hour, unless otherwise mentioned, in aerated unlabeled urea or bicarbonate solutions (in $10^{-4}M$ $CaSO_4$) of the highest concentration and the same pH as used in the experiment. This treatment removed isotopes from the free space (FS) and eliminated any loosely bound radioactive carbon. That treatment hereafter will be referred to as washing of the FS. The plants were then taken out of the solutions, rinsed with distilled water, separated into leaves, stems, and roots, placed in paper bags and dried in a forced-draft oven at 70°C. The dry plant material was ground with a Wiley mill to pass a 20-mesh screen, weighed and counted for C^{14} with a Nuclear-Chicago thin window gas flow counter in metal planchets. Background was subtracted and corrections for self absorption to the 10-mg. basis was made using self absorption factors, obtained as described by Hendler (1959). The specific activity was determined by mixing a known volume of stock solutions of radioactive urea or bicarbonate with 1 g. ground plant material, in each case, and counting 10 mg. of it. The so-found specific activity of the stock solutions was 1,021,000 cpm./ml. for C^{14}-urea and 137,000 cpm./ml. for C^{14}-bicarbonate. These values were used to calculate the specific activities of test solutions at 10 mg. dry plant material.

That amount of C^{14} that was detected in the dry plant material accounts only for that not respired. The part lost, through respiration, would represent a higher per cent in the cases of lower concentrations of the experimental solutions than with higher concentrations. These losses, however, were not measured. The large losses of C^{14} from the experimental solutions to the air are discussed later. The depletion of the external solution due to absorption of C^{14} by the plant was negligible in the case of urea since less than 2% of the C^{14} was taken up and recovered after twenty-four hours.

Assuming that the whole plant and each part contained 85% water, the concentration of C^{14} in the external solution and in the cell solution can be estimated. This statistic was used as an indication of uptake with or against a concentration gradient. Some of the C^{14}, however, very likely was incorporated into different organic compounds and removed from solution in the cell sap.

Results with C^{14}-Urea

Urease in C^{14}-Urea Solutions and Losses of C^{14}

To find if C^{14} was lost from C^{14}-urea solutions the experiment detailed in table 1 was conducted. The results indicate that radioactive carbon was lost from the external solutions especially when low urea concentrations were used. This loss might have been caused by excretion of traces of urease from the plant roots to the external solution. The loss of C^{14} from the external solution is assumed to occur after urease hydrolyzes C^{14}-urea to $C^{14}O_2$ and NH_3, the $C^{14}O_2$ being exchanged with the CO_2 of the atmosphere. Excretion of organic substances and absorption of such, including proteins such as urease, by plant roots, has been reported (Jensen and McLaren, 1960; Martin, 1959; Bhide and Brachet, 1960). Urease, however, might have come from the microbial populations that have been shown to be living on root surfaces (Esterman and McLaren, 1961). A further indication that urease was in the external solution was obtained by the observation that in the absence of plants, $10^{-3}M$ urea solution in a beaker open to the air for 24 hours at room temperature did not lose any C^{14}. Considerable of the $C^{14}O_2$ produced by urease will exist as such and not as $HC^{14}O_3^-$ because of the lower pH used in the urea experiments as compared to that used in the bicarbonate experiments. No correction has been made in the results of these studies to account for the losses of C^{14} from the external solutions since it is not known precisely the curve of concentration changes with time and how the uptake related to the existing concentration. Further, many of the experiments lasted only 6 hours in which time the losses were small for all except the $10^{-4}\underline{M}$ urea concentrations.

Table 1.   Losses of C^{14}-urea from a 100 ml. nutrient solution to bean plants and to the atmosphere.

	Urea concentration, $\underline{M}$			
	10^{-1}	10^{-2}	10^{-3}	10^{-4}
	Recovery of C^{14} in μmoles and losses of C^{14}.			
At start, μmoles added in 100 ml. solution*	10,000	1000	100	10
After 6 hrs., μmoles recovered in 100 ml. solution*	9,200	920	92	7.23
% decrease	8	8	8	27.7
After 24 hrs., μmoles recovered in 100 ml. solution*	8,000	740	58.5	3.54
% decrease	20	26	41.5	64.6
Recovery in plants in 24 hrs.	180	8.7	0.67	0.069
% taken by plants	1.8	0.87	0.67	0.69
% loss to air	18.2	25.1	40.8	63.9

*Calculated by fan-drying 0.2 ml. of solution on a glass planchet, and counting.

Influx—Efflux

The hypothesis was made that some urea enters the cell passively and is there hydrolyzed by urease and the C^{14} is then fixed into organic compounds. If urease were limiting and if part of the urea in the cells were not immediately hydrolyzed, the urea could be expected to be washed out of the roots in the post-treatments. To test the hypothesis, excised roots were incubated in labeled urea solutions of concentrations ranging from $10^{-1}\underline{M}$ to $10^{-4}\underline{M}$ for 6 hours. Following that period the labeled solutions were replaced by $10^{-1}\underline{M}$ nonlabeled ones for varying time periods, then the roots were rinsed with distilled water and counted. The results (table 2) indicate that for the $10^{-1}\underline{M}$ concentration considerable of the C^{14} was replaced in roots by the $10^{-1}\underline{M}$ nonlabeled urea. In lower concentrations no decreases were evident. At low external concentrations all the urea entering the cells appeared to be readily hydrolyzed and the C^{14} fixed into organic compounds. A pool of free urea in cells is probably formed when the rate of urea uptake is greater than the rate of hydrolysis.

The data in table 2 indicate that a 5-minute equilibration period was enough to remove C^{14} from FS of roots except for the $10^{-1}\underline{M}$ urea. Therefore, the results reported hereafter, when roots are used, concern 5-minute washings. Urea is not likely to be bound to exchange sites on the surfaces of the cell walls.

Table 2.   Effect of time of washing on C^{14} retention from C^{14}-urea solution by excised roots incubated for 6 hours.

Time of Washing	Urea Concentration, $\underline{M}$				
	10^{-1}	5×10^{-3}	2.5×10^{-3}	10^{-3}	10^{-4}
Minutes	μmoles C^{14} taken up/g. dry weight				
5	341	11.0	6.6	2.8	0.23
30	139	11.3	6.5	2.4	0.21
60	103	7.7	5.3	2.5	0.25
150	70	8.7	4.6	2.3	0.26
300	56	10.1	5.8	2.6	0.20

Effects of Concentration, Time and Temperature on Uptake of Urea

The concentration ratios, defined as the ratio of uptake from two external concentrations differing by 10 times were calculated. The ratios were somewhat constant at 10 which give a plot of uptake vs. concentration as a straight line. The uptake increased in direct proportion to urea concentration as shown in table 3 for intact plants. Results for excised whole roots were similar. The concentration ratios probably indicate nonmetabolic uptake.

Table 3.   Effect of urea concentration on C^{14} uptake from urea by intact plants in 6 hours.

Urea concentration, $\underline{M}$			
10^{-1}	10^{-2}	10^{-3}	10^{-4}
μmoles C^{14}/g. dry weight in plants			
77	4.3	0.61	0.055

Ratios of uptake at various concentrations, $\underline{M}$					
$\dfrac{10^{-1}}{10^{-2}}$	$\dfrac{10^{-2}}{10^{-3}}$	$\dfrac{10^{-3}}{10^{-4}}$	$\dfrac{10^{-1}}{10^{-3}}$	$\dfrac{10^{-2}}{10^{-4}}$	$\dfrac{10^{-1}}{10^{-4}}$
Concentration ratios in plants					
17.9	7.0	11.0	11.2	8.8	11.2

In table 4 the distribution of C^{14} in the different plant parts is shown. The high L/R ratio (the C^{14} in the leaves/C^{14} in the roots per g. dry weight) in the case of $10^{-1}M$ concentration as compared to that in the lower concentrations used, indicates that when urea enters the root cells some of the urea is not hydrolyzed. When $10^{-1}M$ and even $10^{-2}M$ were used, more of the urea appeared to move to the leaves so that a high L/R ratio resulted. At the lower concentrations used, little C^{14} was found in the leaves (L/R ratio low) and practically all the C^{14} was apparently fixed in the roots.

The uptake of C^{14} from $10^{-2}M$ urea by intact bean plants versus the duration of the experiment is given in figure 1. A resulting straight line when the uptake is plotted against time would be explainable if 1) urea is taken up passively, 2) the label (C^{14}) is fixed after getting into the cell, 3) the fixing mechanism is not limiting. The uptake of C^{14} by excised whole roots from a $10^{-4}M$ urea solution for a 72-hour period is also given in figure 1. With both concentrations the plot of uptake vs. time gave a hyperbola rather than a straight line indicating possibly that the fixing mechanism is limiting.

Table 4.   Distribution of C^{14} taken up from different urea concentrations by intact plants in 24 hours.

| Plant part | Urea Concentration, $\underline{M}$ | | | |
	10^{-1}	10^{-2}	10^{-3}	10^{-4}
	μmoles C^{14}/g. dry weight			
Leaf	287	5.3	0.27	0.028
Stem	121	13.1	0.86	0.068
Root	278	27.0	3.55	0.333
	L/R ratios			
	1.03	0.20	0.08	0.08

The low root temperatures used in this type of experiment can cause plants to wilt, and to avoid wilting the plants were kept in an atmosphere of high humidity. The low temperatures were achieved and kept constant with ice and water in a synthetic plastic insulated container. The experimental solutions were cooled before the plants were immersed. Results in table 5 for excised roots indicate little temperature dependency on urea uptake. The uptake appeared to be more dependent on temperature at low than at high external concentrations between 5 and 20° C.

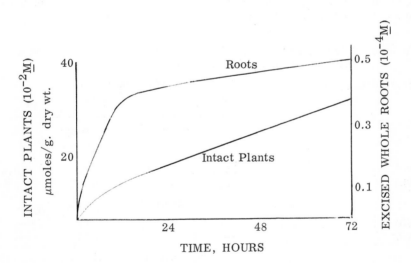

Figure 1. C^{14} uptake from $10^{-2}\underline{M}$ urea by intact plants and from $10^{-4}\underline{M}$ urea by excised whole roots in relation to the duration of treatment.

Effects of Aeration with Nitrogen

In this experiment with intact plants the usual CO_2-free air was bubbled into the external solutions of half of the plants and pure N_2 in the external solutions of the other half as detailed in table 6 (1 hour pretreatment in N_2 was used). The results in table 6 indicate a 41 to 52 per cent inhibition of uptake in the anaerobically treated plants. All the plants were kept in a high humidity atmosphere since the N_2-treated plants tended to wilt. There was no wilting in the humid atmosphere. Anaerobiosis inhibited translocation much more than uptake at high urea concentrations as seen from the leaf/root ratios (table 6). When excised whole roots were used, as shown in table 6, 90 per cent inhibition in C^{14} uptake resulted from the N_2 aeration.

Table 5. Effect of temperature on C^{14} uptake from urea by excised roots in 5 hours.

Urea Concentration	Temperature, $^{\circ}$C.			Q_{10} values between temperatures, $^{\circ}$C	
	5	20	30	5 & 20	20 & 30
$\underline{M}$	μmoles* C^{14} taken up/g. dry wt.				
10^{-1}	633	693	693	1.03	1.00
10^{-2}	20.3	25.9	33.7	1.17	1.19
10^{-3}	1.88	5.23	5.50	1.98	1.03
10^{-4}	0.198	0.485	0.736	1.82	1.32

*Calculated from specific activity relationships.

Effects of Inhibitors

Cyanide (CN^-) inhibited C^{14} uptake from urea (table 7). The inhibition of cyanide, however, may be due to formation of the cyanhydrin between urea and cyanide. A larger molecule would meet more resistance to diffusion.

Table 6. Effect of aeration on C^{14} uptake from urea by intact plants and excised whole roots in 6 hours.

Treatment	Urea Concentration, $\underline{M}$			
	10^{-1}	3×10^{-3}	10^{-3}	10^{-4}
	μmoles C^{14}/g. dry weight			
	Whole Plant			
With air	51.	1.28	0.52	0.046
With N_2	26.	0.61	0.305	0.026
	Excised Whole Roots			
With air	—	—	2.62	—
With N_2	—	—	0.27	—
	Inhibition for N_2, %			
Whole plant	48	52	41	43
Excised whole roots	—	—	90	—
	Leaf/Root Ratios for C^{14}			
With air	1.18	0.43	0.21	0.30
With N_2	0.14	0.26	0.25	0.26

The inhibition of urea uptake by intact plants from 4 different urea concentrations was slight in the presence of 2,4-DNP and much greater with NaN_3 in a 6-hour period as shown in table 8. The inhibition was greater at low urea concentrations than at high. The L/R ratio was increased in the presence of NaN$_3$ especially at low urea concentrations. NaN$_3$, thus, inhibited absorption but not the translocation. Double reciprocal plots made from the data in table 8 indicated competitive inhibition for both 10^{-4}M 2, 4-DNP and 5 x 10^{-3}M NaN$_3$. This should not obtain if urea is absorbed passively but may be due to the urease reactions or to CO_2 fixation in the root cells.

Table 7.   Inhibition of C^{14} uptake from urea by intact plants over a 5 hour period in the presence of and with 2. 5 hour pretreatment with CN^-.

NaCN concentration	Urea concentration, $\underline{M}$			
$\underline{M}$	10^{-1}	10^{-2}	10^{-3}	10^{-4}
	μmoles C^{14}/g. dry weight whole plant			
0	82	3. 9	0. 80	0. 071
10^{-4}	80	2. 7	0. 68	0. 065
10^{-3}	63	2. 4	0. 33	0. 010

In the presence of p-OHMBA, which may be expected to inhibit urease, the uptake of urea by intact plants and by excised whole roots was inhibited as shown in table 9.   The plot of the reciprocals of the uptake and concentration indicates that this inhibition was also competitive.

Table 8.   Effects of 2, 4-DNP and NaN$_3$ on C^{14} uptake from urea by intact plants in 6 hours.

Treatment	Urea concentration, $\underline{M}$			
	10^{-1}	10^{-2}	10^{-3}	10^{-4}
	uptake in μmoles C^{14}/g. dry weight			
	Data for whole plant			
Control	72. 4	2. 42	0. 558	0. 0490
5 x 10^{-4}M 2, 4-DNP	35. 3	1. 66	0. 098	0. 0134
10^{-4}M 2, 4-DNP	72. 9	2. 42	0. 343	0. 0370
5 x 10^{-3}M NaN$_3$	32. 5	0. 43	0. 047	0. 0034
10^{-3}M NaN$_3$	31. 4	0. 72	0. 050	0. 0074
	Leaf/Root Ratios			
Control	0. 020	0. 050	0. 047	0. 042
5 x 10^{-4}M 2, 4-DNP	0. 023	0. 042	0. 190	0. 056
10^{-4}M 2, 4-DNP	0. 010	0. 043	0. 045	0. 042
5 x 10^{-3}M NaN$_3$	0. 042	0. 076	0. 238	0. 162
10^{-3}M NaN$_3$	0. 020	0. 197	0. 233	0. 127

Results with C^{14}-Bicarbonate

Losses of C^{14} from Bicarbonate Solutions

Hurd (1958) reported that at least 50 percent of the C^{14} from 2. 3 x 10^{-3}M C^{14}-bicarbonate solutions was lost in 6 hours to the atmosphere. This is due to the isotopic exchange of $C^{14}O_2$ with the CO_2 of the air and to spontaneous losses of $C^{14}O_2$ to the air.

Table 9　　Effect of p-OHMBA on C^{14} uptake from urea in 6 hours.

Treatment	Urea concentration, $\underline{M}$				
	5×10^{-3}	10^{-3}	5×10^{-4}	10^{-4}	10^{-2}
	Excised Whole Roots				Intact Plant
	μmoles C^{14} taken up/g. dry weight				
Control	8.85	1.67	0.91	0.24	35.0
$5\times10^{-4}\underline{M}$ p-OHMBA	6.82	0.67	0.58	0.07	20.5
Inhibition, %	23	60	36	69	41

To study the losses of C^{14} from variously labeled bicarbonate solutions, different concentrations of it were prepared and the radioactivity in cpm./ml. of solution was determined at different times in the presence of intact plants with aeration with CO_2-free air. The experiment is detailed and the results are reported in table 10. The radioactivity was corrected for background and self absorption according to Hendler (1959). The radioactive carbon was added after the pH of the solution was adjusted at 8.5 and it was not allowed to drop below 8.0 during the experiment. The losses were higher at lower pH. The results in table 10 are in good agreement with Hurd's. The results obtained for plants were not corrected for that type of decrease in radioactivity for the same reasons reported for urea and also because most of the experiments have comparative value only. Some data with corrections are given on page 62.

Table 10.　　Losses of C^{14} from C^{14}-bicarbonate solutions to the atmosphere at pH 8.5 in 6 hours when aerated with CO_2-free air.

Added HCO$_3^-$*	pH**			cpm./ml.		decreases in 6 hrs.
	at start	after 3 hr.	after 6 hr.	at start	after 6 hr.	%
$\underline{M}$						
10^{-1}	8.5	9.2	9.2	2,200	2,000	9
10^{-2}	8.4	8.9	8.9	1,000	900	10
10^{-3}	7.2	8.1	8.1	550	90	83

*The concentrations of $10^{-2}\underline{M}$ HCO$_3^-$ or lower have been increased in the calculations given later by a factor of $6\times10^{-4}\underline{M}$ to correct for the atmospheric CO_2.
** The final reading of pH is recorded here but after each reading it was adjusted to 8.5.

Influx—Efflux

To find out the time necessary to wash the C^{14} from the free space in roots in the uptake experiments and obtain some information about the magnitude of fluxes and about possible enzyme involvement in uptake the experiment detailed in table 11 was run. The results indicate that for all concentrations of bicarbonate used except 10^{-1}M, 5 minutes was enough time to wash the roots. A gradual decrease in C^{14} content with time of washing was attributed to loss by respiration. There was little efflux.

Table 11. Effect of washing time on C^{14} retention from C^{14}-HCO_3^- solutions by excised roots incubated for 6 hours.

Time of washing	Added HCO_3^- concentration, $\underline{M}$				
	10^{-1}	5×10^{-3}	2.5×10^{-3}	10^{-3}	10^{-4}
min.	μmoles C^{14} taken up/g. dry weight				
5	350	33.7	14.7	9.14	5.56
30	183	34.0	13.6	7.82	4.86
60	209	31.6	14.7	8.36	5.02
150	209	23.5	16.8	6.69	3.64
300	167	25.3	12.1	6.35	3.67

Effects of Concentration, Time, and Temperature

The uptake increased as the concentration increased (table 12). The 10-fold increases in external concentration averaged about a 5-fold increase in uptake instead of 10 for C^{14} from urea. Excised roots gave the same results as intact plants.

Table 12   Effect of external bicarbonate concentration on C^{14} uptake from bicarbonate solution in 6 hours.

Plant Part	HCO_3^- concentration, $\underline{M}$		
	10^{-1}	106×10^{-4}	16×10^{-4}
	μmoles C^{14} taken up/g. dry weight		
Intact plant			
Whole plant	69.0	14.5	2.80
Leaf	45.2	10.4	1.67
Stem	69.5	13.4	2.37
Root	142.0	36.3	8.27
Leaf/Root ratio	0.32	0.28	0.20
	Concentration ratios (for 10-fold)		
	$10^{-1}/10^{-2}$	$10^{-2}/10^{-3}$	$10^{-1}/10^{-3}$
	ratios		
Whole plant	5.1	7.7	6.3

The uptake was related to the time of treatment as shown in figure 2. The curve is hyperbolic. The pH of the solutions was adjusted to 8.0 and readjusted to 8.0 whenever some of the plants were harvested. It tended to increase to 8.5. Results in table 13 where Q_{10} values have also been calculated indicate some temperature dependency on $HC^{14}O_3^-$ uptake. A greater loss of $C^{14}O_2$ to the atmosphere at high than at low temperature would increase the Q_{10} values.

Effects of Aeration with N_2 and Inhibitors

C^{14} uptake in the presence of N_2 by excised whole roots from $10^{-3}\underline{M}$ bicarbonate was 0.54 μmoles per g. dry weight as compared to 18.5 μmoles per g. dry weight of the control. The experiment lasted 6 hours.

Concentrations of $5 \times 10^{-4}\underline{M}$ 2,4-DNP and $5 \times 10^{-3}\underline{M}$ NaN_3 gave almost

Table 13.   Effect of temperature on C^{14} uptake from bicarbonate in 6 hrs.

HCO_3^- concn. *	Whole plant	Leaf/ Root	Whole plant	Leaf/ Root	Whole plant
$\underline{M}$	μmoles C^{14}/g. dry weight	ratio	μmoles C^{14}/g. dry weight	ratio	Q_{10}
	1^oC		21^oC		
10^{-1}	41.0	0.67	121.0	0.42	1.72
106×10^{-4}	12.3	0.20	38.1	0.30	1.78
16×10^{-4}	4.0	0.35	12.3	0.10	1.80
7×10^{-4}	1.9	0.11	6.4	0.10	1.83

Excised whole roots**

	5^oC		25^oC		
16×10^{-4}	2.64		18.52		2.65

*Corrected for CO_2 of the air.
**The Ea value between 5^oC and 25^oC was 16,000 cal./mole.

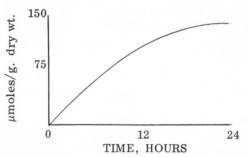

Figure 2. C^{14} uptake from $10^{-2}\underline{M}$ HCO_3^- by intact plants in relation to time of treatment.

Table 14.   Effects of different concentrations of 2,4-DNP and NaN_3 on C^{14} uptake from $10^{-2}\underline{M}$ bicarbonate by intact plants in 6 hrs.

Inhibitor Concentration	Whole plant	Leaf	L/R	Whole Plant, Inhibition
$\underline{M}$	μmoles C^{14} taken up/g. dry weight		ratio	%
0	3.58	0.45	0.02	—
		2,4-DNP		
10^{-4}	3.35	0.50	0.04	6
5×10^{-4}	1.51	0.35	0.06	58
10^{-3}	1.18	0.35	0.07	67
		NaN_3		
10^{-3}	1.95	0.44	0.07	46
5×10^{-3}	1.13	0.42	0.10	69
10^{-2}	0.85	0.45	0.15	76

maximum inhibition of $HC^{14}O_3^-$ accumulation (table 14). Both inhibitors, especially NaN_3, did not inhibit translocation to the leaves so that the leaf/root ratios were higher in the presence of the inhibitors than in the control.

The uptake by intact plants in the presence of p-OHMBA over a 6-hour period was inhibited as shown in table 15. This sulfhydryl inhibitor had some inhibiting effect and the enzyme fixing CO_2 is known to be a sulfhydryl enzyme.

Table 15. Inhibition of C^{14} uptake from bicarbonate by intact plants in the presence of p-OHMBA for 6 hours.

	HCO_3^- Concentration, $\underline{M}$		
	10^{-1}	1.06×10^{-2}	1.6×10^{-3}
	μmoles C^{14} taken up/g. dry weight		
Control	125	23.6	4.90
With 5 x $10^{-4}\underline{M}$ p-OHMBA	150	14.0	2.78
	Inhibition, Whole Plant, %		
	0	41	43
	Leaf/Root ratios for C^{14}		
Control	0.83	0.79	0.43
With 5 x $10^{-4}\underline{M}$ p-OHMBA	2.0	1.06	0.47

Results with Both Urea and Bicarbonate

Results with Intact Plants

The C^{14} uptake from C^{14}-labeled urea solutions in the presence of $10^{-2}M$ nonlabeled bicarbonate and vice versa was studied. Possible competition between the carbon dioxide of the two solutes would decrease C^{14} uptake below the control. If the C^{14} label in both cases were absorbed or fixed as $C^{14}O_2$, competition from non-labeled CO_2 could be expected. If there is no competition some speculation on rate limiting steps may be made.

The effect of the chelating agent, ethylenediaminetetraacetic acid (EDTA), on C^{14} uptake from C^{14}-labeled urea and bicarbonate solutions also was studied. EDTA binds the Ca in a solution (Chaberek and Martell, 1959). The presence of Ca increases K accumulation (Viets, 1944) and this is attributed, by some, to the activation of adenosinetriphosphatases (ATPases) by Ca (Honda and Robertson, 1956) and production of ADP required for K accumulation. The use of EDTA then was to decrease the Ca level to determine whether or not Ca had an effect on uptake of the C^{14}-containing solutes.

The results in table 16 show no dilution of the carbon from either solute in the presence of the other. EDTA inhibited C^{14} uptake from both urea and bicarbonate to a very small extent only indicating possibly that the presence of Ca^{++} was not essential to the uptake of either.

Results with Excised Whole Roots

In this experiment excised whole roots were subjected for 6 hours to different treatments known to inhibit metabolic reactions. The details and results in table 17 showed no inhibition of uptake by fluoride. This obtained for both urea and bicarbonate. EDTA inhibited uptake slightly (18%) from urea and more (44%) from bicarbonate which may be indicative of a Ca^{++} requirement.

All other treatments and inhibitors used, except fluoride, strongly inhibited C^{14} uptake. The inhibition of the other metabolic inhibitors used may be due to changes in the permeability status of the cells as was suggested by Robertson et al. (1951) for mitochondria. The HCO_3^- appeared to be accumulated against a concentration gradient but the urea was not.

Table 16. Effect of bicarbonate on C^{14} uptake from C^{14}-urea and vice versa and effect of EDTA on C^{14} uptake from C^{14}-labeled urea and bicarbonate by intact plants.

Treatment	Whole Plant	Leaf	Stem	Root	L/R
	μmoles C^{14}/g. dry weight				ratio
10^{-3}M urea*	0.99	0.69	0.95	1.84	0.37
10^{-3}M urea* + 10^{-2}M KHCO$_3$	0.83	0.58	0.81	1.80	0.32
10^{-3}M urea* + 10^{-3}M EDTA	0.92	0.39	1.33	1.00	0.39
10^{-4}M urea*	0.114	0.065	0.119	0.259	0.25
10^{-4}M urea* + 10^{-2}M KHCO$_3$	0.145	0.105	0.136	0.305	0.34
10^{-3}M KHCO$_3$*	10.0	7.1	9.5	23.2	0.30
10^{-3}M KHCO$_3$* + 10^{-2}M urea	12.4	11.8	9.7	27.9	0.42
10^{-3}M KHCO$_3$* + 10^{-3}M EDTA	9.2	8.5	10.1	8.1	1.05
10^{-4}M KHCO$_3$*	1.04	0.50	1.06	2.91	0.17
10^{-4}M KHCO$_3$* + 10^{-2}M urea	2.20	1.93	2.06	3.98	0.48

*Labeled with C^{14}.

Table 17. C^{14} uptake from urea or bicarbonate by excised whole roots in 6 hours.

Treatment	Urea	HCO_3^-	Urea	HCO_3^-
	μmoles C^{14} taken up/g. dry weight		% Inhibition	
Control (10^{-3}M, 25°C)	2.62	18.52	—	—
Anaerobiosis (with N$_2$)	0.27	0.54	90	97
At 5°C	0.52*	2.64*	80	86
With 10^{-3}M NaF	3.01	16.62	0	10
With 5 x 10^{-3}M NaN$_3$	0.16	2.27	94	88
With 5 x 10^{-4}M p-OHMBA	0.96	10.01	63	46
With 10^{-3}M EDTA	2.14	10.43	18	44

*The Q_{10} values between 5°C and 25°C were 2.24 for urea and 2.65 for bicarbonate. For urea the amount of C^{14} in roots appeared to be 31% of that in the external solution while for HCO_3^- it appeared to be 135%.

Discussion and Conclusions

Obtaining information about the uptake by plants of either C^{14}-urea or $HC^{14}O_3^-$ is difficult, in part, because of enzymatic reactions within the plants. C^{14}-urea is subject to the following reaction sequence (Hinsvark et al., 1953):

$$C^{14}\text{-urea} + 2H_2O \xrightarrow{\text{urease}} H_2C^{14}O_3 + 2NH_3$$

$$C^{14}\text{-urea} + H_2O \xrightarrow[\text{or}]{\text{urease}} C^{14}O_2 + 2NH_3$$

$$C^{14}O_2 + PEP \xrightarrow{\text{PEPcarboxylase}} C^{14}\text{-oxaloacetate} + H_2PO_4^-$$

Net reaction:

$$C^{14}\text{-urea} + H_2O + PEP \longrightarrow C^{14}\text{-oxaloacetate} + 2NH_3 + H_2PO_4^-$$

Most if not all of the ammonia would be aminated to yield amino acids.

The HCO_3^- would be subject to the following reaction sequence (Bandurski and Greiner, 1953; Bandurski, 1955).

$$HCO_3^- \longrightarrow C^{14}O_2 + OH^-$$

$$C^{14}O_2 + PEP \xrightarrow{\text{PEPcarboxylase}} C^{14}\text{-oxaloacetate} + H_2PO_4^-$$

or (Maruyama and Love, 1962)

$$HC^{14}O_3^- + PEP \xrightarrow{\text{PEPcarboxylase}} C^{14}\text{-oxaloacetate} + H_2PO_4^-$$

With both urea and bicarbonate therefore, the C^{14} label can be fixed enzymatically within cells. This complicates any interpretation of experiments designed to yield data that would provide information on the mechanism of uptake of the two C^{14}-labeled solutes used in this study.

The following major differences were observed for uptake of the two solutes:

(a) Much more C^{14} from the external solutions was lost from bicarbonate than from urea. These losses are due to physical reasons only in the case of bicarbonate. For urea they are due to enzymatic reactions plus the same physical reasons. The C^{14} losses and the large changes in the pH make bicarbonate solutions much more unstable and difficult to work with than the urea solutions. On the other hand the interpretation of the results with urea is difficult because of urease in the external solution. In the low urea concentrations and longer experimental periods but less so in the higher concentrations and shorter periods, urease results in bicarbonate production and this would interfere in this study. What is measured then as C^{14} uptake from low urea concentrations is, in part, C^{14} uptake from low bicarbonate concentrations. However, addition of $10^{-2}M$ HCO_3^- to $10^{-3}M$ and $10^{-4}M$ C^{14}-urea solutions did not decrease C^{14} uptake, as compared with the controls, over a 6 hour period, indicating that HCO_3^- did not unduly dilute the label of C^{14}-urea.

The presence of urease and hydrolysis of the urea with production of HCO_3^- in the external solution can explain results obtained with urea by Wallace and Ashcroft (1956). These workers found that urea suppressed cation uptake by bush beans and rough lemon cuttings but to a smaller extent than ammonium did. Bicarbonate also suppressed cation uptake as was reported by Goss and Romney (1957). Since the present results demonstrated the hydrolysis of some urea in the external solution, the suppression of cation uptake observed by Wallace and Ashcroft (1956) could have been caused by ammonium and bicarbonate ions.

(b) For concentrations of urea and bicarbonate of $10^{-2}M$ or lower, 5 minutes washing of the free space removed essentially all C^{14} that could be washed out. For $10^{-1}M$ concentrations in less than 30 minutes washing, all C^{14} from HCO_3^- not yet accumulated had been removed but, from urea, 5 or more hours washing was required. This is interpreted as indicating that bicarbonate entered the cells and was incorporated into organic compounds and that C^{14} from urea was also incorporated after its hydrolysis by urease which was slower than urea uptake. The rate limiting step in fixation of C^{14} from urea appeared to be the step mediated by urease and not PEPcarboxylase. (See d below.)

(c) Concentration ratios defined as uptake for 10-fold differences in concentrations supplied to roots were in the case of urea close to 10. For bicarbonate the concentration ratios were around 5. Ratios of 10 are considered as indicative of passive uptake and ratios of less than 10 are more difficult to interpret.

(d) The C^{14} uptake in 6-hour experiments was about 10 times higher when bicarbonate was the source of carbon than when urea was. It was less than 10 times but always higher with bicarbonate than urea in 24-hour experiments. The higher C^{14} uptake from bicarbonate indicates that C^{14} entered the cells faster from bicarbonate than from urea. This is expected if the C^{14} enters the cells as HCO_3^- (or CO_2) and as urea (Jacobs, 1924; Collander, 1959) rather then as decomposition products. However, the fact that more C^{14} from high urea than from HCO_3^- can be washed out of the cells, indicates that at least at high external concentrations the limiting step is not to be found in the different ability of the two C^{14} forms to enter the cells. If the C^{14} fixing mechanism after CO_2 is liberated is the same for both C^{14} sources (PEPcarboxylase), then the urease is the limiting step and would be one reason for less C^{14} uptake from urea than from HCO_3^-. In no case was there evidence that the plant roots were able to concentrate the urea against a gradient. The concentrations of urea inside the plants appeared to be lower than that in the external solution. In the case of bicarbonate there could have been some concentration against the gradient.

(e) The Q_{10} values were higher for bicarbonate than for urea. The high (about 2) Q_{10} values for low urea concentrations may be due to its hydrolysis by urease in the external solutions and production of labeled bicarbonate.

(f) The leaf/root ratio was generally 0. 05 - 0. 5 for both solutes, indicating that most C^{14} per g. dry weight was trapped in the roots probably through dark fixation of CO_2. These values for leaf/root ratios were found for all the bicarbonate and all but the $10^{-1}\underline{M}$ urea concentrations. In the highest urea concentration the leaf/root ratio was sometimes much higher. This is in agreement with the idea that from $10^{-1}\underline{M}$ urea, a pool of free urea apparently forms in the roots (Webster et al. , 1955) and some of it moves to the leaves. There was no such a pool or it was much smaller in the case of low urea concentrations.

(g) Generally, the inhibitors used inhibited equally the uptake from all bicarbonate concentrations. In contrast they inhibited more at low than at high urea concentrations indicating that at high urea concentrations some uptake was independent of metabolism. This is in agreement with the observation that at high urea concentrations C^{14} moved out of the cells during washing. On the other hand, 2, 4-DNP, NaN_3, and CN^- incubated for 10 minutes with PEP, Mg, and bush bean root homogenates did not inhibit C^{14} fixation from bicarbonate or $C^{14}O_2$ liberation from urea. The inhibitory effect of these inhibitors then cannot be on urease or on PEPcarboxylase but an effect either on an uptake mechanism or on the permeability of the cells (Robertson et al. , 1951). The inhibitors 2, 4-DNP, NaN_3 and p-OHMBA appeared to competitively inhibit uptake of C^{14} from urea even though the first two did not react with the two enzyme systems. The leaf/root ratio in the presence of any inhibitor tested was higher than was the control with bicarbonate. To a lesser extent the same occurred with urea. Azide was most pronounced in its ability to increase the ratio for both solutes.

(h) EDTA inhibited C^{14} uptake from bicarbonate more than from urea. This may indicate a Ca^{++} requirement for the mechanism for bicarbonate uptake.

The following similarities were observed for uptake of the two solutes:

(a) The distribution of the C^{14} in the plant parts was similar for the two solutes. Most of it was usually found in the roots followed by the stem and leaves.

(b) The uptake with time increased similarly for both solutes, especially if the losses of C^{14} from the external solutions and through respiration were considered.

(c) Anaerobiosis similarly and seriously affected the C^{14} uptake from both solutes.

(d) In the presence of metabolic inhibitors the uptake of C^{14} from both solutes was similarly inhibited. There was inhibition by $10^{-4}M$ or higher 2, 4-DNP; $10^{-3}M$ or higher NaN_3; 5 x $10^{-4}M$ p-OHMBA. The 2, 4-DNP and NaN_3 inhibited uptake as much as 90%. p-OHMBA inhibited less, usually about 50%, in the concentration used. NaF at $10^{-3}M$ had no effect on uptake of the two solutes. (It should be borne in mind that the pH of the solutions was higher in the case of bicarbonate. It varied from 7. 7 to 9. 0 as the concentrations increased from $10^{-4}M$ to $10^{-1}M$. For urea, it varied from 6. 8 to 8 for the same increase in concentration.)

One of the problems in comparing urea with bicarbonate in the present studies was the ammonia released from the urea inside plants. This means that with urea compared with bicarbonate much more of the C^{14} label would be found with amino acids. If ammonium ion or another ammonia compound had been applied with bicarbonate, the two types of studies would have been more comparable. Even so it does not appear that this is the major source of the differences in the results. The major difference is as was reported by Kuykendall and Wallace (1954), for leaves, that urea seems at least at higher concentrations, to enter the roots passively before the C^{14} is enzymatically fixed. All but the inhibitor data indicate this.

Bicarbonate may be subject to metabolic forces in uptake before it is enzymatically fixed in the cell to other compounds. The enzyme reactions in the plants that fix both of the C^{14} labeled compounds, and probably the hydrolysis of C^{14}-urea in the external solution with the production of $HC^{14}O_3^-$, do make it appear in some cases that both are taken up metabolically even though urea may not be. The ideas of Dainty (1962) on electrochemical gradients must be considered for bicarbonate even though they will be complicated by metabolism of bicarbonate. Many unanswered questions remain concerning urea and bicarbonate uptake by plants.

After this report was completed a new reference in German was noted (Mueller, 1961) in which the absorption of urea by plants was described as a passive process. The evidence was based upon failure to be absorbed against a gradient, no temperature dependency, and no effect of metabolic inhibitors beyond their effects on cell permeability.

Summary

The uptake of C^{14} from C^{14}-labeled urea and bicarbonate solutions by intact bush beans under different concentrations, temperatures, times of incubation, anaerobiosis, and metabolic inhibitors was examined.

Evidence was presented that urease was excreted from either intact roots or microorganisms to the external solution and this phenomenon is of considerable importance in interpreting the effects of urea.

Most but not all of the evidence indicated that unhydrolyzed urea entered the plant cells passively and was free to move out again. C^{14} from bicarbonate appeared to be taken up by a metabolic process. The step mediated by urease seems to be the limiting one in C^{14} accumulation from urea in that there appeared to be a pool of unhydrolyzed urea in plants when a high concentration of urea was applied. From 5 to 10 times more C^{14} was taken up from bicarbonate than from urea and all C^{14} from bicarbonate entering the cells appeared to be readily fixed. That from bicarbonate appeared to be absorbed against a gradient but that from urea was not. Most of the C^{14} absorbed remained in roots of intact plants from both sources. In the presence of metabolic inhibitors the leaf/root ratios for C^{14} were increased. Metabolic inhibitors, especially azide, that have no effect on urease or PEPcarboxylase inhibited uptake from both urea and HCO_3^-. Aeration with N_2 decreased C^{14} uptake from both sources.

K^{42} VS. $HC^{14}O_3^-$ UPTAKE (LESS-FREE SPACE COMPONENTS) FROM $KHCO_3$ SOLUTIONS

With R. T. Mueller

In a previous study of this type, we concluded that HCO_3^- and not necessarily CO_2 was taken up by plant roots (Huffaker et al. , 1960). We also concluded that so far as could be determined from the radioactive isotopes, about 3 times as much K as HCO_3^- entered the plants from the external solutions. This was from a high concentration and even much more K than HCO_3^- than this was absorbed from lower concentrations. The balance of the CO_2 for formation of organic acids via phosphoenolpyruvate carboxylase activity in roots to maintain the anion-cation balance with K was assumed to come from internal respiration. Since we later learned that considerable C^{14} from $HC^{14}O_3^-$ could be lost to the air from the nutrient solution an experiment was made to reassess the ratio of K to HCO_3^- that was taken up.

At pH 8. 0 the equilibrium between CO_2 and HCO_3^- gives about 2. 7% CO_2 and 97. 3% HCO_3^-. By starting at pH of 8. 7 it should be possible to avoid much C^{14} loss to the atmosphere because, at that pH, CO_2 is about 0. 6% and HCO_3^- is 99. 4%. The loss is occasioned either by the exchange of $C^{14}O_2$ with CO_2 from the air or by sweeping $C^{14}O_2$ out with CO_2-free air. The latter results in a pH increase of the nutrient solutions containing HCO_3^- which has been demonstrated, Bhan (1959). The reaction is as follows:

$$HC^{14}O_3^- \longrightarrow OH^- + C^{14}O_2 \uparrow .$$

In the present experiment aeration was made with regular air so that the pH did not increase. It actually decreased meaning that little $C^{14}O_2$ was lost to the air. The $C^{14}O_2$ loss was great only with the $10^{-4}\underline{M}$ concentration (the lowest one used).

The bush beans used in this study were germinated in sand and after 10 days transferred to test tubes containing 100 ml. of a 1/4-strength nutrient solution as in experiments described in previous reports in this series. The solution received 1. 25 ppm. iron as FeEDDHA but no other micronutrients. The solutions were aerated and the plants were grown thusly for 4 days. The nutrient solutions were carefully poured out so that roots would not be injured and the solutions were replaced by the test solutions.

The test solutions are described in table 1. The solutions were adjusted to pH 8.5 before the HC^{14}O$_3^-$ was added so that the loss of C^{14} would be minimized. The test began at 2:45 p.m. and the plants were exposed to the test solutions for 5 hours with aeration with regular air. At this time the final pH of the solutions was measured and samples saved for isotope measurement. The solutions were replaced with 10^{-2}M CaCl$_2$ and aerated for another hour. The plants were then washed with water, separated into leaves, stems, and roots and counted for K^{42} with the scintillation well-counter or prepared for counting for C^{14} with the Q-gas counter. Ground aliquots were counted for C^{14} and the results corrected to a standard self-absorption by the method of Hendler (1959). The results were calculated as μmoles from the specific activity relationships. The C^{14} contents of the solutions at the end of the test are in table 1.

Table 1. Description of nutrient solutions used in test.

Concentration	pH		% C^{14}O$_2$ loss from solutions in 5 hrs.
	Initial	Final	
M	K^{42}HCO$_3$ series		
10^{-1}	8.5	8.7	—
10^{-2}	8.5	8.6	—
10^{-3}	8.5	7.9	—
	KHC^{14}O$_3$ series		
10^{-1}	8.5	8.6	19.7
1.06 x 10^{-2}*	8.5	8.2	34.0
1.6 x 10^{-3}*	8.5	7.5	91.4

All solutions contained 10^{-5}M CaCl$_2$.

*Concentration corrected to account for CO$_2$ of air.

The results in table 2 indicate a greater accumulation of K$^+$ than of HCO$_3^-$ just as did the previous study. Even with corrections made for C^{14} loss from the solutions to the atmosphere the lowest ratio of K/HCO$_3^-$ was 2.51. The conclusion must still be that most of the CO$_2$ for synthesis of organic acids to balance the K accumulation arises from internal respiration rather than from the HCO$_3^-$ of the external solution. This is probably a common phenomenon with anions other than HCO$_3^-$. For example in the concentration studies (page 24) K was absorbed to a much greater extent than was Br; the difference was apparently compensated for by reassimilation of respiratory CO$_2$ or HCO$_3^-$ to form organic acids.

Summary

Even with corrections made for losses of C^{14}O$_2$ from HC^{14}O$_3^-$ from the nutrient solution, as the most narrow ratio, 2.5 times as much K was taken up as was HCO$_3^-$ from a KHCO$_3$ solution by bush beans. At dilute solutions the ratio was much wider. Fixation into organic acids of respiratory CO$_2$ apparently makes up the difference to maintain the electrostatic balance.

Radioactive C^{14} was lost from HC^{14}O$_3^-$-containing solutions and aeration of HCO$_3^-$ solutions with CO$_2$-free air consequently resulted in pH increases.

Table 2. Calculated amounts of K^+ and HCO_3^- taken up less the free-space components in the 5-hour test.

Plant Part	Concentration, $\underline{M}$		
	10^{-1}	10^{-2}	10^{-3}
	μmoles/g. dry weight		
	Tagged K in plants		
Leaf	10.2	4.6	3.0
Stem	57.5	17.2	9.0
Root	516.	277.	192.
Whole plant	122.	51.9	47.5
	Tagged HCO_3^- in plants		
Leaf	5.1	8.7	1.9
Stem	48.5	5.2	2.5
Root	181.	47.5	19.1
Whole plant	43.9	13.1	4.6
Whole plant (corrected)*	48.5	15.7	8.5
	Ratios, K^+/HCO_3^- taken up (whole plant)		
	2.77	3.96	10.3
	Ratios on basis of corrected values for loss of C^{14} to the air*		
	2.51	3.30	5.59

*Corrected values for HCO_3^- for whole plant on basis of assuming that the loss of $C^{14}O_2$ from nutrient solution (table 1) was exchanged with $C^{12}O_2$. The correction assumes a linear loss of CO_2 from solutions with time and a linear effect of concentration on uptake.

STUDIES ON THE ABSORPTION AND DISTRIBUTION OF Na^{22} IN BUSH BEAN PLANTS

With N. Hemaidan

It has been reported that many plant species excluded Na (Collander, 1941). Recent studies (Barbier and Chabannes, 1951; Cooper and Peynado, 1954; Huffaker and Wallace, 1959a,b; McLean, 1956) showed that Na was absorbed in relatively large quantities by roots of species not accumulating Na in stems or leaves, and that both K and Na levels and the plant species (Huffaker and Wallace, 1959a,b) influenced the amount of Na being translocated from roots. The purpose of this work was to study in more detail various factors which influence the uptake, distribution and translocation of Na in bush bean plants.

Materials and Methods

Experiments were conducted on bush beans (Phaseolus vulgaris, variety Tendergreen). The plants were grown by germinating seeds in sterilized quartz sand in wooden flats in a glasshouse. The flats were watered regularly with distilled water. Five to six days from germination, sound uniform seedlings were transferred to 100-ml. culture tubes containing 1/4-strength nutrient solution formed of the following salts in moles/liter: KNO_3, 0.001;

$NH_4H_2PO_4$, 0.002; $MgSO_4$, 0.004; H_2SO_4, 0.002; and $Ca(NO_3)_2$, 0.005. Micronutrient elements were added in the following concentrations: 1.0 ppm. as $MnSO_4$, 0.1 ppm. B as H_3BO_3, 0.12 ppm. Zn as $ZnSO_4 \cdot 7H_2O$, 0.03 ppm. Mo as H_2MoO_4, and 1 ppm. Fe as FeEDDHA.

The nutrient media were continuously aerated during the entire growing period. After eight to nine days, the nutrient solution was carefully poured out and the roots washed with distilled water before adding the experimental solutions. The solutions contained 10^{-4} molar $CaSO_4$ to preserve the integrity of the roots and of metabolic absorption mechanisms. The pH was adjusted to 7.

The absorption period selected was 24 hours unless otherwise indicated. The absorption media were also aerated during the entire experimental period. At the end of the absorption period, the experimental solution was poured out and the free space was washed for one hour in 10^{-2} molar $CaCl_2$. The plants were then washed for one or two minutes in running tap water and separated into roots, stems, and leaves. These plant sections were then forced to the lowest one centimeter portions of glass test tubes and counted with a scintillation-well counter. Samples were then dried and weighed. The amount of sodium absorbed was calculated from specific activity relationships and expressed in micromoles per gram of dry weight.

Results

Na Distribution in Various Plant Parts

This experiment was conducted in order to study the effect of the concentration of Na in the external solution on Na accumulation and its pattern of distribution in the various parts of the bush bean plant. Results are shown in table 1. The apparent accumulation of Na was in the following order: roots > stems > leaves. The Na content found in each plant part increased progressively as the external concentration of Na was increased. Of special interest was the fact that Na, at all concentrations, tended to accumulate more in the lower half than in the upper half of the stem. However, Na appeared to be translocated further into the stem at a high Na level than at a low Na level. This was evident from the Na ratio of the lower half to that of the upper half of the stem, being about 35 at 10^{-4}, 31 at 10^{-3}, 16 at 10^{-2}, and 5 at $10^{-1}\underline{M}$. Root-stem ratios showed the same pattern.

Table 1. The content of Na (less free-space constituents) from Na^{22}Cl in leaves, stems, roots of bush bean plants in a period of 24 hours at room temperature.

Plant Part	Concentration in moles/liter			
	10^{-1}	10^{-2}	10^{-3}	10^{-4}
	μmoles/g. dry weight			
Leaves	1.07	0.47	0.03	0.003
Upper half of stem	67.7	2.48	0.04	0.004
Lower half of stem	328.2	40.0	1.26	0.14
Entire stem	219.7	28.6	0.77	0.08
Roots	894.4	195.1	49.83	8.75
Whole plant	253.9	37.4	10.53	1.78

Table 2 shows the concentration ratios for leaves, stems, roots, and whole plant. Concentration ratios are defined in this study as the ratios between the accumulation for two concentrations, one being 10 times the concentration of the other. The means of the concentration ratios for the roots and whole plant were 4.73 and 5.42 respectively, while those for the leaves and stems were inconsistent. The concentration ratios for the roots and whole plant reported here seem to follow closely the relationship,

$$\text{Uptake} = \text{constant} \times 2^{\ln c}$$

where c is the concentration of Na in the external solution. This is in agreement with findings on page 24 where concentration ratios (whole-plant basis) of 3.9, 4.6 and 4.7 were found for Rb, K and Sr respectively.

Table 2.   Concentration ratios for Na accumulated from NaCl at different concentrations. (Calculated from table 1.)

Plant Part	$10^{-1}/10^{-2}$	$10^{-2}/10^{-3}$	$10^{-3}/10^{-4}$	Means
Leaves	2.28	15.67	10.00	9.32
Stems	7.68	37.16	9.62	18.15
Roots	4.58	3.92	5.69	4.73
Whole plant	6.79	3.55	5.92	5.42

Effect of Inhibitors on Na Uptake by Bush Beans

It has been reported that certain inhibitors affect the accumulation and distribution of cations in plants (Fried et al., 1961; Hagen et al., 1957; Jacobson et al., 1960; Pearson, 1962; Russel et al., 1953; Bhan et al., 1960). In this study, the following inhibitors were used: 2,4-DNP at 10^{-4}M, methylene blue at 10^{-3}M, and KCN at 10^{-3}M. The external concentration of $Na^{22}Cl$ ranged from 10^{-1}M to 10^{-4}M. Results are reported in table 3.

Table 3.   Effect of various metabolic inhibitors on Na accumulation and distribution in bush beans for a period of five hours at room temperature.

$Na^{22}Cl$ Concn.	Plant Part	10^{-4}M 2,4-DNP	10^{-3}M Methylene blue	10^{-3}M KCN
M			% of control	
10^{-1}	Leaves	325	378	3230
10^{-1}	Stems	145	67	139
10^{-1}	Roots	58	90	59
10^{-1}	Whole plant	66	89	77
10^{-2}	Leaves	103	46	501
10^{-2}	Stems	133	21	130
10^{-2}	Roots	66	59	51
10^{-2}	Whole plant	90	54	59
10^{-3}	Leaves	52	25	153
10^{-3}	Stems	748	161	1058
10^{-3}	Roots	26	26	13
10^{-3}	Whole plant	34	25	16
10^{-4}	Leaves	14	51	—
10^{-4}	Stems	333	225	—
10^{-4}	Roots	15	12	—
10^{-4}	Whole plant	18	11	—

There was a reduction in the amount of Na taken up by the whole plant and that which accumulated in the roots with all the inhibitors. The reduction became greater as the external concentration of NaCl decreased. As for the amount of Na translocated to the stem, 2, 4-DNP and KCN caused an increase at all the concentrations, the increase being much greater at 10^{-3} and 10^{-4} than at 10^{-1} and 10^{-2}M Na. Methylene blue, however, reduced the amount of Na translocated to the stem at 10^{-1} and 10^{-2} and increased it at 10^{-3} and 10^{-4}M. Regarding Na translocated to the leaves, the amount was approximately tripled in the presence of 2, 4-DNP and increased by four times in the presence of methylene blue at 10^{-1}M concentration only, while it was considerably reduced at 10^{-2}, 10^{-3}, and 10^{-4}M. In the presence of KCN, however, the amount of Na translocated to the leaves was 32 times that of the control at 10^{-1}M, 5 times at 10^{-2} and $1\frac{1}{2}$ times at 10^{-3}M. KCN seemed, therefore, to facilitate the transfer of Na from the roots to the leaves and stems more effectively than 2, 4-DNP and methylene blue even though it inhibited uptake into roots.

Effect of Temperature on Na Uptake and Distribution by Bush Beans

This experiment was conducted in order to study the effect of root temperature on Na uptake and distribution at various external concentrations of $Na^{22}Cl$. Two root temperatures were used—$25^{\circ}C$ and $5^{\circ}C$. In the latter treatment, the experimental solution was cooled to $5^{\circ}C$ first (by packing chopped ice around the culture tubes) before inserting the plants in the tubes. It was feasible to maintain the temperature between $4\text{-}5^{\circ}C$ by adding chopped ice whenever it was required. The stems and leaves in both treatments were at room temperature. The results are shown in table 4.

Table 4. The effect of root temperature on Na uptake (less free-space consitiuents) and distribution in bush beans for a period of five hours.

Plant Part	$Na^{22}Cl$ Concentration Moles/Liter			
	10^{-1}	10^{-2}	10^{-3}	10^{-4}
	For $5^{\circ}C$ as % of control			
Leaves	461	316	240	200
Stems	31	151	247	120
Roots	39	57	55	38
Whole plant	40	60	60	49

The effect of low temperature seemed to be similar to that of KCN regarding its ability to facilitate the transfer of Na from the roots to the leaves. At $5^{\circ}C$ the amount of Na translocated to the leaves increased by approximately 5 times, 3 times, $2\frac{1}{2}$ times, and 2 times at 10^{-1} to 10^{-4}M, respectively. There was also an increase in Na content of the stems except at 10^{-1}. The amount of Na taken up by the whole plant and that which accumulated in the roots was appreciably reduced by low temperature at all the concentrations.

Effect of Absence of Light on Na Uptake and Distribution in Bush Beans

This experiment was started at 10 a. m. at room temperature ($25^{\circ}C$) in the glasshouse. Only one external concentration (10^{-1}M) of $Na^{22}Cl$ was used.

The plants were divided into two groups—one group was in natural daylight (control) while plants of the second group were placed in a cardboard box and covered with a black cloth to exclude light. The results are shown in table 5.

Table 5.   Effect of absence of light on Na acumulation and distribution from $10^{-1}\underline{M}$ Na^{22}Cl in bush beans for a period of 24 hours.

Plant Part	Absence of light
	% of control
Leaves	132
Stems	96
Roots	88
Whole plant	95

The amount of Na that accumulated in the stem and that which was taken up by the whole plant was not affected by the absence of light. There was a reduction of 12% in the Na content of the roots and an increase of 32% in the leaves. These data indicated that absence of light facilitated somewhat the transfer of Na from the roots to the leaves.

Na Distribution in Various Plant Parts When Applied to the Stem of Bush Bean

Plants

In the previous experiments (table 1), it was shown that Na concentration in the leaves was relatively insignificant compared to that which accumulated in the stems and roots. The purpose of this experiment was to study the distribution of Na in the various plant parts when applied to the stem of the plant. A thin cotton thread was forced through the middle of the stem with a regular sewing needle. Both ends of the thread were then cut and dipped into a small, narrow glass vial containing $10^{-2}\underline{M}$ Na^{22}Cl and which was placed in a position parallel to the stem. The plants were in culture tubes containing 1/4-strength nutrient solution. The duration of the experiment was 48 hours. The results are shown in table 6.

Table 6.   Distribution of Na in various plant parts when applied to the stem of bush bean plants by a thread dipped into a vial containing Na^{22}.

Plant Part	μmoles/g. dry weight
Leaves	0.00
Upper half of stem	6.02
Lower half of stem	14.45
Roots	11.21
Whole plant	5.05

The distribution of the Na^{22} was in the following order: stems > roots > leaves. Again Na was essentially excluded from the leaves. It is possible that downward movement of the Na^{22} in this experiment would be related to its uptake into the phloem through the thread. Also 2.4 times more Na accumulated in the lower half than in the upper half of the stem.

In another series of plants, Na was injected into the middle of the stem. Very small glass tubing with a fine pointed head was filled with $10^{-2}\underline{M}$ Na^{22}Cl by capillary action, and inserted into the middle of the stem. The plants were in culture tubes containing 1/4-strength nutrient solution. At the end of 24 hours, all the Na^{22}Cl was taken up by the plant. The same treatment was applied simultaneously to other plants with the addition of 10^{-3}M KCN. The results are shown in table 7.

Table 7.   Distribution on Na in various plant parts when injected into the stem of bush bean plants.

Plant Part	10^{-2}M Na^{22}Cl + 10^{-3}M KCl (control)	10^{-2}M Na^{22}Cl + 10^{-3}M KCN	Increase (+) Decrease (-) for KCN
	μmoles/g. dry weight		%
Leaves	0. 71	1. 94	+173
Upper half of stem	9. 77	11. 33	+16
Lower half of stem	24. 17	15. 95	-34
Entire stem	18. 85	14. 30	-24
Roots	4. 67	5. 57	+19
Whole plant	7. 51	7. 38	-2
$\dfrac{\text{Lower half of stem}}{\text{Upper half of stem}}$, ratio	2. 47	1. 41	

The distribution of Na was similar to that in table 6, i. e. , stems > roots > leaves. Also 2. 47 times more Na was accumulated in the lower half than in the upper half of the stem. When 10^{-3}M KCN was included, the lower half of the stem contained only 1. 41 times more Na than the upper compared to 2. 47 in the control. Also there were increases of 173%, 16% and 19% in the Na content of the leaves, upper half of the stem, and the roots respectively as the result of KCN and simultaneously a decrease of 34% and 24% in the Na content of the lower half of the stem and the entire stem respectively. KCN appeared to facilitate the translocation of Na further into the shoots resulting in a more uniform distribution of Na throughout the plant.

Distribution of Na in Various Plant Parts When Injected into the Petiole of the Leaf

The bush bean plants had two primary leaves and a relatively small secondary one. Solutions of 10^{-1}M Na^{22}Cl + 10^{-3}M KCl (control) and 10^{-1}M Na^{22}Cl + 10^{-3}M KCN were injected into the petiole of one of the two primary leaves as described earlier for the stem injection. The plants were in culture tubes containing a 1/4-strength nutrient solution. The duration of the experiment was 24 hours. The data in table 8 showed an equal distribution of Na in both the lower and the upper half of the stem. More Na was concentrated in the stem than in roots. Of special interest was the exclusion of Na from the opposite leaves in the control treatment in spite of the fact that the opposite petioles contained a considerable amount of Na. However, when 10^{-3}M KCN was included, about 11. 5 times more Na accumulated in the opposite leaves. There was also a considerable increase in the accumulation of Na in all the plant parts except the roots which showed a decrease of 22%.

Since KCN partially broke down the mechanism responsible for the exclusion of Na from the leaves, the following experiment was conducted to confirm that point: 10^{-1}M Na^{22}Cl was injected into the petiole of one of the primary leaves (control) as mentioned earlier.   The other primary leaf was dipped in $10^{-3}\underline{M}$ KCN solution for one minute.   The plants were then put in culture tubes containing 1/4-strength nutrient solution.   The duration of the experiment was 24 hours.

Table 8.   Distribution of Na from $Na^{22}Cl$ in various parts of the bush bean plant when injected into the leaf petiole.

Plant Part	$10^{-1}\underline{M}$ $Na^{22}Cl$ $+ 10^{-3}\underline{M}$ KCl (control)	$10^{-1}\underline{M}$ $Na^{22}Cl$ $+ 10^{-3}\underline{M}$ KCN	Increase (+) Decrease (-) for KCN
	μmoles/g. dry weight		%
Injected Petiole	39. 71	50. 22	+26
Leaf of injected Petiole	12. 08	14. 27	+18
Leaf opposite injection	0. 74	9. 26	+1150
Petiole opposite injection	10. 39	10. 42	0
Upper half of stem	10. 20	14. 98	+47
Lower half of stem	9. 79	13. 72	+40
Entire stem	9. 34	14. 19	+52
Roots	4. 09	3. 19	-22
Whole plant	8. 35	11. 12	+33
$\dfrac{\text{Lower half of stem}}{\text{Upper half of stem}}$, ratio	0. 96	0. 92	

The data in table 9 indicated that two times more Na was accumulated in the upper half than in the lower half of the stem.   The opposite leaves in the control treatment effectively excluded Na.   When these leaves were dipped in $10^{-3}\underline{M}$ KCN, however, they accumulated about 10 times more Na, confirming the results in table 8 to the effect that KCN helps in partially breaking down the mechanism responsible for Na exclusion from the leaves of bush bean plants.   Also there was an increase in the amount of Na accumulated in all the plant parts except the opposite petioles and roots.

Distribution of Na in Various Plant Parts when Applied to the Leaves of Bush

Bean Plants

Huffaker and Wallace (1959a) reported that more Na accumulated in the shoots of radish plants than in the roots, while in soybean, Na was excluded from the leaves and the pattern of Na distribution was in the following order: roots > stems > leaves, i. e. , similar to the pattern reported for bush beans in these studies (table 1).   Unpublished data (Hemaidan, 1961) on Na uptake and accumulation by radish and bush bean plants confirmed the results obtained by Huffaker and Wallace (1959a), and showed that the radish accumulated about 2000 times more Na in the leaves than bush beans.

The following experiment was conducted in order to compare the accumulation and distribution of Na in radish and bush beans when applied to the leaves. The leaves were dipped in $10^{-2}\underline{M}$ $Na^{22}Cl$ for one minute, allowed to dry off for a few minutes at room temperature, then the plants were put into culture tubes containing 1/4-strength nutrient solution and allowed to grow for 72 hours. The results are shown in table 10.

The pattern of distribution of Na in bush beans was in the following order:

roots > stems > leaves, similar to the pattern obtained when Na^{22} was applied to roots (table 1). Much less Na accumulated in the leaves than in roots giving a leaf/root ratio of 0.39. In radishes, the pattern of Na distribution was reversed—leaves > stems > roots—similar to the pattern observed when Na was supplied to roots. Much more Na accumulated in the leaves than in roots giving a leaf/root ratio of 7.20. This illustrates clearly the difference among plant species regarding accumulation and distribution of Na.

Table 9. The distribution of Na from Na^{22}Cl in various plant parts of the bush bean plant when injected into the petiole of one of the primary leaves while the second primary leaf was dipped in 10^{-3}M KCN.

Plant Part	10^{-1}M Na^{22}Cl + Dipping second primary leaf in 10^{-3}M KCl (control)	10^{-1}M Na^{22}Cl + Dipping second primary leaf in 10^{-3}M KCN	Increase (+) or Decrease (-) for KCN
	μmoles/g. dry weight		%
Injected petiole	93.66	107.5	+15
Leaf of injected petiole	3.93	7.92	+102
Opposite leaf (KCN- or KCl-dipped)	0.29	3.30	+1040
Opposite petiole	13.42	11.88	-12
Upper half of stem	12.04	14.10	+17
Lower half of stem	5.75	7.01	+22
Entire stem	6.54	6.97	+6
Roots	6.94	5.14	-26
Whole plant	7.96	9.93	+25
$\frac{\text{Lower half of stem}}{\text{Upper half of stem}}$, ratio	0.48	0.50	

From the studies on injecting Na into stems and petioles (tables 8, 9), it was shown that KCN facilitated the transport of Na further into the stems and leaves. The following experiment was conducted in order to study the effect of KCN on accumulation and distribution of Na when applied to the leaves of bush bean plants. The leaves were dipped for one minute in 10^{-1}M Na^{22}Cl without KCN (control) and in 10^{-1}M Na^{22}Cl + 10^{-3}M KCN. The plants were put in culture tubes containing 1/4-strength nutrient solution and allowed to grow for 24 hours. The results of this experiment are shown in table 11.

Table 10. Distribution of Na in roots, stems, and leaves when applied to the leaves of radish and bush bean plants.

Plant Part	Bush Beans	Radish
	μmoles/g. dry weight	μmoles/g. dry weight
Root	9.66	1.38
Stem	8.78	3.08
Leaf	3.76	9.93
Whole plant	6.67	8.48
Leaf/Root	0.39	7.20

KCN resulted in more Na^{22} in leaves and stems by 47% and 24% respectively, and a reduction of 8% in roots. This confirms the results reported earlier to the effect that KCN facilitates the transfer of Na further into the stems and leaves.

Table 11. Distribution of NaCl in leaves, stems, and roots of bush bean plants when $Na^{22}Cl$ was applied to the leaves.

Plant Part	$10^{-1}\underline{M}\ Na^{22}Cl$ (control)	$10^{-1}\underline{M}\ Na^{22}Cl$ + $10^{-3}\underline{M}$ KCN	Increase (+) or Decrease (-) for KCN
	μmoles/g. dry weight		%
Leaves	83. 9	123. 2	+47
Petioles	70. 2	80. 1	+14
Upper half of stem	64. 4	74. 7	+16
Lower half of stem	34. 4	43. 6	+27
Entire stem	44. 8	55. 4	+24
Roots	17. 7	16. 3	-8
Whole plant	58. 7	74. 0	+26
$\dfrac{\text{Lower half of stem}}{\text{Upper half of stem}}$, ratio	0. 53	0. 58	

Exclusion of Na from Leaves of Bush Beans

It was shown above (tables 1, 6, 7, 8, 9) that leaves of bush beans partially excluded Na. The data from experiments on injecting Na into the petioles (tables 8, 9) indicated that the mechanism could be located in the leaves. In order to check this point further, the following experiment was conducted: leaves of bush beans were dipped in $10^{-3}M\ Na^{22}Cl$ for one minute and allowed to dry for a few minutes at room temperature. The plants were then divided into four groups and put in culture tubes containing four different concentrations of non-labeled NaCl ranging from 0 to $10^{-2}\underline{M}$, adjusted to pH 7. 0, and the experiment was allowed to proceed for 24 hours at room temperature. The results are shown in table 12.

Table 12. Distribution of Na from $10^{-3}M\ Na^{22}Cl$ in leaves, stems and roots of bush beans when applied to the leaves while roots were in different concentrations of non-labeled NaCl.

Plant Part	Concentrations of NaCl in external solutions with roots			
	0	$10^{-4}\underline{M}$	$10^{-3}\underline{M}$	$10^{-2}\underline{M}$
	μmoles/g. dry weight from leaf application			
Leaves	1. 88	1. 80	1. 39	1. 35
Upper half of stem	3. 13	3. 19	3. 33	3. 73
Lower half of stem	1. 44	1. 16	1. 26	1. 45
Entire stem	2. 44	2. 07	2. 38	2. 25
Roots	0. 22	0. 16	0. 05	0. 05
Whole plant	1. 65	1. 62	1. 66	1. 63

The upper half of the stem accumulated the largest amount of Na. The leaves accumulated approximately the same amount of Na regardless of the concentration of the external solution. The same pattern was observed for the upper half of the stem, lower half of the stem, and the entire stem. The roots at 0 NaCl and 10^{-4}M NaCl, however, accumulated four times and three times more Na^{22} than the roots at 10^{-3}M and 10^{-2}M NaCl respectively. This could be explained by the difficulty of Na moving from the leaves to the roots against a concentration gradient. The ability of the leaves to accumulate approximately the same amount of Na regardless of the external concentration of the roots is further evidence that Na exclusion from the leaves is a function of the leaf itself.

Uptake and Distribution of Na^{22}Cl by Bush Beans at Various Time Intervals

Absorption and distribution of 10^{-2}M NaCl by bush beans was studied at various time intervals ranging from 30 minutes to 8 hours as shown in table 13 and figures 1, 2, and 3. The differences in leaves were not significant.

Table 13. Time-course of Na absorption and distribution in bush beans from application to roots of 10^{-2}M Na^{22}Cl at room temperature.

Time	Leaves	Stems	Roots	Whole Plant
		μmoles/g. dry weight		
$\frac{1}{2}$ hour	0.026	0.68	8.21	1.26
1 hour	0.108	0.72	16.33	2.50
$1\frac{1}{2}$ hours	0.123	1.40	26.00	3.90
2 hours	0.354	1.38	28.25	4.65
$2\frac{1}{2}$ hours	0.152	0.78	34.64	4.46
3 hours	0.344	2.86	50.54	7.90
$3\frac{1}{2}$ hours	0.000	1.14	48.12	9.04
4 hours	0.213	3.40	58.68	9.25
5 hours	0.108	3.91	77.34	11.58
6 hours	0.047	3.41	78.50	13.18
7 hours	0.359	4.36	94.01	14.62
8 hours	0.093	2.97	97.97	15.03

There was a steady increase in the amount of Na accumulated in the roots between 30 minutes and 8 hours (figure 1). The same trend was observed regarding the amount of Na taken up by the whole plant between 30 minutes and $3\frac{1}{2}$ hours, after which the rate of accumulation tapered off (figure 2). Of special interest was the Na content of the leaves (figure 3). The Na^{22} in leaves was very variable. This particular experiment was repeated three additional times and similar results were obtained It was not possible to determine if the leaf content actually fluctuated.

Accumulation of Na in Split Bush Bean Roots

The following experiment was conducted in order to study the accumulation of Na in the roots when Na^{22} was applied to one-half the root only while the other half was in 10^{-4}M CaCl$_2$. The roots of each plant were divided into halves. Each half was inserted carefully into a different 100-ml. culture tube. CaCl$_2$ (100 ml. of 10^{-4}M) was added to one-half and 100 ml. of 10^{-2}M Na^{22}Cl was added to the other half. The results are shown in table 14.

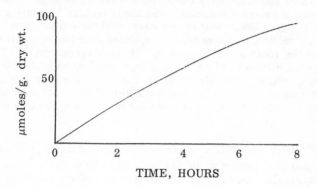

Figure 1. Time-course of Na uptake in bush bean roots from application to roots of $10^{-2}\underline{M}$ $Na^{22}Cl$.

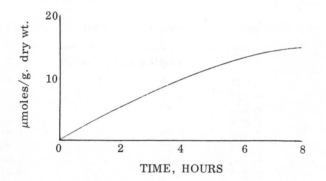

Figure 2. Time-course of Na uptake on a whole-plant basis from application to roots of $10^{-2}\underline{M}$ $Na^{22}Cl$.

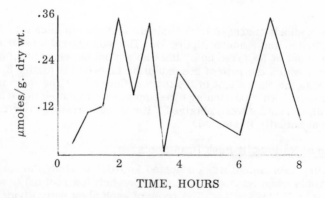

Figure 3. Time-course of Na transfer to bush bean leaves from application to roots of $10^{-2}\underline{M}$ $Na^{22}Cl$.

The pattern of Na distribution followed the pattern previously reported in table 1, i.e., root> stem> leaf. Both halves of the root accumulated more Na than the leaves. There was about 68 times more Na in the half which was furnished with $Na^{22}Cl$ than the half which was not.

Table 14.   Accumulation of Na in bush bean roots in which $10^{-2}\underline{M}$ $Na^{22}Cl$ was furnished to half the roots only.

Plant Part	μmoles/g. dry weight
Roots in $10^{-4}\underline{M}$ $CaCl_2$ only	6.24
Roots in $Na^{22}\overline{C}l$	425
Stems	38.60
Leaves	0.05
Whole plant	65.32

Discussion

The distribution of Na in bush beans was in the following order: roots> stems> leaves. The amount of Na present in the leaves at any of the concentrations used was negligible compared to that which was in the roots when the Na was supplied to the roots. Of special interest also was the fact that Na tended to accumulate more in the lower half than in the upper half of the stem. This is in agreement with findings of Huffaker and Wallace (1959a,b) and Neil, (1962) who reported a similar pattern for Na distribution in beans as evident from radioautographs.

The apparent exclusion of Na from leaves presents difficult problems. Barbier and Chabannes (1951) suggested that Na may circulate in plants from roots to foliage to roots and there finally remain. The present studies do indicate that Na moves readily from leaves to roots of bush bean plants. The irregular data obtained for Na in leaves vs. time of uptake may be indicative of a circulation pattern. Na entering the leaves appeared to be lost from them. Some individual cells have an outwardly directed Na pump coupled with an inwardly directed K pump which to a degree results in Na exclusion. Just how this may relate to an entire organ like a leaf is unknown. A coupled pump could explain the synergistic or Viets-like effect of Na in enhancing K uptake and vise versa (Huffaker and Wallace, 1959b; Prevot and Ollagnier, 1961).

The effect of the concentration of Na in the external solution on Na accumulation gave concentration ratios of 4.73 and 5.42 for roots and whole plant respectively. These concentration ratios seemed to follow the relationship,

$$\text{Uptake} = \text{constant} \times 2^{\ln c}$$

where c is the concentration of Na in the external solution. This is in agreement with results for K and other ions (see page 24).

The use of inhibitors reduced the amount of Na taken up by the whole plant and that which accumulated in the roots. The reduction became greater as the external concentration of NaCl decreased. This increased dependency on metabolism as the external concentration is decreased may suggest that two processes are involved as suggested for K by Bange and van Vliet (1961) in the uptake of Na as follows:

(a)   A passive process operating at higher external concentrations which requires no energy from metabolism and is thus not sensitive to inhibitors.

(b)   An active process operating at lower external concentrations which is dependent on metabolic energy and is thus more sensitive to inhibitors.

Another possible explanation is a one-mechanism process but merely differences in the energy barrier for low and high external concentrations.

The studies with metabolic inhibitors, especially with KCN, indicated a differential effect on Na accumulating in roots vs. that transferred to leaves. Similar results were obtained by Bhan et al. (1960). Bange and van Vliet (1961), as have other workers, proposed separate mechanisms that lead to shoot vs. root accumulation. The fact that low temperature and anaerobiosis, Letey et al. (1961), as well as metabolic inhibitors increased Na transfer to shoots indicates that metabolism is a barrier to such transfer. Na accumulation into roots behaves differently. Considerable is known about active transport of Na in animal cells (Tosteson and Hoffman, 1960) but little is known for plant cells.

The inability of bush bean leaves to accumulate Na could be due either to a physical barrier in leaf cells or to Na expulsion dependent on metabolism. The data on uptake vs. time (table 13, figure 3) seems to favor the latter. As shown in figure 3, Na did enter the leaf but it appeared that perhaps it could be expelled. Barbier and Chabannes (1951) reported that Na absorbed by pea roots completed a circuit of the plant and returned to the roots. Operation of a Na expulsion "pump" is indicated also by the inhibitor data, where poisoning resulted in more Na accumulation in the leaves. Letey et al. (1961) reported a very marked increase of Na in shoots of snap-dragons with decreasing oxygen levels. Low oxygen levels could have similar effects on the enzyme system as that of low root temperature. The possibility of a Na "pump" is further substantiated by the work of Bergquist (1958) on the alga <u>Hormosira banksii</u>. He obtained a marked increase in free space Na, cytoplasmic Na, and bound Na with 2, 4-DNP, KCN and pCMB as compared to controls. He suggested the Na expulsion "pump" could be a redox pump of the type suggested by Conway (1951, 1953) which would provide a suitable mechanism for the transfer of electrons to oxygen, for a cation to be expelled, and for an anion to diffuse out to maintain electrical neutrality.

Summary

Studies on absorption and translocation of Na with Na^{22} in bush beans indicated that the roots contained much more Na than the stems or leaves. Na appeared to be translocated further into the stem at a high Na level than at a low Na level. It also tended to accumulate more in the lower half than in the upper half of the stem. The exclusion of Na by the leaves was evident at low and at high Na levels.

Na applied to leaves or to stems of bush beans appeared to move in a downward direction. KCN no matter where applied increased upward movement and retention in leaves. When Na was supplied to leaves of bush bean and radish, the same distribution pattern was obtained as when it was supplied to roots.

The inhibitors, 2, 4-DNP, methylene blue, and KCN influenced the absorption and translocation of Na. The reduction in absorption became greater as the external concentration of Na decreased. KCN facilitated the translocation of Na from the roots further into the stem and leaves and resulted in a more uniform distribution of Na throughout the plant. Low root temperature reduced absorption but resulted in more Na translocation to the leaves. Absence of light resulted also in more Na translocation to the leaves. It was shown that Na did enter the leaf but it seemed to be expelled. Plant species differences seem to be the most important factor influencing the distribution of Na.

It was suggested that Na expulsion or some other analogous process which is dependent upon metabolism is responsible for the exclusion or removal of Na from leaves of bush beans.

EFFECT OF SOME CHEMICALS ON LEAKINESS OF
BEAN ROOT CELLS TO Na^{22}

With N. Hemaidan

In studies of inhibitor effects on salt uptake it is necessary to know whether or not the inhibitors influence the permeability of the cells and make them leaky. Hayes and Rothstein (1962) have reported that Hg salts make yeast cells leaky to K and Na. The present study was made to see if a similar phenomenon obtained for bush bean root cells.

Bush bean plants (two per culture tube) that had been grown in 1/10-strength nutrient solution for 13 days were exposed to 100 ml. 10^{-3}M Na^{22}Cl + 10^{-3}M CaCl$_2$ at pH 7 for 24 hours. The specific activity was 36,100 cpm./μmole Na. These solutions were then discarded, the tubes rinsed with distilled water and the solutions were replaced with the solutions outlined in table 1. One set of controls was not subjected to a post treatment. CaCl$_2$ (10^{-4}M) was used in the post treatments because Gardos (1960) had shown that Ca was not only necessary for K accumulation but possibly also for K outflow.

Table 1. Effect of inhibitors on leakiness of bush bean roots to Na^{22}.

Post Treatment	Leaf	Stem	Root	Whole Plant
	μmoles/g. dry weight			
10^{-4}M CaCl$_2$	.004	2.46	35.7	6.0
" + 10^{-6}M HgCl$_2$	.008	1.04	27.4	4.7
" + 10^{-5}M HgCl$_2$	.006	1.38	34.5	5.9
" + 10^{-4}M HgCl$_2$	.004	1.39	35.4	3.9
" + 10^{-3}M HgCl$_2$	.002	1.32	13.2	2.1
" + 10^{-3}M KCN	.003	1.39	28.6	4.3
" + 10^{-3}M KCl	.004	1.68	30.9	5.6
" + 10^{-3}M 2,4-DNP	.007	1.45	26.9	4.8
" + 10^{-4}M pCMB	.004	1.18	26.3	4.4
" + 10^{-4}M CuSO$_4$	.007	1.71	30.0	5.9
" + 10^{-4}M MnSO$_4$	.003	1.92	33.7	5.6
L. S. D. (.05)	N.S.	0.74	4.9	1.4

After 4 hours in the respective solutions, the solutions were again changed, this time to a 10^{-2}M CaCl$_2$ solution to replace exchangeable Na^{22} on the cation exchange sites. All solutions were aerated.

The results for plant parts are in table 1. Hg^{++} appeared to make the roots leaky. At 10^{-3}M HgCl$_2$ the roots lost considerable Na^{22}. Some of the other metabolic inhibitors (KCN, pCMB, 2,4-DNP) may have caused some leakiness but not nearly as much as did 10^{-3}M HgCl$_2$. It is doubtful that the results on pages 31 and 88 are the result of metabolic inhibitor effects on root cell permeability if the present results can be generalized.

CATION CONTENTS OF FIVE VEGETABLE CROPS
GROWN IN THE FIELD

Among the reasons given for variations in the mineral content of plants are the following: (a) differences in the mineral composition of the nutrient substrate, (b) differences in distribution of nutrients among various plant parts as result of differences in size and proportion of plant parts, and (c) concentration and dilution effects from differences in carbohydrate accumulation. All three of these points should be considered when assigning critical levels for the various plant nutrients.

This study was undertaken to determine: (a) the ability of various plants to utilize Na, (b) if plants other than alfalfa (Bear and Prince, 1945) exhibit cation-equivalent constancy, (c) if a higher degree of cation-equivalent constancy exists in a particular plant portion such as was found for the alfalfa leaf (Wallace et al. , 1948a), and (d) the possible relationship of the P content of plants to cation interrelationships (Truog et al. , 1947).

Glasshouse studies with alfalfa have shown that constancy of the cation me. sum is a phenomenon secondary to the cation-anion ratio and that this ratio is a function that involves the whole plant (Wallace and Bear, 1949). Differences in dilution caused by growth can influence the cation content but not the cation-anion ratio. A true test for constancy of the cation me. sum in plants must make corrections for carbohydrate concentration and dilution and should consider the whole plant.

Methods

Certain vegetable crops were grown in a Nixon loam soil in New Jersey during the 1947 growing season in field plots that had been fertilized with different combinations of K, Mg, and Na. Relatively large quantities of fertilizers were applied and the field was in a fair state of fertility before the experiment was started. Six plots having wide variations in the cation content of the fertilizer, especially K and Na, were selected for study of the cation contents of the plant tissues.

The cation contents of the fertilizers applied to these plots are given in table 1. All fertilizers were disced-in before seeding. Varieties of vegetables, planting and harvesting dates are given in tables with the chemical analyses and relative yields of the crops.

Table 1. Fertilizer treatment of vegetable plots expressed as me. per 100 gram soil. *

Treatment Designation	K (60% muriate)	Mg (Epson salts)	Na (NaCl)	Cl content of K and Na salts
2 K, Mg	. 4 (630)	1. 2 (3000)	. 0	. 4
0 K, Na	. 0 (0)	. 0	. 4 (470)	. 4
K, Na	. 2 (315)	. 0	. 4 (470)	. 6
2 K, Na	. 4 (630)	. 0	. 4 (470)	. 8
0 K	. 0 (0)	. 0	. 0	. 0
4 K	. 8 (1260)	. 0	. 0	. 8

* Numbers in parentheses represent the application in pounds per acre of the respective salt. All fertilizer was disced-in before seeding. An overall fertilizer treatment of one ton per acre of 5-10-0 was made before seeding. The soil was limed to pH 6. 5.

The plant materials were oven-dried, ground, and analyzed for K, Ca, Mg, Na, and P by methods outlined by Toth et al. (1948). N, modified to include nitrate-N, and Cl were determined on certain samples according to A. O. A. C. procedures. All analyses, except P, are reported as me. per 100 g. dry tissue.

In determining relative yields, the smallest plant in each group was considered as 100.

Where sampling procedure justified, the analyses of the various plant parts were combined to calculate the composition of the plant as a whole from the relative size of each part.

Results and Discussion

In many cases there were relatively little differences in the cation values of plants from different plots possibly due to the prior fertility status of the field. No conclusions for constancy of cation me. values of a plant tissue can be made unless wide variations exist in the content of the individual cations. With plants, the yields varied greatly with very small changes in the individual cation contents.

Radish (table 2)

The K treatments were reflected in the K content of tops, roots, and in the plant as a whole. Large quantities of Na were absorbed where it was supplied and the Na was uniformly distributed between the top and the root in contrast to alfalfa (Wallace, Toth, and Bear, 1948c). Small amounts of Na were present in the plants grown on plots not receiving Na. Radish has been classified as a plant that will absorb Na even if the nutrient medium is low in Na (Wallace, Toth, and Bear, 1948b). Its ability to do this is largely dependent on the amount of available K. This has been shown also for a plant in a different classification of ability to absorb Na (Wallace, Toth, and Bear, 1948c). The Na content of these radish plants was greatly reduced by the application of K.

Plants were classified (Wallace, Toth, and Bear, 1948b) into the following categories in respect to their ability to accumulate Na:

    (I) Plants not accumulating Na.
    (II) Plants accumulating Na if present in abundance.
    (III) Plants accumulating Na whether abundant or not.
    (IV) Plants native to saline habitats and normally high in Na.

Radish was classified as a group III plant.

The K supply is an environmental factor that can, according to the present data, greatly modify such a classification scheme. A high content of K may be the reason why a plant like turnip was tentatively classified (Wallace, Toth, and Bear, 1948b) in group I while other workers have reported turnip as a plant that absorbs appreciable quantities of Na. Turnip undoubtedly belongs in the same class III as radish.

Radish plants when low in K tended to have increased contents of Ca although this was modified by the Na contents. Of some interest is the very low retention of Ca in roots.

The plants from the plot receiving Mg and the plot receiving no K, Na, or Mg contained the highest amounts of Mg. The latter effect is indicative of the competition between K and Mg for absorption.

The K content of the roots was generally higher than leaves whereas Ca and Mg contents were considerably lower in the roots. The leaves contained the largest cation me. sum.

Table 2.   Relative yields and cation contents of Early Scarlet Globe
radishes grown in soil receiving varying amounts of cations
in the fertilizers.   (Planted April 29, 1947—Harvested
June 3, 1947)

Treatments	Relative yield	K	Ca	Mg	Na	Cation Sum	P
	%			me. per 100 g. dry weight			% of dry wt.
				Tops			
2 K, Mg	113	140	158	86	3	387	.64
0 K, Na	100	77	187	61	71	416	.51
1 K, Na	151	99	144	44	36	321	.42
2 K, Na	113	145	120	48	24	337	.53
0 K	135	103	202	83	3	391	.52
4 K	138	136	141	46	0	323	.45
				Roots			
2 K, Mg	185	174	17	26	2	219	.53
0 K, Na	100	127	21	22	67	237	.58
1 K, Na	164	164	20	25	33	242	.58
2 K, Na	164	186	18	20	19	243	.58
0 K	156	140	20	24	5	189	.48
4 K	177	186	14	18	1	219	.53
				Whole Plant			
2 K, Mg	135	155	99	61	3	318	.59
0 K, Na	100	92	135	49	70	346	.53
1 K, Na	150	118	107	39	32	299	.46
2 K, Na	123	160	83	37	22	302	.55
0 K	135	114	143	65	3	325	.55
4 K	150	155	95	36	0	286	.48

The cation me. sum of the tops (leaves and stems) varied from 321-416
(28.6%); those in the roots from 189-243 (28.6%); and those in the whole plant
from 286-346 (21.0%).   The cation me. sum of the whole plant was thus more
constant than either tops or roots alone.

The plant lowest in K contained the highest cation me. sum and also the
smallest yield.   Lack of sufficient K possibly resulted in diminished carbohydrate production that resulted in an apparent increased concentration of minerals.   This, however, does not necessarily explain all the variations in the
cation me. sum.

The P content did not follow any of the individual cation contents but there
was a slight tendency for P to follow the total cation content.   Factors that
concentrate the cation values would have the same influence on the anions.

Most experiments that have resulted in increases in Mg with simultaneous
increases in the P contents of plants have been carefully controlled in a glasshouse and are less complicated than field conditions.   Some factors that could
cause failure to observe a Mg-P relationship in plants are as follows:

(a) Concentration or dilution of carbohydrates resulting from differences in

mineral nutrition,
(b) Low available P when conditions are such that permit an increase in absorption of Mg and vice versa,
(c) Competition with P from other mineral anions for absorption such as $SO_4^=$, NO_3^-, and Cl^-,
(d) The genetic failure of some plants to exhibit Mg-P relations,
(e) Loss of minerals from foliage from leaching by rain water, or
(f) A combination of many factors.

Information is as yet lacking in regard to most of these points.

Carrot (table 3)

As in radish there was a general trend for the K treatments to be reflected in the K content of the plant. Ca and Mg were higher in the top than in the root as obtained for the radish plants. In contrast to radish the K content of the tops was higher than of the roots and less Na was absorbed than in radish. The increase in Na and slightly decreased K when Na was added was more conducive to higher yields in carrot than in radish. Small quantities of Na were absorbed even when none was added to the soil. The Na of plants supplied no K, 1 K, and 2 K in addition to the Na was 23, 21, and 8 me. per 100 g. Under usual amounts of K-fertilization carrot can be regarded as a type III plant like radish. There was no difference in this plant in the distribution of Na between root and shoot.

Table 3. Relative yields and cation contents of Chantenay carrots grown in soil receiving varying amounts of cations in the fertilizers. (Planted April 29, 1947—Harvested October 15, 1947)

Treatment	Relative yield	K	Ca	Mg	Na	Cation Sum	P
	%			me. per 100 g. dry weight			% of dry wt.
				Tops			
2 K, Mg	248	136	133	49	0	318	.17
0 K, Na	198	96	109	37	31	273	.20
1 K, Na	180	96	120	54	24	294	.18
2 K, Na	141	128	90	37	14	279	.20
0 K	100	63	118	53	3	237	.18
4 K	136	136	89	35	2	262	.20
				Roots			
2 K, Mg	179	72	15	22	2	111	.32
0 K, Na	165	72	15	21	18	126	.35
1 K, Na	122	63	12	26	20	121	.37
2 K, Na	122	77	15	17	13	122	.35
0 K	100	41	12	22	8	83	.30
4 K	107	96	15	18	3	132	.35
				Whole Plant			
2 K, Mg	199	91	50	30	1	172	.27
0 K, Na	176	81	48	27	23	179	.30
1 K, Na	149	73	43	34	21	171	.32
2 K, Na	129	95	42	24	13	169	.30
0 K	100	49	53	34	6	142	.25
4 K	117	109	39	23	3	174	.30

The range in variation of the cation me. sum of the carrot shoots was 237-318 (34. 2%); those in the roots from 83-132 (59. 0%); and those in the whole plant from 142-179 (26. 1%).   Again the whole plant exhibited less variation in the cation sum than shoots and roots alone.   This is due to compensating influences resulting from differential distribution of nutrients among the various plant parts which in turn arises partly from differences in the size of the various parts.   A similar compensating influence was noted for alfalfa (Wallace, Toth, and Bear, 1948a; Wallace and Bear, 1949).

Of particular interest was the variation in cation content of 5 of the 6 plants which was 21. 3% for tops, 15. 8% for roots, and only 5. 9% for the whole plant indicating the extent of compensating influences.   The wide variation for all 6 plants was that the other was lowest in K, lowest in yield, and highest in proportion of shoot to root.   The K deficiency in this plant evidently resulted in decreased cation and anion absorption.   The P content of the whole plant was decreased also in about the same proportion as was that of the total cations.

There was no apparent Mg-P trends in this plant.

It was noted that certain plants such as carrot and radish have very high mineral contents in their top portions.   These tops have no particular market value yet they are marketed with the edible portion.   In the interests of conservation it may eventually be of value to return these materials to the soil. The top portion of the carrots in this experiment are equivalent approximately to 1000 lb. per acre of a 9-1-14 (N, P_2O_5, K_2O) fertilizer.

Snap Bean

Plants on plots not receiving K contained only slightly smaller amounts of K than on the other plots.   No detectable Na was absorbed by any of the plants and this is then a type I plant under the K supplies encountered.   Yields were smallest in the plot receiving no K, Na, or Mg and were highest in the plot receiving 2 K and Mg but the yields were not consistent with any of the chemical analyses.   The treatments influenced the yields more than they did the chemical composition.

The range of cation me. sums for the leaves was 331-386 (16. 3% variation); those in the stems from 116-150 (29. 2%); those in the seed pods from 108-142 me. (31. 4%); and those in the whole plant from 179-210 me. (17. 3%).   This plant and potato were the only ones in which the leaves were analyzed separately.   This plant like alfalfa (Wallace, Toth, and Bear, 1948a) tended to have more constant cation me. values in the leaves than in the whole plant. Both are legumes.   Variations in the cation me. sum were related to both K and Ca.

The difference in the Mg content of these plants was not great enough to have any influence on the P content.

The fact that the pods comprised nearly 50 per cent both the weight of the above-ground portion of the plant and the cation me. sum of the plant illustrates the tremendous drain on the plant by fruiting.

Potato

No roots were analyzed and the samples of leaves, stems, and tubers were taken at different times making comparison between plant parts difficult.

The K content of stems and tubers but not the yields was smallest on the plot receiving no K, Mg, or Na.   No detectable Na was absorbed by any of the plants.   Potato can, therefore, be classified as a type I plant under conditions of this experiment.

The variations of individual cations were very small so that a high degree of constancy of cation me. sum existed for all plant parts. This cannot be accepted as absolute evidence that this plant exhibits constancy of cation me. values.

Ca was strongly excluded from the potato tuber. Much smaller quantities of Ca were present in all portions of the potato plant than in the other plants studied.

Cation-P trends were inconclusive.

Large K and Na treatments appeared to decrease the yield of tubers. Since no Na was absorbed by any of the plants and since the largest K application did not result in large increases in the K content nor appreciable reductions in Ca or Mg, another limiting factor was believed to be involved. For this reason the Cl content of these plant tissues was determined. The plants not receiving Cl as a carrier in the fertilizer contained the smallest content of Cl in the leaf, stem, and tuber portions. Cl in the fertilizer materially increased the Cl content of the plants (up to 2.72% in the stems). The Cl contents of the plants was related to the Cl applied in the fertilizer but they could not be consistently related inversely to the yield of potatoes. The data, however, do indicate a possible negative relationship between Cl content and yield of potatoes. This point should be further investigated in the light of the influence of Cl in the overall cation/anion in plants (Wallace, Toth, and Bear, 1949).

Lettuce

The shoot portion only of lettuce was analyzed. The K treatments were reflected in the K content of the plants, the range being from 93-217 me. (3.63-8.42 per cent).

Na absorption in lettuce was similar to that of carrot and again related to the K treatments. Where no Na was applied the Na content of the plants was very small even where the K content was decreased. Lettuce then is classified as a type II Na plant when moderate amounts of K are present.

The range of the cation me. sum was from 188-306 (63.0%). This is a large variation that would unlikely be compensated for by root composition and root size or by carbohydrate accumulation but it is possible that both factors might combine to give this effect. Hoagland (1944, p. 166), however, states that decreased absorption of K will not always be fully compensated by increased absorption of other bases. Ca and Mg were not absorbed rapidly enough to replace K in this plant when K was low. Since this work was undertaken other data have been obtained (Wallace, Toth, and Bear, 1949; Wallace and Bear, 1949; Wallace, 1952) showing that the cation me. sum is secondary in importance to the cation-anion ratio. It was wondered what adjustments in anion content would take place in these lettuce plants where the cation content was reduced when Ca and Mg did not compensate for low K. The anions, N and Cl, were determined. There was a tendency for the combined contents of these 2 anions to be reduced as the cation me. sum was reduced. If a constant cation/anion exists for this plant it could mean that increasing K may greatly increase the N content of this and similar plants. The cation me. sum of this plant definitely increased with K. Cl did not apparently decrease the N content of this plant possibly because the cation and anion me. sums increased with K.

The Mg content of the lettuce plants was greater than that of their Ca. The plant with the largest Mg content contained the highest P content.

The data indicate that not all plants exhibit constancy of the cation me. sum. This phenomenon is in addition to that of concentration-dilution resulting from differences in carbohydrate accumulation.

Increasing K was associated with an increased cation me. sum that was most pronounced in the case of lettuce and potato. These are non-Ca-accumulating plants and correspond to those referred to by Hoagland in which Ca and Mg do not compensate fully for decreases in K.

The cation me. sum of radish, a Ca-accumulating plant tended to increase with the Ca content in contrast to the above plants and also in contrast to alfalfa and other plants that maintain a constant cation me. sum.

Carrots and beans tended to be intermediate plants in that their total cation contents did not follow exactly the K or the Ca trends but were related to the sum of both. Alfalfa would be in this class.

Summary

A study of the yields and cation and P contents of various portions of 5 vegetable crops grown in the field resulted in the following conclusions:

1. K content of the nutrient medium and genetic factors greatly influenced the absorption of Na. Genetic factors sometimes are secondary to the influence of K. The classes of plants with respect to their behavior towards Na must, therefore, be defined to include the influence of K.

2. In general when the entire plant could be considered as a single unit, the whole-plant basis exhibited a more constant cation me. sum than did most of the individual plant parts. This is consistent with a concept of constancy of cation-anion ratios for the whole plant and differential distribution of nutrients among plant parts according to the relative size of each. Proportion of leaves, stems, reproductive organs, and roots as well as carbohydrate production then have a large influence on the cation me. sum of the various plant parts.

3. The cation me. sum of the leaf portions of bean and potato plants maintained a higher degree of constancy than did other plant parts. These were the only two plants in which leaves were analyzed separately.

4. Mg-P correlation is either restricted to certain plants or is so complicated by field conditions that it is not easily discernible.

5. A possible negative relationship between Cl in fertilizer and yields of potatoes was indicated.

6. The tops of certain vegetables are extremely high in fertilizer elements and as conservation measures the tops of these plants when they have no market value may profitably be returned to the soil.

7. Some plants, particularly lettuce, may not exhibit constancy of the cation me. sum because Ca and Mg are absorbed too slowly to compensate for K when the K content is low. Corresponding relations, however, appear to exist for the anions.

8. Plants were tentatively classified into 3 groups according to their cation accumulation characteristics as follows: (a) cation me. sum increases with increasing K, (b) cation me. sum increases with increasing Ca, and (c) cation me. sum tends to be constant. These differences were most pronounced in the leaf or shoot portions.

9. In some species Ca was not accumulated in root tissues but was largely translocated to the leaves.

10. Cl decreased the N content of potatoes but not of lettuce.

11. Large amounts of K fertilizer tended to decrease the Mg contents of the plants.

(This report was originally written in 1949.)

EFFECT OF HUMIDITY DIFFERENCES (THEREFORE TRANSPIRATION DIFFERENCES) ON SALT UPTAKE AND DISTRIBUTION IN INTACT PLANTS

With G. A. Wallace and C. R. Carmack

Whether or not transpiration influences salt uptake has been one of the most controversial aspects of the problem of salt uptake by intact plants. The general problem has been discussed in the books of Briggs, Hope, and Robertson (1961) and Sutcliffe (1962). Salts are carried upward in the transpirational stream. The evidence for this was summarized by Sutcliffe as follows: (a) tracheal sap does contain quantities of salt, (b) ringing of the bark does not directly interfere with solute movement to shoots but severing of the xylem does (these results were confirmed here with N^{15} salts applied to citrus, Wallace et al., 1954), (c) the upward movement of salts in the xylem has been demonstrated with radioactive isotopes, (d) the rate of movement of radioactive isotopes through stems has been shown to be a function of the intensity of transpiration, and (e) when transpiration is stopped in a particular leaf or leaflet, salt movement to that leaf is practically stopped.

By influencing the internal concentration of salts in the xylem sap, transpiration supposedly can indirectly exert an influence on salt absorption into the roots. The salt concentration in xylem sap influences the rate of movement of salts from the cortical cells to the stele. This influence is therefore exerted on the concentration gradient between the external solution and the cortical cells. Slow water movement would then decrease salt absorption.

Briggs, Hope, and Robertson (1961, p. 197) have reviewed the work which indicates that salt passes into the xylem without passing through the vacuoles. This could imply that salts moving to the shoot may do so under the influence of the transpirational stream. A question is whether or not the influence of the transpirational stream extends to the external solution of roots through a free space. Dainty (1962) says that the evidence is overwhelming that free space does not extend beyond the plasmalemma. Emmert (1961b) has reported evidence of a barrier against P^{32} movement laterally across roots. Salts therefore must be accumulated before they can be transferred to the xylem and explanations other than continuous free space must be sought for the problem of apparent transpiration effect on salt uptake. One possible explanation was given above.

In 1960 Russell and Barber reviewed the problem of the relationship of water absorption by intact plants to salt uptake by plants. They discussed the two above conflicting views of how transpiration can influence salt uptake by intact plants. One of these is ".... the transfer of ions across the root symplast to the vascular stele is an active process dependent on the release of energy through metabolic processes and that the effect of transpiration is to accelerate the movement of ions in water after they have been released into the vascular tissues" (p. 127). The other is "...that ions moved passively in water from the outer surface of the root upward to the shoot" (p. 127). This latter involves a continuous free space from root surface to the leaf. Russell and Barber favor the first concept and come to the following 4 conclusions: (p. 137) (a) ions can enter into the free space of the cortical tissues of roots, though other mechanisms whereby ions may be transferred across the cortex cannot be excluded, (b) at some sites external to the vascular tissue there is a barrier to the free movement of ions which, under some circumstances, is capable of maintaining considerably higher concentrations of ions within the vascular stele than in the ambient medium, (c) the transfer of ions across this barrier depends on the expenditure of metabolic energy, and (d) some

step in the overall process whereby ions are transferred from the outer medium to the shoot can, under certain circumstances, be accelerated by increasing the rate of transpiration.

In 1942 Hoagland and Broyer showed that salt uptake in plants of low salt
status was affected very little by the rate of transpiration while in plants of
high salt status large increases in absorption of salts could be obtained by increasing the rate of transpiration. The results have been verified by Russell
and Shorrocks (1959). If movement of salt into the xylem were the rate-limiting step in salt absorption of plants that were transpiring slowly under high
salt conditions, increasing the transpiration rate under such conditions would
increase salt uptake.

Bernstein and Gardner (1961) have offered an explanation for a transpiration affect on salt uptake. If water is being moved into the root at a greater
relative rate than the salt in the external solution then the salt concentration
in the free space can be increased for a short time. This increase in concentration would result in the usual increase in uptake by the roots. This physical
effect of rapid transpiration would be exerted at the root surface rather than
at the xylem according to other explanations.

Several workers have recognized the problem of apparent differences in
salt absorption in root and salt transfer to shoot (Freeland, 1936; Hylmo, 1953,
1955, 1958; Epstein, 1956a, 1956c; Kramer, 1957; Kylin and Hylmo, 1957;
Fried et al. , 1961; Bange, 1959). Some of these workers thought that transpiration was an important factor in transfer to the shoot. At least Kylin and
Hylmo (1957) wanted to divide the absorption of salt into two components, i.e.,
mostly metabolically controlled at low external concentrations and mostly passively controlled at high external concentrations. In the latter condition the
absorption would be greatly dependent upon transpiration. Because of the ar-
guments reviewed above it is very apparent that an increase in salt absorption
as a result of increased transpiration is not evidence of passive uptake of salt.
It is rather important to consider the experimental conditions as a source of
explanation of variable results (Briggs et al. , 1961). It was found here that
broken root segments in solution cultures could influence results (Wallace and
Hale, 1962b, p. 57). This suggests that the problem of salt and water movement in
old roots as a result of transpirational pull should be investigated. The complex effects of concentration of external solutions on salt uptake can be better
understood (see page 19).

Solutes moving from roots to shoots must pass from the cortical cells into
the xylem of the stele. Lundegardh (1950, 1954—in Briggs et al.) has suggested that this movement into the xylem is largely a passive movement or leakage. Sandstrom (1950) (see Briggs et al.) has shown that removal of the epidermis from roots resulted in an increased salt absorption which was wholly
passive and related to transpiration. The argument is that once ions pass a
metabolic barrier in the epidermis, they are free to pass into the xylem.
More recently decorticated roots have been used and shown to behave similarly (Branton and Jacobson, 1962). The transpiration effect on salt uptake may
be due to technique. An unanswered question seems to be whether or not old
portions of roots have breaks in appropriate places in the epidermis and in the
cortex also to allow free entry to the xylem without going through metabolic
centers. Brouwer (1953) reported that different zones of the root differed in
water uptake. He felt that there was no relationship to salt uptake because
metabolic inhibitors hindered salt uptake but were thought to have no effect on
water movement. Actually some metabolic inhibitors do cause plants to wilt
and there is the problem of some inhibitors causing an increased amount of

salt transfer to shoot, Hale et al. (1962) and page 64.

One possible experimental use of differential transpiration in salt uptake is to get information on whether or not components of a salt are passively or actively moved into plants. This type of evidence of course cannot be conclusive (Dainty, 1962) but it can be part of a total picture. Since calcium had been reported as an ion passively accumulated by plant cells (Moore et al., 1961), an experiment was conducted to find out if transpiration would increase calcium uptake. Bush beans were used for this experiment. The bush beans were first germinated in sand. When the bush beans were five days old, they were transferred to 1/4-strength nutrient solutions. One-hundred-ml. culture tubes were used to hold the plants. Each contained 2 plants and solutions were aerated. When the bush beans were nine days old, the experiment was started.

The experiment was conducted in two parts. The first half of the tubes (two) was put into a humidity chamber with approximately 60% relative humidity, then the second half was put into the humidity chamber with approximately 90% relative humidity. Each half was in the chamber for 24 hours. $CaCl_2$ at $10^{-3}M$ and $10^{-2}M$ was used in the experiment. The calcium was tagged with 600,000 cpm. of Ca^{47} in the 100 ml. solution. The initial pH was 6 and the final pH was between 5.0 and 5.4. Each tube was given a post treatment of 100 ml. of aerated $10^{-2}M$ $CaCl_2$ for one hour after removal of the test solutions. The temperature varied between $25.5°C$ and $24°C$. Fluorescent lights were on 12 hours of the 24 hours.

The results for calcium uptake less free-space components of the experiment are given in table 1 in μmoles per gram dry weight. The results were very inconclusive. There was no effect of low humidity and hence of increased transpiration to increase the Ca movement to shoots. At the low concentration ($10^{-3}M$) there appeared to be an increased Ca movement into roots at low humidity (as would be expected for greater transpiration if Ca were moving into roots passively) but this did not obtain at the high ($10^{-2}M$) Ca concentration. The differential effects for root vs. shoot may coincide with the report (p. 142) that Ca uptake into roots may be a passive process while transfer of it to shoots depends on metabolism.

Table 1.   Effect of humidity on Ca^{47} uptake and translocated by bush bean plants.

Humidity	Leaf	Stem	Root	Whole plant
		μmoles/g. dry weight for $10^{-3}M$ $Ca^{47}Cl_2$		
Low	0.25	10.1	192.0	30.7
High	0.44	9.4	91.2	18.6
		for $10^{-2}M$ $Ca^{47}Cl_2$		
Low	0.11	39.8	2390.	334.
High	3.15	53.1	2300.	385.

Each value is the mean of two determinations and the experiment was duplicated.

Barber and Koontz (1963) have made a very similar study with barley seedlings and found that transpiration had a slight effect only on Ca movement into the shoot and none on Ca movement into roots.

Partly as a means of checking the effect of the anion and to verify that K (presumably) is metabolically accumulated, a similar experiment was made with KCl. Bush beans were germinated in sand and transferred, when 5 days old as before, to 100-ml. culture tubes that contained 1/4-strength nutrient solution. The bush beans were aerated and kept at 25°C while in solution culture. The experiment was conducted in a humidity chamber. For 20 hours previous to the experiment, the plants were in the dark.

Half of the plants were placed in the humidity chamber for 2 hours at 60% relative humidity. Then the relative humidity was raised to 90% and the second half was put in the humidity chamber for 2 hours while the first half was taken out. The bush beans were given a post treatment of $10^{-2}M$ $CaCl_2$ for 1 hour immediately after coming out of the humidity chamber. KCl at $10^{-2}M$ and $10^{-3}M$ was used in the experiment. $CaCl_2$ at $10^{-5}M$ was in all the solution cultures. The potassium was tagged with K^{42} at a specific activity of 150,000 cpm./100 ml. at counting time of samples. The final pH was between 5.5 and 6.5. The transpirational differences seemed to have no effect on K uptake (table 2).

Table 2.　Effect of relative humidity on K uptake less free-space components by intact bush beans.

Relative Humidity	Leaves	Stems	Roots	Whole plant
	μmoles/g. dry weight from $10^{-3}M$ KCl			
High	2.30	3.88	39.2	9.12
Low	0.92	2.78	40.0	8.83
	from $10^{-2}M$ KCl			
High	13.7	15.4	107.0	27.7
Low	15.9	21.0	96.8	32.5

Each value mean of 4 plants.

Summary

Literature was reveiwed which indicates there is not a free-space channel between leaves and the outside of roots through which salts can move under influence of the transpirational stream. Under some conditions transpiration can influence the rate of salt movement to leaves; however, studies with Ca^{47} and K^{42} indicated no effect of transpiration on movement of the isotopes to the shoots.

SOME EFFECTS OF HEAVY METALS ON UPTAKE OF K AND Ca
BY BUSH BEAN PLANTS
With G. A. Wallace and C. R. Carmack

Many mineral elements have some specific functions in plants and some functions for which there is some interchangeability with other mineral elements. Investigators speak of specific carriers, specific binding sites, specific transport mechanisms but questions as to the degree of specificity still

remain. Biological systems may have complete specificity, for example, outwardly directed sodium pumps vs. inwardly directed potassium pumps in cells
but, even so, metal binding by chelating agents is only relatively specific.
Kroll and Gordon (1960) were unsuccessful in producing a chemical that would
chelate Sr to a greater extent than Ca. The relative ability to chelate Sr vs.
Ca for a few chelating agents varied from 0.54 to 0.0085. A degree of specificity, however, was attained. Kroll (unpublished) has found that a combination resin-chelating agent can completely separate Ca from Sr. He suggested
that this may be the means by which biological systems achieve full specificity.

The chelating agent, ethylenediamine di (o-hydroxyphenyl acetate), has a
measure of specificity for iron because of its extremely high stability constant
(about 10^{33}). If iron is absent and other cations are present it will chelate
them. In other words it is not absolutely specific for iron.

A logical question therefore is how specific are various uptake mechanisms
for metal ions in plants. Epstein (1961) showed that there was specificity of K
accumulation in the presence of Na when Ca^{++} was present but that without
Ca^{++} the specificity was at least in part lost. Wallace (1962a, p. 28) reviewed
literature which implied that heavy metals could compete with each other
either for uptake or in some of their specific functions in the cells of plants.
There was a relationship between ability to induce an iron chlorosis and stability constants of metals with chelating agents. Similar findings were reported by El Kholi (1961) except that his results extended to heavy metal inhibition
of K, Ca, and Mg uptake as well.

Since heavy metals such as Zn and Cu have stability constants with chelating agents several orders of magnitude greater than do alkali or alkaline-
earth metals, the effect of some metals on uptake (less free-space components
in roots) of K and Ca by plants was studied.

In the first experiment the effect of Zn, Mn, Cu, and Ni on K uptake was
studied. Bush beans were used for this experiment. The bush beans were
first germinated in sand. When the plants were seven days old they were
transferred to 100-ml. culture tubes that contained 1/4-strength nutrient solution minus micronutrients and iron. Each culture tube contained two plants
and the solutions were aerated. The temperature of the solutions in the culture tubes was regulated at $25^{O}C$ in a water bath. When the plants were elev-
en-days old, the experiment was conducted. Solutions of $10^{-3}\underline{M}$ KCl and
$10^{-4}\underline{M}$ $CaCl_2$ were used for all plants. The potassium was tagged with 140,000
cpm./100 ml. of K^{42} as counted with a scintillation-well counter at time of
counting the plant samples. The different treatments were: control, $10^{-4}\underline{M}$
$ZnSO_4$, $10^{-4}\underline{M}$ $MnCl_2$, $10^{-4}\underline{M}$ $MnCl_2$ + $10^{-4}\underline{M}$ $ZnSO_4$, $10^{-4}\underline{M}$ $CuSO_4$, $10^{-4}\underline{M}$
$ZnSO_4$ + $10^{-4}\underline{M}$ $MnCl_2$ + $10^{-4}\underline{M}$ $CuSO_4$, $10^{-5}\underline{M}$ $CuSO_4$, and $10^{-4}\underline{M}$ $NiSO_4$.
The experiment lasted two hours. A post treatment of $10^{-2}\underline{M}$ $CaCl_2$ was
given for one hour to remove K^{42} from the free space.

The results of the experiment are given in table 1. The per cent inhibition
of uptake of K^{42} by Cu, Ni, Zn, and Mn ($10^{-4}\underline{M}$ each) was 85, 81, 57, and 0
respectively. The stability constants or log $\overline{K}$ of each with ethylenediamine
(a representative chelating agent) are given by Chaberek and Martell (1959) as
10.55, 7.66, 5.71, and 2.73, respectively for the 4 metal ions. These values
indicate that the heavy metals may compete with the K binding site. No double
reciprocal plots, as yet, have been made with the effect. There is, even so,
some uncertainty concerning the specificity of the K binding site. A test was
made to determine if Cu merely made the cells leaky to K^{42} (see also page 75).
Plants that had been exposed to K^{42} for 4 hours were exposed to $10^{-4}\underline{M}$ solu-

tions of $CuSO_4$, $NiSO_4$, $ZnSO_4$, and a control. Each solution also contained $10^{-5}M$ $CaCl_2$. Only in the case of $CuSO_4$ was there any loss of K^{42} in the post treatment. There was no loss with Ni and Zn. With Na^{22} (page 75) there was only a slight tendency for Cu to cause leakiness. With K^{42} (but not with Na^{22}) the Cu effect may have been in removing the K^{42} from the Donnan free space.

Table 1.   Influence of heavy metals on uptake and distribution of K from a $10^{-3}M$ KCl solution.

Treatment	Leaf	Stem	Root	Whole Plant
		μmoles/g. dry weight		
Control	9. 85	24. 1	708.	101. 0
$10^{-4}M$ Zn	5. 82	24. 5	240.	43. 0
$10^{-4}\underline{M}$ Mn	7. 44	19. 2	632.	100. 0
$10^{-4}\underline{M}$ Mn + Zn	15. 0	32. 8	574.	97. 5
$10^{-4}\underline{M}$ Cu	0. 87	2. 95	93. 5	15. 5
$10^{-4}\underline{M}$ Zn, Mn, Cu	1. 14	3. 68	70. 6	12. 4
$10^{-5}\underline{M}$ Cu	2. 28	12. 1	550.	76. 4
$10^{-4}\underline{M}$ Ni	4. 98	22. 0	200.	19. 4

Each solution contained $10^{-4}\underline{M}$ $CaCl_2$ and each value was the mean for 4 determinations.

A study was made of heavy metal effect on Ca uptake. Bush beans were used for this experiment. The bush beans were first germinated in sand; when the plants were seven days old, they were transferred to 1/4-strength nutrient solution minus added micronutrients. Culture tubes (100 ml.) were used to hold the plants. Each tube had two plants and was aerated. The temperature of the nutrient solutions was again held at 25°C. When the bush beans were ten days old, the experiment was conducted.

$Ca^{47}Cl_2$ $(10^{-3}\underline{M})$ was used in all treatments. The treatments were similar to those in table 1. The exposure period was two hours. The pH was initially adjusted at 7. 0. A post treatment of aerated $10^{-2}M$ $CaCl_2$ for one hour was used. The calcium was tagged with 100,000 cpm. $\overline{C}a^{47}/100$ ml.

Table 2.   Influence of heavy metals on uptake and distribution of Ca from a $10^{-3}\underline{M}$ solution of $CaCl_2$.

Treatment	Leaf	Stem	Root	Whole Plant
		μmoles/g. dry weight		
Control	. 200	2. 69	64. 2	9. 63
$10^{-4}M$ Zn	. 248	2. 34	43. 8	7. 77
$10^{-4}\underline{M}$ Mn	. 181	2. 52	60. 3	9. 28
$10^{-4}\underline{M}$ Zn + Mn	. 259	0. 97	38. 8	5. 74
$10^{-4}\underline{M}$ Cu	. 258	2. 37	58. 8	9. 78
$10^{-4}\underline{M}$ Zn + Mn + Cu	. 372	2. 42	61. 2	9. 30
$10^{-5}\underline{M}$ Cu	. 374	1. 73	62. 2	10. 1
$10^{-4}\underline{M}$ Ni	. 202	1. 95	46. 5	7. 55

The results are in table 2. There were no real differences in Ca uptake as result of the heavy metals in contrast to K. This may be related to the observations that imply that K is accumulated as a result of metabolic processes while Ca is taken up passively at least into roots (page 142).

If one metal ion competes with another for a given site, then H^+ should do the same. Also if K^+ is bound to a site and Ca is not, H^+ should compete with K for uptake but not for Ca. Results for 4-hour uptake studies with K^{42} and Ca^{47} gave such results (table 3).

Table 3. Effect of pH on K and Ca uptake (less free-space constituents) by intact bush bean plants.

pH	Leaf	Stem	Root	Whole Plant
		μmoles/g. dry weight		
		K from KCl, $10^{-4}M$		
3.5	.16	.52	7.17	1.76
5.0	.09	.55	14.10	2.72
6.5	.22	.82	23.80	4.53
8.0	.30	1.39	27.40	5.02
9.5	.30	.93	20.20	4.15
		K from KCl, $10^{-3}M$		
3.5	.57	1.33	21.0	4.59
5.0	1.24	3.22	39.5	10.50
6.5	.94	3.08	44.1	9.54
8.0	.90	3.10	50.9	11.50
9.5	.46	1.78	46.2	9.22
		Ca from $CaCl_2$, $10^{-4}M$		
3.5	.14	.29	12.20	1.54
5.0	.02	.22	4.46	0.74
6.5	.02	.21	4.76	0.73
8.0	.04	.56	4.68	1.14
9.5	.03	.18	9.92	1.55
		Ca from $CaCl_2$, $10^{-3}M$		
3.5	.77	1.24	118.0	13.60
5.0	.30	3.49	36.4	7.34
6.5	.14	1.61	37.0	6.62
8.0	.15	2.90	39.2	7.10
9.5	.26	3.22	78.7	13.10

Each value is the mean of 4.

Summary

Zn, Ni, and Cu ($10^{-4}M$) inhibited accumulation (uptake less free-space constituents in roots) of K ($10^{-3}M$) by intact bush bean plants but not of Ca. The inhibition of K was correlated with stability constants of the metals with chelating agents. H^+ competed with K for entry into bush beans but did not seem to do so with Ca.

UPTAKE OF MANNITOL BY BUSH BEAN PLANTS AND DISTRIBUTION IN PLANT PARTS

Mannitol was presumed for a long time to be physiologically inert, and of very slow permeation (Collander and Barlund, 1933). The use of such a substance not absorbed by the plant would be useful in studies on water relations of plants.

It was not until 1956 that some workers presented evidence for mannitol absorption by the vacuole in addition to its permeation into the free space of plants (Ordin et al. , 1956).

Some data concerning the uptake of C^{14}-mannitol was given in the sections beginning on pages 19, 26, and 29. Because most of these studies with mannitol were made before we learned that broken root tips resulted in transfer of solutes from the external solution to the leaves of plants without their going through the metabolic mechanism of the roots, additional studies were made. The studies with the ions had been verified earlier. Present studies were made with plants in which we were quite certain that there were no broken root tips. The previous results are believed to be reasonably valid.

The uptake by plant materials of mannitol has been reported recently (Dalev et al. , 1957; Thimann et al. , 1960; Groenewegen and Mills, 1960; Bidwell and Ghosh, 1962). Thimann et al. reported that mannitol readily penetrated the free space but only sluggishly penetrated a second compartment. Bidwell and Ghosh reported that mannitol was taken up passively by <u>Fucus vesiculosus</u>, a marine alga.

The results of the studies on pages 19, 26, and 29 in general did indicate that mannitol was taken into plants passively. The effect of root temperature (page 35), however, may indicate otherwise for roots but not for transfer to leaves. Because of these questions in addition to the one of broken roots and also for the purpose of noting distribution patterns among plant parts, this new study was made.

Experiments were conducted on bush beans (<u>Phaseolus vulgaris</u>, variety Tendergreen). The plants were started by germinating seeds in sterilized quartz sand in wooden flats in a glasshouse. The flats were watered regularly with distilled water. Five to six days from germination, sound uniform seedlings were transferred to 100-ml. culture tubes containing 1/4-strength nutrient solution which was formed of the following salts in moles/liter: KNO_3, 0.001; $NH_4H_2PO_4$, 0.002; $MgSO_4$, 0.004; K_2SO_4, 0.002; and $Ca(NO_3)_2$, 0.005.

The nutrient media were continuously aerated in the tubes during the entire growing period. After eight days, the nutrient solution was carefully poured out and the roots washed with distilled water before adding the experimental solutions. These solutions in addition to mannitol contained 10^{-4} molar $CaCl_2$ to preserve the integrity of the roots. These were also aerated. The pH of the experimental solutions was always adjusted to 7 and checked frequently. The absorption period selected was 6 hours. At the end of the absorption period, roots were rinsed with distilled water and washed for 5 minutes with aeration as a post treatment. After that, the plants were washed again in running tap water for 2 or 3 minutes and separated into roots, stems, and leaves. These parts were then put into paper bags and dried in a forced-draft oven at $70^{\circ}C$. The dried plant material was ground in a Wiley mill, then weighed and aliquots were spread evenly in metal planchets. These were then counted for C^{14} with a thin window gas flow counter. Corrections for self-absorption were made, and the amounts of mannitol were calculated from specific activity relationships according to the principles of Hendler (1959) and expressed as micromoles per gram of dry weight.

Evidence that mannitol was absorbed by the roots and transported to the shoots was demonstrated by Groenewegen and Mills in 1960 and confirmed by the results obtained in the present study, table 1. The effects of concentration, temperature, and metabolic inhibitors on uptake of mannitol and its distribution among leaves, stems, and roots in 6 hours are indicated in table 1. The concentration ratios on the whole-plant basis for $10^{-1}/10^{-2}$, $10^{-2}/10^{-3}$, and $10^{-3}/10^{-4}$M were 9.7, 4.6, and 3.0 respectively. For leaves they were 9.2, 7.1, and 12.0. Similar results were obtained in a repeat experiment.

Table 1.   Uptake of mannitol in 6 hours by bush bean plants with variations of experimental conditions.

Concentrations of C^{14}-mannitol in external solution	Leaves	Stems	Roots	Whole Plant	Leaf / Root
M	\multicolumn{4}{c}{μmoles/g. dry weight}	ratio
	\multicolumn{4}{c}{$21^{\circ}C$}	
10^{-1}	15.8	1.3	80.2	19.0	0.19
10^{-2}	1.71	0.08	8.6	1.95	0.20
10^{-3}	0.18	0.03	2.03	0.42	0.09
10^{-4}	0.02	0.01	0.73	0.14	0.03
Root Temperature $^{\circ}C$	\multicolumn{4}{c}{at 10^{-3}M}	
1	0.09	0.04	0.18	0.09	0.50
11	0.18	0.02	0.80	0.18	0.23
21	0.18	0.03	2.03	0.42	0.09
31	0.87	0.05	4.21	0.87	0.21
Inhibitor	\multicolumn{4}{c}{at 10^{-3}M and $21^{\circ}C$}	
Control	0.18	0.03	2.03	0.42	0.09
10^{-4}M 2,4-DNP	0.21	0.02	1.25	0.29	0.17
10^{-3}M KCN	0.55	0.06	0.50	0.30	1.11
Dark	0.14	0.07	2.10	0.43	0.07

Each value is the mean of determinations for 4 plants.

The Q_{10} values for 11/1, 21/11, and 31/21 $^{\circ}C$ were on the whole-plant basis 2.0, 2.3, and 2.1 respectively. For roots they were 4.4, 2.5, and 2.1. Similar results for roots were obtained in a prior experiment. Cyanide and dinitrophenol might have depressed the uptake but they did not depress that transferred to leaves. Cyanide appeared to increase that transferred to leaves.

Since the results with temperature and inhibitors did not support the concept that mannitol was passively absorbed as reported elsewhere for other species, estimates were made for the gradient between C^{14}-mannitol in roots for 10^{-1} to 10^{-4}M solutions. That in roots was approximately 10, 10, 20, and 70% respectively. These values for 6 hours indicate that mannitol was taken up sluggishly.

The reason for inclusion of a dark treatment was to evaluate the effect of transpiration on uptake. The mannitol uptake was independent of the light vs. dark during the period of test. Transfer of mannitol to shoots, however, appeared to be reduced by keeping the plants in the dark.

Increasing external concentrations of mannitol caused a greater percentage transfer to the leaves.

The physiological implications of the presence of mannitol in the shoots of intact plants are of great importance. In studies of plant-water relations the use of mannitol as a substance to increase osmotic pressure will therefore be impossible and studies using it will be open to question. Mannitol increases the osmotic concentration in the ambient solutions and, being absorbed, the osmotic concentration of the plant cell would also be increased.

Summary

The non-ionizable compound, mannitol, appeared to be absorbed by plant roots and transported to the leaves of bush beans. The presence of absorbed mannitol in the shoots of intact plants has considerable implications in studies of the physiology of plants. Between 10^{-1} and $10^{-2}\underline{M}$, the mannitol was absorbed in direct proportion to its external concentration but at lower concentrations a hyperbolic relationship obtained. Uptake appeared to be dependent upon temperature and influenced by metabolic inhibitors but the mannitol was not absorbed against a concentration gradient. Transfer of mannitol to leaves was decreased by keeping plants in the dark. Increasing external concentration resulted in a greater proportion of mannitol transferred to leaves.

EFFECT OF PRETREATMENT OF BUSH BEAN ROOTS WITH SODIUM ON THE TRANSFER OF Na^{22} TO THE SHOOTS

Arisz (1956) suggested that low salt roots were better than high salt roots for study of salt accumulation into vacuoles but that high salt roots were better than low salt roots for study of transport of salts to shoots. This is because the test salts would have less tendency to be transported to vacuoles of cells in the roots instead of to the shoots in plants where root vacuoles already have high salt concentrations. Helder (1957) reported that pretreatment of roots with potassium decreased subsequent rubidium absorption but that it increased rubidium transfer to the shoots. Although some workers have reported that all salts present in roots can be mobilized and transferred to the shoot, questions do remain as to whether or not salts in the vacuole are readily transported to shoots or whether or not transport to the vacuole is prerequisite to transfer to the shoot. Epstein (1956b) has said that certain ions that are metabolically accumulated in the roots are largely unavailable for transfer to the shoots. The purpose of this study was to see if pretreatment with sodium of plant roots of a species that, in the presence of sodium, accumulates it in the roots but not in the shoots (Huffaker and Wallace, 1959a) would result in an increased transfer of Na^{22} to shoots.

Methods in general were similar to those on page 62. Eight-day old seedlings were transferred to culture tubes and pretreated for 5 days with 1/10-strength nutrient solution with 0 Na, $10^{-3}\underline{N}$ Na_2SO_4, and $10^{-2}\underline{N}$ Na_2SO_4 for 5 days. These solutions were then removed and replaced with $\overline{10}^{-2}\underline{N}$ $Na_2{}^{22}SO_4$ + $10^{-5}\underline{N}$ $CaCl_2$ at pH 7 for periods of 2, 4, and 24 hours. One hundred ml. test solution was used per tube and each ml. contained 4090 cpm. Na^{22} per ml. as determined with the scintillation-well counter. There were two culture tubes and 4 plants per treatment. At the end of each respective test period the

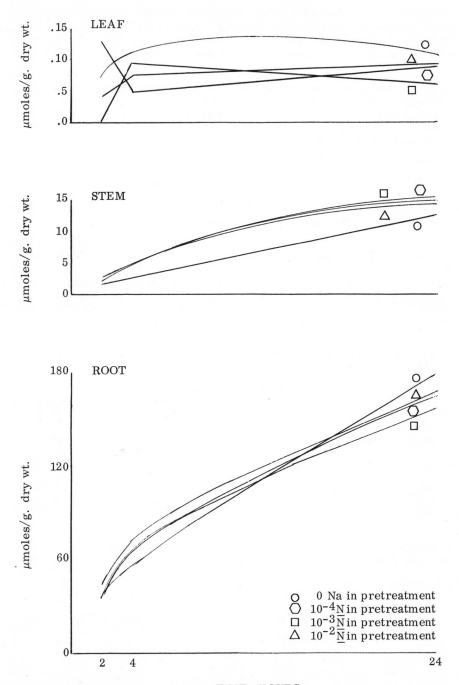

Figure 1. Na^{22} in some plant parts when applied following pretreatment of bush bean plants with Na$_2$SO$_4$.

shoots were removed and divided into leaves and stems.   The detopped roots received a post-treatment of 100 ml., aerated, 10^{-2}M $CaCl_2$ for one hour to remove Na^{22} from the free space.   Results were reported as μmoles Na per gram dry weight as the means of the 4 separate determinations.

The results in figure 1 indicate that there was essentially no effect of sodium pretreatment on subsequent uptake (less free-space components) and distribution of Na^{22}.   The only plant part where an effect was indicated was the bottom 1/3 of the stem where the effect suggested by Arisz seemed to hold, namely that when the root capacity was satisfied more ion would be transferred to the shoot.

AMMONIUM AND NITRATE NITROGEN IN CATION AND ANION
RELATIONSHIPS IN PLANTS
With C. R. Carmack and R. T. Mueller

There are many reports that indicate the NH_4^+ cation decreases the uptake of other cations (K + Ca + Mg) (Drosdoff et al. , 1955; Van der Merwe, 1952-1953; Nightingale, 1948; and Wallace et al. , 1949).   Bhan et al. (1960), however, noted that at pH 8. 5 the K + Ca + Mg content in soybeans was the same for all-NO_3^- vs. all-NH_4^+ as nitrogen sources (table 1).   At pH 5-6 nitrate plants did have more K + Ca + Mg than did ammonium plants but at pH 4 they were both again equal, possibly the result of H^+ competition.

Table 1.   Effect of pH of nitrogen source on some characteristics of soybeans (Bhan et al. , 1960).

N treatment and pH	K + Ca + Mg	Yield	N
	me./100 g. dry weight	g./8 plants	% of dry weight
NO_3^-, 3-4	155	3. 2	3. 19
NO_3^-, 5-6	201	3. 5	3. 41
NO_3^-, HCO_3^- (8. 5)	211	5. 3	3. 83
NH_4^+, 3-4	165	2. 7	4. 06
NH_4^+, 5-6	149	3. 0	4. 44
NH_4^+, HCO_3 (8. 5)	209	2. 3	4. 11

Assumptions may be made then that if cation uptake equals anion uptake the following relationships would hold when different nitrogen sources are used:

at pH 8. 5 (see table 1):
(a) $NH_4^+ + K + Ca + Mg = HCO_3^- + H_2PO_4^- + SO_4^=$
or
(b) $K + Ca + Mg = HCO_3^- + NO_3^- + H_2PO_4^- + SO_4^=$

at acid pH (see table 1):
(c) $H^+ + NH_4^+ + K + Ca + Mg = CO_2 + H_2PO_4^- + SO_4^=$
or
(d) $H^+ + K + Ca + Mg = CO_2 + NO_3^- + H_2PO_4^- + SO_4^=$.

In case (a) it would be expected that less K should be taken up by plants than in case (b) and that less HCO_3^- would be taken up in case (b) than in case (a). This latter hypothesis was tested (solutions 1 and 2 in table 2).   In addition to these, the uptake of $KHC^{14}O_3$ was compared in the presence of $NH_4H_2PO_4$ vs. $NaNO_3$ (table 2, solutions 4 and 6). Solution 3 was identical with solution 4 and solution 5 was identical with solution 6 except K^{42} was used in 3 and 5 in contrast to C^{14} in 4 and 6. It would be expected that NO_3^- vs. $H_2PO_4^-$ would influence the results but less than would that of NH_4^+ vs. NO_3^-.

Table 2. Nutrient solutions used in first experiment.

	Numbers of the experimental solutions					
Ion	1	2	3	4	5	6
	m. molar concentration					
K	9	9	4*	4	4*	4
Ca	1	1	.01	.01	.01	.01
Mg	1	1	—	—	—	—
NH_4^+	5	0	4	4	0	0
NO_3^-	0	5	—	—	4	4
$SO_4^=$	11	1	—	—	—	—
$H_2PO_4^-$	1	1	4	4	—	—
HCO_3^-	4*	4*	4	4*	4	4*
Na	—	—	—	—	4	4

*Radioisotopic label indicated by *.

The results of these tests are in table 3. As predicted the all-NO_3^- plants (case b above) had about $\frac{1}{2}$ the C^{14} that the all-NH_4^+ plants had (case a above). These relative values are reasonably accurate even though the exact values are complicated because of exchange with CO_2 of the air. CO_2 from respiration is probably more important than external bicarbonate in preserving the balances described in case (a) and case (b). Greater differences in C^{14} uptake were expected than were obtained in treatments 1 and 2.

Table 3. Uptake of K and HCO_3^- by bush beans as influenced by different nitrogen sources or by anions (treatments in table 2).

Treatment numbers from table 2	Leaf	Stem	Root	Whole plant
	μmoles/g. dry weight			
	C^{14}-bicarbonate from complete nutrient solutions			
1(NH_4^+)	0.38	0.76	13.90	2.29
2(NO_3^-)	0.90	1.06	2.81	1.21
	K^{42} from $NH_4H_2PO_4$ vs. $NaNO_3$ solutions			
3(NH_4^+)	0.79	4.40	155.1	19.4
5(NO_3^-)	23.6	35.8	239.4	53.9
	C^{14}-bicarbonate from $NH_4H_2PO_4$ vs. $NaNO_3$ solutions			
4(NH_4^+)	0.20	0.75	10.01	1.80
6(NO_3^-)	0.80	0.30	3.90	1.18

NH_4^+-N in solution 4 resulted in about twice as much $HC^{14}O_3^-$ in the plants as did NO_3^--N in solution 6 (table 3). The results were quite similar to those of solutions 1 and 2. NO_3^--N resulted in a greater amount of C^{14} translocated to leaves than did NH_4^+-N in both cases (table 3).

More K^{42} (solutions 3 and 5 of table 2) was absorbed in the presence of NO_3^- than in the presence of NH_4^+ (table 3) as predicted for case (a) vs. case (b). An item of great interest was the large increase of K transported to shoots in the presence of NO_3^- relative to the presence of NH_4^+.

Since NH_4^+ did appear to compete with K^{42} for uptake some studies were undertaken to determine the type of inhibition involved. The double-reciprocal plot technique of Lineweaver and Burk (1934) was used. Four concentrations of K^{42}Cl with bush bean plants prepared as described in preceding reports were exposed for 4 hours to the radioisotope. At that time the plant roots were subjected to a 1-hour post treatment consisting of 10^{-2}M $CaCl_2$. The solutions were 10^{-4}, 2×10^{-4}, 5×10^{-4}, and 10^{-3}M. Three pH systems were used, pH 4, pH 7, and pH 8 (HCO_3^-), to test H^+ as an inhibitor of K uptake. In one set of plants at pH 7, 10^{-2}M NH_4Cl was used to determine the effect of NH_4^+. The results in figure 1 indicate that both H^+ and NH_4^+ competed competitively with K for uptake.

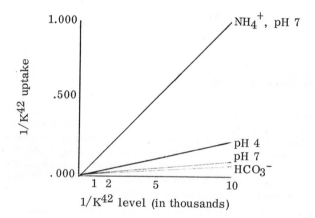

Figure 1. Double reciprocal plots of K^{42} uptake with H^+ and NH_4^+ as inhibitors.

Since recent studies indicate that Ca may be taken up nonmetabolically by bean roots (page 142), a study was made with Ca^{47} to see if NH_4^+ had any effect on Ca uptake as it does for K. The results were completely negative (table 4).

Table 4. Effect of NH_4^+ on Ca^{47} uptake by bush beans. *

$CaCl_2$	NH_4^+ levels, M		
M	0	10^{-3}	10^{-2}
	μmoles/g. dry weight whole plant		
10^{-4}	2.3	2.2	1.8
2×10^{-4}	3.7	3.9	3.2
5×10^{-4}	6.6	6.8	7.0
10^{-3}	14.9	14.4	18.2

*Plants were prepared and handled as in previous experiments with a 1-hour 10^{-2}M $CaCl_2$ post treatment.

If there are major differences in uptake mechanisms for K and Ca it was wondered if the NO_3^-, Cl^-, or $SO_4^=$ salts of each in single-salt solutions would have differential effects on pH changes in the external solution. This is the well-known effect of pH drifting in nutrient solutions in which plants are grown. Nitrate nitrogen usually results in an upward pH drift in complete solutions and ammonium nitrogen in a downward drift (Trelease and Trelease, 1935). It has been assumed that NO_3^- is taken up slightly faster than cations and NH_4^+ slightly faster than anions with H^+ or OH^- exchange causing the pH drift. In table 5 are some results of drift with single salts where the initial pH was 7.0. With all anions Ca resulted in a higher pH than K but it did result in H^+ exchange or production as did K. With Ca, nitrate resulted in increased pH as is commonly experienced for nitrate in nutrient solutions. This would mean that nitrate was absorbed faster than Ca, but for all other salts used the cation appeared to be absorbed faster than the anion.

Table 5.   pH drift of single salt solutions in which bush beans were growing (initial pH at 7.0).

$10^{-3}M$ solution of	Time, hours			
	0	3.5	26	48
		pH		
$Ca(NO_3)_2$	7.0	7.0	7.2	7.6
KNO_3	7.0	6.0	5.9	5.7
$CaSO_4$	7.0	6.5	6.1	5.4
K_2SO_4	7.0	4.8	4.2	3.9
$CaCl_2$	7.0	6.6	5.7	5.3
KCl	7.0	5.6	4.6	4.3

Summary

From a complete nutrient solution about twice as much $HC^{14}O_3^-$ was absorbed by plants receiving NH_4^+ as the sole source of nitrogen compared with those receiving NO_3^- as the sole source of nitrogen. If cation uptake equaled anion uptake, however, the difference should have been much greater.

With both N sources much more K was taken up than was HCO_3^-. With NO_3^--N the ratio was 44 and with NH_4^+-N it was 8.

pH is an important factor determining how effectively NH_4^+ will compete with cations for absorption by plants.

Not only was more K^{42} absorbed when NO_3^- was the nitrogen source compared with NH_4^+, but also much more of it was translocated to leaves and stems with nitrate than with NH_4^+.

NH_4^+ and H^+ both appeared to competitively inhibit K^{42} uptake according to the double reciprocal plot technique.

NH_4^+ did not influence the uptake of Ca^{47} in short-time studies.

As measured by pH changes in the external solution, K and Ca were taken up faster than the complementary anion except with $Ca(NO_3)_2$ where nitrate was taken up faster. K caused a greater pH decrease than did Ca with three different anions.

ADDITIONAL STUDIES ON THE EFFECT OF CYANIDE ON UPTAKE
OF POTASSIUM BY BUSH BEAN PLANTS

Because of the apparent effect of cyanide on the distribution of cations in leaves and roots of bush beans (pages 39 and 64), additional studies were made in an attempt to better characterize the phenomenon.

In a 5-hour experiment bush bean plants that had been previously grown for 6 days in 1/10-strength nutrient solution were exposed to $10^{-3}M$ $K^{42}Cl$ (4680 cpm./μmole at counting time) with $10^{-5}M$ $CaCl_2$. These treatments were combined with 10^{-5}, 10^{-4}, 10^{-3}, and $10^{-2}M$ of either NaCl or NaCN and replicated sets of each were run at root temperatures of 5 and 20°C. The roots received a post treatment of $10^{-2}M$ $CaCl_2$.

In another experiment similar bush beans were exposed to combinations of KCN and KCl so that the K^+ concentration was $10^{-3}M$ and that of CN^- varied from zero to $10^{-3}M$. K^{42} (5070 cpm./μmole K at counting time) was used in this experiment which ran for 5 hours at pH 7. $CaCl_2$ at $10^{-5}M$ was used in each solution. All solutions were aerated. The roots received the usual $CaCl_2$ post treatment.

The results of the first experiment are summarized in table 1. The specific effects of cyanide, temperature, and sodium are given in tables 2, 3, and 4 respectively.

Table 1. Uptake (less free-space components) of K^{42} from KCl as influenced by temperature, cyanide, and Na.

NaCl or NaCN	With NaCl				With NaCN			
	Leaf	Stem	Root	Whole Plant	Leaf	Stem	Root	Whole Plant
M			μmoles K per g. dry weight					
			at 20°C					
10^{-5}	21.0	25.7	273.4	61.2	19.1	26.0	228.5	56.1
10^{-4}	21.5	28.7	311.5	65.0	11.5	16.4	209.7	41.6
10^{-3}	23.7	30.3	270.0	64.5	1.7	9.7	126.5	24.1
10^{-2}	18.2	24.5	240.1	53.4	0.2	2.4	39.0	7.6
			at 5°C					
10^{-5}	0.17	5.3	92.8	16.7	0.07	2.9	82.7	14.5
10^{-4}	0.15	4.6	85.8	14.6	0.00	3.3	58.6	10.8
10^{-3}	0.16	4.2	76.3	13.7	0.06	3.2	54.0	8.7
10^{-2}	0.37	2.8	61.2	10.3	0.02	1.2	26.6	5.0

Each value is the mean of 4 replications.

Cyanide inhibited K accumulation by roots somewhat more at the high temperature than at the low (tables 1, 2, 3). This would be expected if cyanide and low temperature were both inhibiting the same component or same mechanism. In general the movement of K^{42} to leaves was inhibited more than into roots. An exception was the lowest cyanide level with the high temperature. A relationship of cyanide concentration vs. translocation to leaves will be discussed below. The general result of the first experiment was that cyanide decreased the leaf/root and stem/root ratios for K^{42} (table 5). From these results it

Table 2.   Effect of cyanide on K^{42} uptake from table 1.

NaCN	Leaf	Stem	Root	Whole Plant
$\underline{M}$		% Inhibition from CN^-		
		at 20°C		
10^{-5}	9	0	16	8
10^{-4}	46	43	33	36
10^{-3}	93	68	53	63
10^{-2}	99	90	84	86
		at 5°C		
10^{-5}	59	45	11	13
10^{-4}	100	28	32	26
10^{-3}	62	24	29	36
10^{-2}	95	57	57	52

Table 3.   Effect of temperature on K^{42} uptake from table 1.

NaCl or NaCN	With NaCl				With NaCN			
	Leaf	Stem	Root	Whole Plant	Leaf	Stem	Root	Whole Plant
$\underline{M}$			% Inhibition by low temperature					
10^{-5}	99	79	66	73	100	89	64	74
10^{-4}	99	84	72	78	100	80	72	74
10^{-3}	99	86	72	79	96	67	57	64
10^{-2}	98	89	75	81	90	50	32	34

Table 4.   Effect of sodium on K^{42} uptake from table 1.   Percentage values are calculated with $10^{-5}\underline{M}$ NaCl or NaCN as controls.

NaCl or NaCN	With NaCl				With NaCN			
	Leaf	Stem	Root	Whole Plant	Leaf	Stem	Root	Whole Plant
$\underline{M}$			% Increase or decrease by Na salt					
			at 20°C					
10^{-4}	+2	+12	+14	+6	-40	-37	-8	-26
10^{-3}	+13	+18	-1	+5	-91	-63	-45	-57
10^{-2}	-13	-5	-12	-13	-99	-91	-83	-86
			at 5°C					
10^{-4}	-12	-13	-8	-13	-100	+14	-29	-26
10^{-3}	-6	-21	-18	-18	-14	+10	-35	-40
10^{-2}	+118	-47	-34	-38	-71	-59	-68	-66

would appear that transport of K^{42} to shoots as well as accumulation in roots was sensitive to cyanide except such a conclusion is not certain. Less may have been transported to shoots because less was taken into roots.

Table 5. Leaf/root and stem/root ratios for K^{42} in plants.

NaCl or NaCN	Leaf/root		Stem/root	
	NaCl	NaCN	NaCl	NaCN
$\underline{M}$	ratios			
	at $20^{o}C$			
10^{-5}	.076	.084	.094	.114
10^{-4}	.069	.055	.092	.078
10^{-3}	.088	.013	.112	.076
10^{-2}	.076	.005	.102	.062
	at $3^{o}C$			
10^{-5}	.0018	.0008	.057	.035
10^{-4}	.0017	.0000	.054	.056
10^{-3}	.0022	.0011	.055	.059
10^{-2}	.0060	.0008	.046	.045

Sodium (without cyanide) in general interfered more with K uptake percentagewise at the low temperature than at the high (table 4). This is consistent with the view that at least two uptake mechanisms for K were present (Bange, 1961) one of which being more inhibited by low temperature than the other. At low temperature the sodium could have interfered with the mechanism for which sodium is a competitive inhibitor (Bange, 1961).

The Viets-like effect where sodium stimulates K uptake (Huffaker and Wallace, 1959b; Prevot and Ollagnier, 1961) was evident at high temperature but not at low (table 4). With cyanide, sodium effects were masked.

When cyanide level was varied without sodium (table 6), low levels of cyanide (below $10^{-4}\underline{M}$) did not inhibit the uptake of K^{42} and it was at these levels where transport to shoots was increased. The effect of cyanide on transport of K^{42} to shoots therefore, appears to be a complex phenomenon.

Table 6. Effect of cyanide levels on K^{42} uptake (less free-space constituents) and distribution (K^+ was at a constant level of $10^{-3}\underline{M}$).

KCN	Leaf	Stem	Root	Whole Plant	Leaf/root
$\underline{M}$	μmoles/g. dry weight				ratio
0	2.3	20.6	191.2	37.9	.012
5×10^{-6}	14.7	23.2	245.3	52.9	.060
10^{-5}	9.1	16.0	267.9	51.7	.034
5×10^{-5}	15.8	20.7	249.6	51.4	.063
10^{-4}	6.7	14.0	214.7	41.9	.026
5×10^{-4}	2.7	8.5	120.3	26.4	.022
10^{-3}	1.0	5.9	109.2	19.2	.010

Summary

Low temperature decreased the percentage of inhibition of K^{42} uptake caused by cyanide with bush beans. In the presence of sodium ions the transfer of K^{42} to shoots was greatly inhibited by both low temperature and levels of cyanide of $10^{-4}M$ or greater. In studies without sodium, cyanide levels lower than $10^{-4}M$ increased K^{42} translocation to leaves and that into whole plants slightly. Sodium decreased K^{42} uptake relatively more at low temperature than at high consistent with a view of 2 uptake mechanisms for K. A Viets-like effect where sodium stimulated K uptake was indicated at $20^{\circ}C$ but not at $5^{\circ}C$.

EFFECT OF NUTRIENT DEFICIENCIES ON K, Na, AND Fe

UPTAKE BY BUSH BEAN PLANTS

Because of the recognized importance of metabolism in the accumulation of at least certain ions by plants an exploratory investigation was made to determine how some specific mineral element deficiencies influenced the uptake (less free-space components) of some cations. If a consistent pattern could be detected it may be possible to speculate concerning the accumulation mechanism. One of the special reasons for using this approach was the observation with sodium that such things as low temperature, metabolic inhibitors, anaerobiosis increased sodium transport to shoots (page 62). It was wondered if nutrient deficiencies had the same effect.

Studies were made with potassium, sodium and iron uptake. Bush beans previously germinated in sand were transferred to complete nutrient solutions in 3700 ml. bottles except where single nutrients were completely omitted as indicated in table 1. For the K^{42} experiment and the first Fe^{59} experiment the plants were mildly deficient only. They were exposed to the differential solutions for 9 days at which point the solutions were replaced with those containing either K^{42} (10,200 cpm./ml. at counting time of plant samples) in $10^{-4}M$ KCl (in $10^{-4}M$ $CaCl_2$) or Fe^{59} (240 cpm./ml.) in $10^{-4}M$ FeEDDHA (in $10^{-4}M$ $CaCl_2$). The plants were exposed to K^{42} for 24 hours and to Fe^{59} for 96 hours. The pH of all solutions was maintained at 7. The K^{42} plants received a post treatment of 1 hour with aerated $10^{-2}M$ $CaCl_2$ to remove K^{42} from the free space and the Fe^{59} plants received a similar treatment except with $10^{-4}M$ EDDHA or $10^{-3}M$ EDDHA. Actually the $10^{-4}M$ solution was too dilute to remove all the Fe^{59} from the surfaces and walls of the roots.

For the study with Na^{24} bush bean seedlings were grown for 18 days before transfer to 3700 ml. bottles, then grown with different nutrient solutions as indicated in the table for 14 days. Iron and nitrogen deficiency symptoms had appeared on plants in the respective solutions. The plants were exposed to Na^{24} for 5 hours and then handled essentially as for the previous plants.

In an additional experiment with Fe^{59}, bush bean seedlings were transferred at eight days to the 3700 ml. bottles and grown with differential nutrient solutions for 15 days. At this time the old solutions were discarded and $10^{-4}M$ Fe^{59} EDDHA in $10^{-4}M$ $CaCl_2$ solutions were substituted. After 6 hours exposure these solutions were removed and $10^{-3}M$ EDDHA was added for 20 hours. All solutions were aerated. The roots were then washed with tap water and aliquots of the plants counted. All radioactive data were calculated as μmoles/gram dry weight using specific activity relationships.

The results are in tables 2 (K^{42}), 3 (Fe^{59}), 4 (Fe^{59}) and 5 (Na^{24}).

Table 1.   Concentrations of nutrient solutions used to produce deficiencies in bush beans used in the experiments.

Treatment Solution	$NH_4H_2PO_4$	$(NH_4)_2SO_4$	$Ca(NO_3)_2$	K_2SO_4	$CaSO_4$	$MgSO_4$	FeEDDHA
			Millinormality in final solution				
Control	1	1	10	5	0	4	0.2
-P	0	1	10	5	0	4	0.2
-K	1	1	10	0	0	4	0.2
-N	0*	0	0	5	10	4	0.2
-P, N	0	0	0	5	10	4	0.2
-Fe	1	1	10	5	0	4	0.0
-Mg	1	1	10	5	0	0	0.2
-Mg, P, N	0	0	0	5	10	0	0.2
-Mg, N	0*	0	0	5	10	0	0.2

*KH_2PO_4 at 1 millinormal was used. All treatments received Zn, Mn, & B.

Table 2.   K* uptake (less free-space components in roots) by bush bean plants with different nutrient element deficiencies.

Treatment	Dry weight of plants	Leaves	Stems	Roots	Whole Plant
	grams		μmoles K/g. dry weight		
Complete	3.8	8.1	2.7	46.3	10.1
-P	1.3	0.7	1.4	3.5	1.8
-K	3.3	12.4	31.5	104.5	29.4
-N	0.9	0.8	1.4	9.3	3.0
-P, N	0.9	0.5	0.8	8.5	2.4
-Fe	0.7	0.4	1.2	11.5	1.8
-Mg	1.4	2.6	11.6	42.6	9.0
-Mg, N, P	0.6	0.9	1.4	17.9	5.0
-Mg, N	0.9	0.8	1.3	16.0	4.6

Each value is the mean of 4 determinations.

Table 3.   Fe* uptake by bush bean plants with different mineral element deficiencies and washed with $10^{-4}M$ EDDHA in post treatment.

Treatment	Dry weight per plant	Leaves	Stems	Roots	Whole plant
	gram		μmoles Fe/g. dry weight		
Complete	3.6	12.00	1.77	24.74	11.06
-P	1.2	1.97	.86	22.16	7.20
-K	3.5	2.17	.82	28.95	4.42
-N	1.0	4.25	1.67	39.19	11.93
-P, N	0.9	4.62	1.60	49.40	14.98
-Fe	0.9	6.48	3.53	61.00	12.08
-Mg	1.9	5.93	1.78	57.01	11.98
-Mg, N, P	0.6	12.65	2.31	56.92	21.18
-Mg, N	0.9	2.44	1.18	49.71	12.61

Each value is the mean of 4 determinations.

Withholding K resulted in a large increase in K^{42} uptake (less free-space components) during the test period relative to the other pretreatments. Humphries (1952) had reported similar results not only for potassium but also for nitrogen and phosphorus where nitrogen deficiencies resulted in an increased subsequent uptake of nitrogen and deficiencies of phosphorus resulted in an increased subsequent uptake of phosphorus. Withholding K in the present study actually had not produced visably deficient plants at the time of the uptake experiment.

Table 4. Fe* uptake by bush bean plants with different mineral element deficiencies with 10^{-3}M EDDHA in post treatment.

Treatments	Leaves	Roots	Whole plant	Root/Leaf Ratio
	grams dry weight per plant			Ratio
Complete	0.40	1.76	3.14	4.4
-P	0.33	0.46	1.17	1.4
-N	0.25	0.28	0.95	1.1
-Mg	0.12	0.60	0.96	5.0
-N, P, Mg	0.19	0.18	0.66	1.0
-Fe	0.18	0.74	1.32	4.1
	μmoles Fe/g. dry weight			
Complete	2.05	1.29	1.47	0.6
-P	0.39	0.58	0.39	1.5
-N	0.21	0.42	0.34	2.0
-Mg	2.61	1.04	1.19	0.4
-N, P, Mg	0.32	0.61	0.40	1.9
-Fe	0.72	0.10	0.20	0.1

Each value is the mean of 4 determinations.

Table 5. Na* concentrations in plants grown in nutrient solutions used to produce deficiencies in bush beans.

Treatment	Leaves	Stems	Roots	Whole plant
	μmoles Na/g. dry weight			
Complete	0.04	16.9	68.1	21.1
-N	0.10	10.4	56.3	13.8
-Fe	0.20	8.4	53.8	11.5
-P	0.27	8.4	34.4	9.6
-Ca	0.12	16.0	111.4	23.6
-K	0.32	20.3	86.1	20.9
-Mg	0.20	11.0	79.3	18.4

Each value is the mean of 4 determinations

Fe and N deficiency symptoms were present on leaves. No symptoms on yield differences were apparent for -P, -Ca, -K, or -Mg.

Withholding Mg had little effect on K^{42} uptake. It would appear that any cation deficiency would result in an increased uptake of another cation because of the tendency for cation-equivalent constancy in some plant species (Bear, 1950). In this study any influence of Mg deficiency on K^{42} uptake may be the result of this phenomenon. This would explain why there was more K^{42} in (-)Mg, N, P plants than in (-)N, P and why there was more in (-)Mg, N than in (-)N.

Deficiencies of N, P, and Fe resulted in large decreases in K^{42} uptake but only Fe deficiency appeared to depress the translocation to the shoots.

In the first Fe^{59} experiment the roots were washed with $10^{-4}\underline{M}$ EDDHA which evidently did not remove all iron adsorbed on root surfaces. There were consequently apparent increases in Fe accumulation in roots as the result of deficiencies. All single element deficiencies, however, appeared to depress the Fe^{59} in the leaves (table 3). When $10^{-3}\underline{M}$ EDDHA was used in the post treatment (table 4) Fe, generally, was decreased in both leaves and roots except that Mg deficiency seemed to have no effect. As in the case of K^{42}, P, N, and Fe deficiencies decreased the uptake of Fe^{59}. The root-leaf ratios for dry matter in table 4 correspond with known effects, at least for nitrogen, on root growth, namely that nitrogen deficiency depresses shoot growth much more so than root growth (Bosemark, 1954). The effect of Fe deficiency to decrease uptake of Fe^{59} was unlike that found by Brown and Jones (1961) and Lingle et al. (1963) for Hawkeye soybean and Tiffin and Brown (1961a) for PI54619-5-1 soybean.

P, N, and Fe deficiencies decreased uptake of Na^{24} also (table 5). Serry and Eid (1959) found that P deficiency decreased uptake of Mg. Ca, K, and Mg deficiencies had no effect on Na^{24} uptake which again may be part of the general cation relationship. Deficiencies of P, N, and Fe tended to result in slight increases in the Na^{24} transported to shoots in keeping with similar results with other factors that decrease metabolism (page 62).

Summary

Deficiencies of P, N, and Fe resulted in decreased uptake of K^{42}, Fe^{59} and Na^{24} by bush bean plants. Fe^{59} had to be washed from roots with EDDHA before the effect of deficiencies could be clearly detected. Where Ca, K, and Mg deficiencies were present there seemed to be little effect on uptake by the three isotopes beyond increases in K and Na due to cation interrelationships.

EFFECT OF ETHYLENEDIAMINE DI (O-HYDROXYPHENYLACETATE) ON YIELDS OF BUSH BEANS

With N. Hemaidan

There is considerable evidence that the chelating agent, ethylenediamine di (o-hydroxyphenylacetate) (EDDHA) increases the yields of plants even when there is no apparent iron deficiency (Wallace, 1962, p. 117). Four possible reasons for the effect were discussed in that report as follows:

(a)   Improved micronutrient balance.
(b)   Auxin-like effects.
(c)   Stimulation of enzyme activity.
(d)   Chelation of calcium in roots.

Toxic effects of excess heavy metals are alleviated by EDDHA and at least part of the effect is in decreased uptake of those metal ions by plants. Wallace

(1963) also suggested that EDDHA increased growth more when the Ca level was high than when it was low.   The results of the present study which was undertaken to further investigate this problem indicated that the Ca effect may be because a low Ca solution is more conducive to micronutrient imbalance in plants than is a high Ca solution.   This effect of Ca and micronutrients has been discussed elsewhere (Wallace and Bhan, 1962; Wallace, 1962, p. 25; and Wallace and Hale, 1962a, p. 28).

Bush bean plants were grown, 4 per pot, in 1800 ml. solutions in glazed pots for 17 days.   There were 3 Ca levels: 10^{-4}M, 2×10^{-3}M, and 6×10^{-3}M. K and Ca combined were kept constant at 7×10^{-3}M.   At each Ca level Cu, Zn, and Mn sulfates and B as boric acid were supplied at 1/10, 1/4, 1/4, and 1/4 ppm. of the metal respectively in the solutions.   In another set they were supplied at 5 times these levels.   Fe was supplied at 10^{-4}M ferric ammonium citrate and the pH was kept around 5 to keep the Fe soluble. NO_3^-, NH_4^+, Mg^{++}, $SO_4^=$, and $H_2PO_4^-$ were supplied at 7, 2, 2, 2, and 2 me. per liter, respectively.   EDDHA treatments were superimposed upon the others (table 1) at 0, 10^{-4}M (equivalent to the Fe), 2×10^{-4}M, and 5×10^{-4}M.

Table 1.   Effect of EDDHA on yields of bush beans when micronutrients and Ca levels were varied (Fe was 10^{-4}M).

EDDHA in nutrient solution M	Zn, Cu, Mn, B normal			Zn, Cu, Mn, B 5 times normal		
	Ca level			Ca level		
	Control	Low	High	Control	Low	High
	g. dry weight per plant*					
0	1.15	1.11	1.25	1.08**	1.21**	1.29**
10^{-4}	1.74	1.62	1.57	1.58	1.25	2.38
2×10^{-4}	1.98	1.70	2.09	1.92	1.52	2.20
5×10^{-4}	2.08	1.85	1.94	2.38	1.93	2.40
	yield as per cent of no EDDHA					
10^{-4}	151	146	126	146	103	185
2×10^{-4}	172	153	167	176	126	171
5×10^{-4}	181	166	155	221	160	186

*Mean of 4.
**Iron chlorosis.

The data in table 1 further verify that EDDHA can increase yields and the effect was other than that of correction of Fe deficiency. Large yield increases were obtained for 10^{-4}M EDDHA relative to none.   Actually the yields for 5×10^{-4}M EDDHA were on the average about 20 per cent greater and for 2×10^{-4}M about 15 per cent greater than for those at 10^{-4}M.   These latter effects most certainly are independent of iron deficiency especially since the zero level of EDDHA without the high level of micronutrients did not show symptoms.

When the five-times level of micronutrients was supplied, the plants without EDDHA did have iron chlorosis and this was most pronounced with the low

Ca plants. This response was as expected (Wallace, 1962, p. 25) including the ability of Ca to overcome some of the heavy metal effects. Even though EDDHA overcame the effects of heavy metals it did so least effectively in the presence of low Ca and most effectively in the presence of high Ca. This may be the nature of the Ca-EDDHA interaction discussed earlier (Wallace, 1963).

Even though EDDHA has important interactions with Ca and micronutrient levels it appears that EDDHA has other effects. Auxin-like effects and other effects on metabolism have been proposed and of course these are likely since EDDHA does get into the foliage of plants from applications to the roots (Wallace, 1962, pp. 41, 53, 57, 62).

Summary

An experiment in which bush beans were grown for 17 days with and without FeEDDHA and with excess EDDHA at different calcium and micronutrient level indicated the following:

1. EDDHA did increase the yields of the test plant independently of supplying iron.

2. EDDHA did improve the yields of plants by overcoming the effects of excesses of heavy metals but this may not be the only effect.

3. Excess heavy metals were most toxic in the presence of low calcium and increasing the Ca level tended to overcome the toxicities.

4. There was an interaction between Ca level and response to chelating agent but this was with the high level of micronutrients. FeEDDHA ($10^{-4}\underline{M}$) failed to improve yields at a low calcium level when the micronutrients were high but did at a high calcium level.

5. A combination of high Ca with EDDHA produced the highest yields and this was in spite of the high level of micronutrients.

PRELIMINARY STUDIES OF IONS IN THE STEM EXUDATE

With C. B. Joven, G. B. Blank, and O. R. Lunt

Root pressures develop in plants that result in the forcing of sap through the shoots of plants. Sap may flow from leaf tips, twigs, or large stems. Many plant species, when detopped, exude sap from the cut surface for a considerable time. The characteristics of sap flow and composition have been the subject of a large number of studies relating to water absorption by plants, particularly regarding the possible involvement of metabolic forces in water absorption by plants. Although agreement is lacking regarding the mechanism responsible for exudation, the preponderance of investigators believe the phenomenon is basically osmotic, i. e. , salts metabolically transferred to the xylem vessels result in osmotic pressures which result in the transfer of water to the xylem. The following statement is condensed from Sutcliffe (1962): "The establishment of a high salt concentration in xylem sap is responsible for the development of so-called root pressure by means of which water is forced to some extent out of the root along the conducting channels into the stem. Root pressure is particularly strong in vines, and it is the cause of bleeding in which a watery sap flows, sometimes for hours, from a cut stem. Water moves from the soil solution—in which the concentration of dissolved substances is low—across the root into the xylem sap, where the concentration is higher. Movement of salts into the sap depends on energy from respiration just as does the accumulation of salts in vacuoles, and as may be expected, root pressure diminishes when roots are placed at low temperature, in the absence of oxygen or in the presence of poisons. "

Little had been known about the rise of sap or its composition until the classic work of Stephen Hales in 1727. Investigating the sap which exuded from the cut end of a branch, Hales found that it had a pressure of 1.5 atmospheres. Hales believed that the movement of water through a plant was primarily caused by the living cells in the root and stem (White, 1938). Hofmeister disagreed that living cells caused water to move up the plant. He concluded that a turgor pressure was built up in the roots and this forced water into the intercellular spaces of the stele and finally into the xylem (Kramer, 1949). It was soon seen, however, that osmosis had something to do with root pressure (Atkins, 1916; Priestly, 1920). According to Priestly, "organic solutes in the xylem sap maintain the osmotic pressure of the sap at a level permitting the manifestation of exudation pressures (stems as well as roots exhibit exudation pressure) when the surrounding parenchymatous tissues are in contact with a more dilute aqueous solution" (Priestley and Armstead, 1922). This phenomenon must be dependent upon living cells for when stems were killed no exudation pressure could be measured.

Sutcliffe (1962) states that "the predominating influence of metabolic mechanisms of absorption in young plants under normal conditions is indicated by the existence of root pressure, and by the preferential transference of certain ions from roots into shoots." Oxygen is needed for exudation. Exudation is inhibited by narcotics; thus exudation is related to respiration.

Although both the exudation pressure and the osmotic pressure of sap varied considerably in trees never did the exudation pressure exceed the osmotic pressure (Ingold, 1935). Van Overbeek (1942) found that the osmotic pressure of the exudate of detopped tomato plants in nutrient solution was lower than the pressure with which roots absorbed water. This would seem to support Atkin's view (1916) that "the solution in the tracheae acting osmotically through the semi-permeable membrance, formed by the outer tissues of the root, determines a flow of water from the soil to the tracheae, and the resulting hydrostatic pressure is responsible for the exhibition of bleeding and root pressure" and contradicts the supposition of James and Baker (1933) that "root and stem exudation pressures are transmitted through the living symplast, and movement of liquids due to these pressures take place principally through the sieve tubes".

Exudation occurs only from those plants whose exudates have an osmotic concentration higher than that of the external solution (Crafts and Broyer, 1938; Laine, 1934). Eaton (1943) found that when the culture solutions, in which cotton plants were growing, were replaced by tap water, a curvilinear relationship was found between exudation rate and the osmotic differential. When extrapolated, this curve appeared to pass through the origin indicating that osmosis was the only force involved in exudation.

Lundegardh (1944) suggested that exudation and salt absorption were two separate processes. He reported that salt absorption is related to anion respiration (sensitive to KCN and O_2 deficiency), while exudation is connected with the glycolytic system (sensitive to IAA and NaF).

When the osmotic pressure of the external solution was increased, the rate of exudation decreased and vice versa, (Laine, 1934; van Andel, 1952; van Nie et al., 1950). Kramer (1949) reported that an increase in the osmotic pressure of the external solution resulted in an increase in the osmotic pressure of the exudate. Lundegardh (1944), however, found that the exudate concentration increased until the external solution concentration was about 40 me./ liter, after which there was no further increase.

Some investigators found that the xylem exudate closely resembles the soil solution moreso than does expressed sap (Lowry and Tabor, 1931). According to Laine (1934), the osmotic pressure of the exudate depends on the osmotic pressure of the soil solution, and the osmotic pressure of the exudate is greater than the mean osmotic pressure of the soil solution.

There seems to be a qualitative correlation between drying of the soil and cessation of exudation from the stumps of decapitated plants (Litvinov and Gebhardt, 1929; Litvinov, 1932). Exudation from coleus, sunflower and tomato stopped at a moisture content about halfway between the moisture equivalent and the wilting percentage (Kramer, 1941). Above the moisture equivalent, exudation decreased and this was probably due to poor aeration. The relation between the rate of exudation and soil moisture was found to be expressed by a parabola (McDermott, 1945).

Fertilized plants were found to contain more sugar in the exudate than those plants without fertilizer (Stoev et al. , 1959). This is attributed to a rapid digestion of starch by those plants which received P fertilizer. This would seem to contradict van Overbeek's (1942) finding of no sugar in the sap of decapitated tomato plants.

About 20% of the P in excised barley root exudate seemed to be phosphoryl choline and glyceryl phosphoryl choline, S was $SO_4^=$, while a large number of metallic cations are transported as free ions (Bollard, 1960; Sutcliffe, 1962).

The concentration of K and Ca in the exudate was highest when the external solution was pH 7-8 and decreased as the pH decreased (Laine, 1934). In corn, however, Pavlinova (1926) found the concentration of Ca in the guttation fluid to be directly proportional to its concentration in the nutrient solution (2. 5 times that in the nutrient solution). Similarly, Shardakov (1928) found that the concentration of Ca, K, Cl, and PO_4 in the sap and guttation fluid depend on the salt concentration of the substrate. Laine (1934) reported that the amount of each ion in the sap is characteristic of that particular ion.

According to Crafts and Broyer (1938) the concentration of ions in exuded sap has no relationship to that in the nutrient solution. The amounts and proportions of ions released depend on the relative rates of absorption and the ability of cells of various tissues to hold them.

Grossenbacher (1939) with decapitated Helianthus showed a definite cycle of exudation by controlling such conditions as temperature, air flow, humidity and light. With Helianthus detopped under water there was a diurnal cycle in exudation with the maximum at midnight and the minimum around noon (Hagan, 1949). The mechanism of the diurnal cycle seems to be related to the mechanism responsible for root pressure. Root activity and respiration may be related, but the diurnal cycle of root pressure has not been shown to parallel the respiration cycle (Grossenbacher, 1938).

Tissue permeability may be able to account for fluctuations in exudation rate, but it cannot explain periodicity in root pressure which goes together with the periodicity of exudation. Vaadia (1960) concluded that salt entry into the xylem of detopped plants is related to metabolism. He suggested that the endodiurnal mechanism, through metabolism, controls the entry, the exudation rate, and the root pressure.

Broyer (1951) suggested that "the average osmotic pressure differences within a particular cultural treatment suggest a metabolic factor to be possibly involved in the pressure of bleeding. " Frey-Wyssling (1929) called bleeding pressure the actual pressure which acts upon the xylem vessels. According to him this pressure is usually hidden by root pressure.

Broyer (1950) suggested that the bleeding sap corresponded to the ions accumulated by individual cells. That bleeding is related to ion accumulation disagrees with earlier ideas that explained bleeding as an osmotic phenomenon caused by a suction force of sugars in the sap (Burstrom and Krogh, 1947; Went, 1944).

Root pressure is related to transpiration (Rufelt, 1956). When the osmotic concentration of the external solution was increased by adding D-mannitol, or by inhibiting respiration with 10^{-3}M Na diethyldithiocarbamate (DIECA), transpiration of wheat plants was slowed down rapidly. When root pressure was inhibited or slowed down transpiration was decreased.

While perhaps most of the work on exudation has been concerned with problems of water uptake, less has been concerned with mineral composition with the objective of studying mineral accumulation and distribution in plants. Some recent developments and observations in this laboratory have led us to believe that studies of exudate composition may be a useful tool in studying solute uptake and distribution. Our studies using C^{14} indicate that synthetic chelating agents, urea, mannitol, and biuret are readily taken up through plant roots and translocated to shoots. These substances, however, apparently are not found in the stem exudate during test periods when placed in the external solution after plants were detopped. This behavior was unexpected and has focused our attention on the potential utility of studies of exudate composition on the general problems of mineral accumulation and distribution.

The subject of the stem exudate has been partially reviewed in recent years (Arisz et al. , 1951; Bollard, 1960; Kramer, 1949; Kramer, 1956; Stocking, 1956; Briggs et al. , 1961). Many attempts have been made to explain the nature of this exudation (Arisz et al. , 1951; Bollard, 1960; Hoagland, 1944; Kramer, 1956; Lundehardh, 1949; Stocking, 1956). Some workers have noted correspondence between composition of the exuded sap and the external solution in which the roots grew (Arisz et al. , 1951; Kramer, 1949). Assay of the stem exudate, consequently, has sometimes been used as a criterion of the need of plants for fertilizer elements (Arisz et al. , 1951; Kramer, 1949) or as an index of whether or not a solute can be accumulated by a plant (Brown and Tiffin, 1960; Tiffin and Brown, 1959), or its composition has been studied as a means of determining the nature of iron transport (Tiffin and Brown, 1961b).

The root pressure theory implies that solutes in the exudate would be actively accumulated from the external solution by root cells and would leak because of low oxygen tension or bleed into the xylem and would, consequently, by osmosis result in solution moving through the cut stems (Arisz et al. , 1951; Hoagland, 1944; Kramer, 1949). The concentration of salts in sap exuded from excised roots can be several times that of the solution in which they were grown (Arisz et al. , 1951; Hoagland, 1944; Kramer, 1949). Mathematical formulae have been worked out for both the volume and concentration of the exuded sap (Arisz et al. , 1951). Bollard (1960), however, says that lack of information on factors influencing the nature and concentration of nutrients in stem exudates has prevented the use of such sap as a guide to nutritional status of crops and that surprisingly little is known about the composition of such sap. The prior salt status of the plants is believed to be important in determining the volume and composition of exudate.

Kramer (1940) "found that exudation from detopped tomato plants attained a maximum at about 25°C and decreased as the soil temperature was increased. "

Several workers in this field have made the assumption that the exudate from detopped plants is identical with the stream that is translocated to the shoots of intact plants. Evidence that this may be incorrect has been obtained in recent studies in this laboratory.

Our thinking and exploring in this direction began as a result of reports of Brown and Tiffin (1960) and Tiffin and Brown (1959) that synthetic chelating agents were not accumulated by plant roots and transported to shoots of plants and their evidence was based in part on the absence of the chelating agents in the stem exudate. Results in this laboratory consistently indicated the presence of the chelating agents in the foliage of plants following applications to the solutions in which the roots were bathed. The results of Brown et al. were verified in this laboratory. Unless extremely high application rates were used there was no C^{14} from labeled chelating agents present in the stem exudates. In the case of high external concentrations of chelating agents they were greatly diluted in the exudate. In intact plants, however, the chelating agents moved through roots to the foliage. As mentioned above extremely interesting observations were made when C^{14}-mannitol, C^{14}-urea, and C^{14}-biuret were applied to the solutions in which roots were bathed. C^{14} from none of these three substances were present in the exudate but large quantities of each were present in the foliage of intact plants from similar applications. Preliminary evidence indicated that these solutes are not removed from the xylem by the living cells along the xylem of the detopped plants. In 4-hour studies there were 3 to 5 times as much C^{14} from two of the solutes in the foliage of the plants as in the roots expressed on a dry weight basis. Separate studies indicated that broken roots were not a cause of the results. K^{42}, Br^{82}, Fe^{59}, and $HC^{14}O_3^-$ were in the exuded sap following root applications. The work of Emmert (1961) may help to understand the nature of the stem exudate. He found that P already in the plant was transported to the stem exudate but the P in the external solution did not readily do so. Van Die (1959) on the other hand reported that C^{14} compounds from $KHC^{14}O_3$ in the external solution appeared in the stem exudate within minutes.

Minshall (1961) found that a soil application of urea increased the amounts of K, P, amino acids, and nitrate in the exudate of detopped tomato. This effect on K has never been reported for intact plants and leads us to further suspect that the substances found in stem exudate are not necessarily those translocated to the shoots of intact plants.

Vaadia et al. (1961) found that topped grape vines did not have Cl^{36} in the exudate but that topped sunflowers did when Cl^{36} was in the root medium. Although this is of considerable interest it does not necessarily coincide with the known observations that grapevines are very sensitive to chloride injury (Woodham, 1956) if the stem exudate is synonymous with the transport stream. Lunt et al. (1960) observed that the transpirational stream of beans contained much less (by 20x) Cl than did an external solution. Our preliminary studies indicate several conditions in which the concentration of an isotope is considerably lower in the stem exudate than in the external solution. The salt concentration in exudate might have been higher, however, than in external solution.

Much of the information on ion accumulation in plants is based on studies with excised roots and with discs from storage tissue. If information obtained with exudates from detopped plants does not fully represent an intact plant, then it logically follows that excised roots and storage tissue also may be different from intact plants. Accumulation of solutes into the vacuoles of roots may indeed be different from the accumulation (at least uptake) of solutes that results in transport to the shoots of the plants. Bange (1959) and more recently Fried et al. (1961) have suggested two (or more) accumulation mechanisms one of which would lead to accumulation in shoots. This concept, however, has been challenged by Tanada (1961). The observation that ions accumulated in the root can essentially all be translocated to the shoot (Hoagland, 1944) also casts some doubt on a concept of different mechanisms for roots and shoots.

Our observations on stem exudates do relate to the question of separate mechanisms for accumulation into shoot or into root. Other unpublished information obtained in this laboratory may possibly indicate that separate mechanisms could be involved in root accumulation and in accumulation that results in transfer to shoots. Some metabolic poisons used with intact plants have inhibited the accumulation of some ions by roots but have actually increased the amounts translocated to shoots. Root temperature studies have indicated some different temperature dependency patterns for root accumulation vs. shoot accumulation. An excess of chelating agents inhibited iron accumulation into potato discs and into roots but not into shoots. Chelating agents appear not to be accumulated by plant cells even though they were readily taken up by roots and translocated to shoots. Other studies have indicated that the effect of Ca on K accumulation differed for roots and shoots. The same occurred for the effect of K on Ca accumulation. Hodges and Vaadia (1962) suggested that ions could arrive at the xylem with or without having been accumulated by the intervening cells.

We are aware of objections to a theory of separate accumulation mechanisms leading to the root or to the shoot or at least to the evidence presented for such. We are also aware of the relative ease with which it is often possible to confirm erroneous observations. If one works from a false assumption, the build-up of circumstantial evidence is often not too difficult. Even though the observations listed above could be and may be evidence for separate mechanisms, we know that alternate explanations are possible for each observation.

The possibility exists that solutes which do not appear in the stem exudates but are translocated to leaves of intact plants may be nonmetabolically absorbed. Previous studies with C^{14}-biuret indicated this possibility (Clark and Wallace, 1961). Mannitol is believed not to be accumulated by plant cells (Thimann et al., 1960) and the same may obtain for other of these solutes. Unpublished studies in this laboratory have indicated that each of the four solutes (chelating agent, mannitol, biuret, urea) not appearing in the exudate can be taken up into plants in direct proportion to the concentration supplied to the roots. A tenfold increase in external concentration resulted in a ten-fold increase in that taken up. If this means passive absorption it may follow that solutes which appeared in the stem exudates are metabolically accumulated.

Emmert (1960) measured the P content of stem exudates. He found a higher content of P in the exudate than in the ambient solution. Most of the exudate P came from internal sources with only a small part coming from the external solution.

Emmert (1961a,b, 1962) has made some recent studies of xylem composition by means of the stem exudate. He found that xylem sap phosphorus was relatively dilute compared with the outside solution. He, however, indicated that the isotope could leave the stream by exchange or loss to adjoining cells. His techniques must be considered in a study of the exudate problem.

Materials and Methods

Bush bean plants (Phaseolus vulgaris, var. Tendergreen) were germinated in sand and transferred in about 10 days after germination to 1/4 strength nutrient solution unless otherwise stated. After 3-4 days in these solutions the plants were detopped and were placed into experimental solutions. Ten plants were used for each beaker containing 300 ml. solution; the stems were bent slightly into a graduated centrifuge tube for collection of exudate. Most of the experiments were run at a constant temperature of 25°C. Additional details are given with each experiment.

The Results of 12 Experiments Will Be Briefly Presented

Experiment 1. $KH_2P^{32}O_4$ in external solution.

Bean plants germinated in sand were transferred at 10 days to 1/4-strength nutrient solution. After three days, 10 plants were placed into each of four different beakers containing 10^{-5}, 10^{-4}, 10^{-3}, and 10^{-2}M $KH_2P^{32}O_4$ with the pH adjusted to 7.0 with NaOH. The predominant anion would then be $HPO_4^=$. The plants were then detopped and the exudate collected at different time intervals and the content of P^{32} was determined.

In no case was the P^{32} in the exudate greater than that in the external solution. In general the volume of exudate increased with increasing external concentration. The recovery of isotope in the exudate decreased with the increase of external concentration. Table 1 shows the results of this experiment. The results indicated as found by Eaton (1943) that an increasing concentration of external solution resulted in an increased volume of exudate.

Table 1. P^{32} in stem exudate in experiment 1.

Time	10^{-5}M	10^{-4}M	10^{-3}M	10^{-2}M
hours		volume of exudate, ml.		
0-23	0.5	0.5	1.2	2.1
23-48	0.5	0.2	0.6	1.2
48-68	0.1	0.1	0.1	0.2
0-68	1.1	0.8	1.9	3.5
		μmoles P^{32}/ml. of exudate*		
0-23	0.006	0.068	0.397	0.909
23-48	0.006	0.045	0.452	1.40
48-68	0.0097	0.065	0.329	1.07
		P^{32} in exudate as % of external concentration		
0-23	60	68	40	9
23-48	60	45	45	14
48-68	97	65	33	11

*Labeled P calculated from specific activity relationships.

In other studies elsewhere, salts of Mn, Zn, Cu, K, and Rb first increased and then decreased the volume of stem exudate; Ca and Mg salts decreased the volume as concentrations of salts increased (Lingle et al., 1963).

Experiment 2. $KH_2P^{32}O_4$ in external solution.

This experiment was similar to the first experiment except that, in addition, a 10^{-1}M $KH_2P^{32}O_4$ solution was used (table 2). The tendency of increasing external concentration to result in an increased volume of exudate was reversed at 10^{-1}M where essentially no exudate was obtained.

Experiment 3.   Plants pretreated with P^{32} before detopping.

Because of the suggestion of Emmert (1960) that ions already in plants before detopping are the ions mainly transported in the stem exudate rather than those of the external solution, a study was made with $KH_2P^{32}O_4$ as pretreatment for four days before the plants were detopped.   The concentrations of $KH_2P^{32}O_4$ used were 10^{-4}, 10^{-3}, and $10^{-2}\underline{M}$ and each of these also received $10^{-4}\underline{M}$ $CaCl_2$ and $10^{-3}\underline{M}$ KCl.

Table 2.   Effect of level of $KH_2P^{32}O_4$ on exudate characteristics.

Time	$\underline{M}$, concentration of $KH_2P^{32}O_4$ in external solution				
	10^{-5}	10^{-4}	10^{-3}	10^{-2}	10^{-1}
hours	volume of exudate, ml.				
0-18	0.2	0.2	0.4	0.4	0.0
18-24	0.3	0.3	0.5	0.7	0.0
24-48	0.5	0.1	0.1	0.3	0.1
0-48	1.0	0.6	1.0	1.4	0.1
	μmoles P^{32}/ml. exudate				
0-18	.0006	.004	.000	0.40	—
18-24	.0087	.090	.456	0.71	—
24-48	.0047	.060	.346	0.36	1.65
	P^{32} in exudate, % of external concentration				
0-18	6	4	0	4	—
18-24	87	90	46	7	—
24-48	47	60	35	4	2

The concentration of P^{32} in the exudate increased with the increase in concentrations of the external solution at 0-24 hours (table 3).   However, from 24-48 hours, the trend was reversed, that is, the P^{32} in the exudate as per cent of the external solution decreased with increase in concentration. With two concentrations, 10^{-4} and $10^{-3}\underline{M}$ $KH_2P^{32}O_4$, the concentrations of P^{32} in the exudate exceeded that of the external solution at the final period, 24-48 hours.   With enough time all perhaps would do the same.

Table 3.   Effect of pretreatment with different concentrations of $KH_2P^{32}O_4$ on P^{32} in the stem exudate.

Time	M concentration of $KH_2P^{32}O_4$ in pretreatment solutions and of KH_2PO_4 in external solutions following detopping		
	10^{-4}	10^{-3}	10^{-2}
hours	Volume of exudate, ml.		
0-24	0.1	0.2	0.5
24-48	0.2	0.1	0.3
0-48	0.3	0.3	0.8
	μmole P^{32}/ml. exudate		
0-24	not counted	0.42	5.16
24-48	0.13	1.12	6.26
	P^{32} in exudate, % of external solution		
0-24	—	42	52
24-48	136	112	63

Experiment 4. Ca^{47} in stem exudate.

Ten bush bean plants were placed into each of five beakers containing 10^{-6}, 10^{-5}, 10^{-4}, 10^{-3}, and $10^{-2}\underline{M}$ $Ca^{47}Cl_2$ in which the pH had been adjusted to 7.0. The plants were detopped and the exudate collected. Table 4 shows the results of the experiment.

Table 4. Ca^{47} in stem exudate.

Time	Molarity of CaCl$_2$				
	10^{-6}	10^{-5}	10^{-4}	10^{-3}	10^{-2}
hours	volume of exudate				
0–24	0.6	0.9	0.7	0.7	0.3
24–48	0.6	0.4	0.3	0.4	0.2
0–48	1.2	1.3	1.0	1.1	0.5
	μmole Ca^{47}/ml. exudate				
0–24	0.0000027	0.000018	0.00016	0.10	1.94
24–48	0.0	0.0	0.023	0.016	4.97
	Ca^{47} in exudate, % of external solution				
0–24	0.3	0.2	0.2	10	19
24–48	0.0	0.0	23	2	50

The uptake of Ca^{47} by intact plants was found to be directly proportional to the external concentration (page 144).   It was wondered if the same obtained for the stem exudate. The results of this experiment showed that the same trend in the stem exudate as in intact plants was followed; that is, the amount of Ca^{47} in the stem exudate was directly proportional to the external concentration for the low concentration range only. Ratios in the exudate for each 10-fold increase in external concentrations were 6.7, 8.8, 62, and 19.4 from 10^{-6} to $10^{-2}\underline{M}$.

Experiment 5. $K^{42}Cl$ in external solution.

Ten bush bean plants were placed into each of five beakers containing 10^{-6}, 10^{-5}, 10^{-4}, 10^{-3}, and $10^{-2}\underline{M}$ $K^{42}Cl$ in which the pH had been adjusted to 7.0. Exudate was collected in the usual manner.

Varying concentrations of $K^{42}Cl$ in the external solution did not appear to influence the amount of exudate (table 5). Concentrations of K^{42} in the exudate showed a tendency to increase with increasing concentration of the external solution. At one concentration, $10^{-2}\underline{M}$, the amount of K^{42} in the exudate exceeded that in the external solution.

Experiment 6. $Rb^{86}Cl$ in external solution.

Bush bean plants were placed into each of four beakers containing 10^{-5}, 10^{-4}, 10^{-3}, and $10^{-2}\underline{M}$ $Rb^{86}Cl$. The pH was adjusted to 7.0 and the exudate collected. Small quantities of Rb were present in the exudate (table 6). This could be the result of there being no Rb in roots prior to treatment with that absorbed being transferred to vacuoles instead of to the exudate. For the time periods 21–27 hours and 27–48 hours, the concentrations of Rb^{86} in the exudate did not differ much from one another at the external concentrations, 10^{-5}, 10^{-4}, and $10^{-3}\underline{M}$ $Rb^{86}Cl$. There was no detectable Rb^{86} in the exudate at the external concentration, $10^{-2}\underline{M}$ $Rb^{86}Cl$, for the period 27-48 hours.

Table 5. Effect of $K^{42}Cl$ on exudate characteristics.

Time	Molarity of KCl				
	10^{-6}	10^{-5}	10^{-4}	10^{-3}	10^{-2}
hours	volume of exudate, ml.				
0-4	0.6	0.6	0.5	0.3	0.4
4-8	0.3	0.4	0.5	0.3	0.3
8-12	0.1	0.1	0.1	0.1	0.2
0-12	1.0	1.1	1.1	0.7	0.9
	μmoles K^{42}/ml. exudate				
0-4	0.00021	0.00238	0.064	0.03	0.15
4-8	0.0000029	0.000268	0.0086	0.78	10.5
8-12	0.00000	0.0000	0.0000	0.00	0.31
	K^{42} in exudate, % of external concentration				
0-4	21	24	64	3	2
4-8	3	3	9	78	106
8-12	0	0	0	0	3

Table 6. Effect of $Rb^{86}Cl$ on exudate characteristics.

Time	Molarity of RbCl			
	10^{-5}	10^{-4}	10^{-3}	10^{-2}
hours	volume of exudate, ml.			
0-5	0.5	0.6	0.7	0.2
5-21	0.4	0.8	0.9	0.6
21-27	0.4	0.6	0.9	0.4
27-48	0.2	0.2	0.3	0.1
0-48	1.5	2.2	2.8	1.3
	μmoles Rb^{86}/ml. exudate			
0-5	0.00000	0.000	0.0076	0.000
5-21	0.0000067	0.000	0.0045	0.00235
21-27	0.000067	0.001	0.041	0.120
27-48	0.000074	0.00184	0.030	0.000
	Rb^{86} in exudate, % of external concentration			
0-5	0.0	0.0	0.8	0.0
5-21	0.07	0.0	0.5	0.02
21-27	0.7	1.0	4.0	1.2
27-48	0.7	1.8	3.1	0.0

Experiment 7. Effect of pretreatment with $10^{-3}\underline{M}$ KH_2PO_4 on the volume of exudate.

Several bush bean plants were placed into each of two crocks, one containing distilled water and the other $10^{-3}\underline{M}$ KH_2PO_4 and left in a constant temperature room over night. The following morning, 10 plants from each of the two treatments were placed into each of four beakers containing 10^{-5}, 10^{-4}, 10^{-3}, and 10^{-2} M KH_2PO_4. Exudate was collected in the usual manner.

Pretreatment of plants with 10^{-3} M KH_2PO_4 showed an effect on the amount of exudate as compared with plants which were pretreated with distilled water (table 7). This seems to be in accord with the observations of Arisz et al. (1951) which showed that the exudation phenomenon is dependent on osmotic differences between the external medium and the plant sap.

Table 7.   Effect of pretreatment with KH_2PO_4 on the volume of exudate.

Time	Molarity of KH_2PO_4							
	10^{-5}		10^{-4}		10^{-3}		10^{-2}	
	T_1	T_2	T_1	T_2	T_1	T_2	T_1	T_2
hours	volume in ml.							
0–24	0	0	0	0.3	0	0.1	0.2	1.3
24–48	0	0	0	0.2	0	0.4	1.8	1.5
48–73½	0	0	0	0.0	0	0.2	0.8	0.4
0–73½	0	0	0	0.5	0	0.7	2.8	3.2

T_1-plants pretreated with distilled water.
T_2-plants pretreated with 10^{-3} M KH_2PO_4.

Experiment 8.   The effect of a combination of K and Ca on the volume of exudate.

Ten bush bean plants transferred to tap water for four days after germination in sand were placed into each beaker, one containing 10^{-3} M KCl, one 10^{-3} M KCl + 10^{-2} M $CaCl_2$, one 10^{-3} M KCl + 10^{-3} M $CaCl_2$, and the other 10^{-3} M KCl + 10^{-5} M $CaCl_2$. The pH was not adjusted. Exudate was collected in the usual manner.

Varying concentrations of $CaCl_2$ with one KCl concentration showed an effect on the amount of exudate collected (table 8). The 10^{-2} M $CaCl_2$ depressed the volume of exudate, 10^{-3} M $CaCl_2$ did not have any appreciable effect, and 10^{-5} M $CaCl_2$ increased the volume of exudate.

Table 8.   Effect of a combination of K and Ca on volume of stem exudate.

Time	Molarity of salts			
	10^{-3} M KCl	10^{-3} M KCl + 10^{-5} M $CaCl_2$	10^{-3} M KCl + 10^{-3} M $CaCl_2$	10^{-3} M KCl + 10^{-2} M $CaCl_2$
hours	volume of exudate, ml.			
0–24	0.5	1.0	0.4	0.1

Experiment 9.   Effect of KCl concentration on the volume of exudate.

Bush bean plants, 11 days old, were placed in distilled water, detopped and left for 19 hours in a constant temperature room. After 19 hours, 10 plants were placed into each of five different beakers containing 10^{-5}, 10^{-4}, 10^{-3}, 10^{-2}, and 10^{-1}M KCl. The usual procedure for collecting exudate was follow-ed. Table 9 shows the results of the experiment. There seemed to be no ef-fect of KCl concentration in the volume of exudate.

Table 9.   Effect of KCl concentration on volume of exudate when pre-treated with distilled water.

| Time | Molarity of KCl | | | | |
	10^{-5}	10^{-4}	10^{-3}	10^{-2}	10^{-1}
hours	volume of exudate, ml.				
0–24	1.3	1.6	1.7	1.0	1.2
24–48	0.1	0.1	0.3	0.4	0.2
0–48	1.4	1.7	2.0	1.4	1.4

Experiment 10. C^{14} D-fructose experiment.

Bush bean plants germinated in sand were transferred after 10 days to tap water for four days. Ten plants were then placed into each of two beakers containing 10^{-5}M and 10^{-4}M C^{14} D-fructose solutions. The usual procedure for collecting exudate was followed. The results in table 10 showed no C^{14} in the exudate. It has also been found earlier in this laboratory that C^{14}-urea, C^{14}-mannitol and C^{14}-biuret were not present in the stem exudate. C^{14} D-fructose seems to follow this trend.

Table 10.   D-fructose in stem exudate.

| Time | Molarity of C^{14}D-fructose | |
	10^{-5}	10^{-4}
hours	volume of exudate, ml.	
0–69	0.2	0.2
	μmole C^{14}/ml. exudate	
0–69	0.000	0.000

Experiment 11.   Effect of pretreatment with K and Ca on K^{42} in exudate.

Bush bean plants were germinated in sand and then after 10 days transfer-red into each of four containers containing (a) 1/10-strength nutrient solution, (b) 1/10-strength nutrient solution + 5 x 10^{-2}M $CaCl_2$, (c) 1/10-strength nutri-end solution + 5 x 10^{-2}M KCl and (d) tap water. They were left in these treat-ments for five days. Ten plants from each of the above mentioned treatments were then placed into separate beakers containing 10^{-3}M K^{42}Cl and the usual procedure for collecting exudate was followed. The pH was 5.6. The results in table 11 indicate that the high levels of Ca in pretreatment increased exudate volume but had little influence on K^{42} in the exudate. Pretreatment of the plants with K did not seem to influence the K^{42} in the exudate either.

Experiment 12. NaH_2PO_4 in external solution.

Bush bean plants were germinated in sand and transferred to 1/4-strength nutrient solution and left in this for three days. After three days, 10 plants were transferred to each of five beakers containing 10^{-5}M NaH_2PO_4, pH = 5.6; 10^{-4}M NaH_2PO_4, pH = 5.6; 10^{-3}M NaH_2PO_4, pH = 5.3; 10^{-2}M NaH_2PO_4, pH = 4.7 and 10^{-1}M NaH_2PO_4, pH = 4.3. The plants were then detopped and the exudate collected in the usual manner.

Table 11.   Effect of pretreatment with $CaCl_2$ and other salts on exudate characteristics from a 10^{-3}M $K^{42}Cl$ solution.

Time	Pretreatment (see text)			
	(a)	(b)	(c)	(d)
hours	volume of exudate, ml.			
0–5	0.3	0.9	0.4	0.4
5–9	0.0	0.4	0.3	0.1
0–9	0.3	1.3	0.7	0.5
	μmole K^{42}/ml. exudate			
0–5	0.00024	0.014	0.0039	0.0298
5–9	—	0.0086	0.0093	0.0495
	K^{42} in exudate, % of external solution			
0–5	0.02	1.4	0.4	3
5–9	—	0.9	0.9	5

The volumes of exudate obtained from each of the treatments 10^{-5}M NaH_2PO_4 through 10^{-2}M NaH_2PO_4 did not differ significantly from one another but a decrease was obtained at 10^{-1}M NaH_2PO_4 (table 12).

These results all indicate that bush bean exudates collected for up to 48 hours do not contain, except for small amounts, isotopes placed in the external solution at time of detopping.

Table 12.   Effect of pretreatment of NaH_2PO_4 on exudate volume.

Time	Molarity of NaH_2PO_4				
	10^{-5}M	10^{-4}M	10^{-3}M	10^{-2}M	10^{-1}M
hours	volume of exudate, ml.				
0–24	0.5	0.7	0.8	0.4	0.2
24–47	0.3	0.2	0.1	0.3	0.1
0–47	0.8	0.9	0.9	0.7	0.3

Summary

Detopped plants are often used as an index of solute uptake and transport in plants. Tiffin and Brown (1961b) observed that when detopped bean plants were supplied iron chelates, iron but not synthetic chelating agents, appeared in the stem exudate. When intact plants were used, however, small quantities of chelating agents were translocated to leaves. Similar results have been obtained repeatedly in this laboratory. There is a considerable lag time between detopping and the appearance of simultaneously added isotopes in the exudate.

When C^{14}-mannitol, C^{14}-urea, and C^{14}-biuret were supplied to the solution in which roots were bathed, C^{14} appeared in the leaves in all three cases but not in the stem exudate in tests made for 24-48 hours.

Some tentative observations when plants were detopped and then placed into test solutions are—

1. The volume of stem exudate increased with increasing external concentration of KH_2PO_4 until the $10^{-1}M$ concentration was reached. NaH_2PO_4 did not give similar increases.
2. The % recovery of P^{32} in the stem exudate relative to the external concentration decreased with increasing KH_2PO_4.
3. With dilute external solutions the P^{32} in the exudate approached that in the external solution.
4. When plants were exposed to P^{32} for four days before they were detopped, the initial exudate contained slightly more P^{32} than in the external solution at a $10^{-4}M$ concentration but not at a $10^{-2}M$ concentration.
5. Ca^{47} appeared in the stem exudate at a concentration much lower than in the external solution, and in amounts at $10^{-6}-10^{-3}M$ in the external concentration the Ca^{47} in the stem exudate was roughly proportional to the external concentration.
6. Recovery of Ca^{47} in exudate was greater at high external concentrations that at low.
7. In a 4—8 hour period, the % recovery of K^{42} in the exudate increased with external concentration and varied from 3 to 106%.
8. In time periods up to 48 hours, the stem exudate contained around 1% of the Rb^{86} in the external solution for several different concentrations.
9. Pretreatment of plants before detopping with 5 x $10^{-2}M$ $CaCl_2$ increased the volume of exudate relative to more dilute pretreatment solution.

pH CHANGES IN A NUTRIENT SOLUTION DURING SALT UPTAKE

The fact that an excess of anion uptake over cation uptake by plant roots causes an increase in pH in the external nutrient solution and that an excess of cation uptake over anion uptake causes a decrease in pH is well known. In 1935, Trelease and Trelease suggested that a balance of NH_4^+ -N to NO_3^- -N (1 to 7) would serve as a buffer against such change in pH.

The purpose of this note is to suggest that a very small difference only in cation vs. anion uptake is necessary to cause the pH changes.

If a solution were completely unbuffered and if the root did not act as a buffer and if one started from a $10^{-3}M$ KCl solution at pH 7.0 and if 10.0% of the K were absorbed in a given time, the resulting pH would be 6.0 if 9.9% of the Cl were simultaneously absorbed. There would be a 1% difference in cation vs. anion uptake. For a 10% difference, i.e., 10.0% K uptake vs. 9.0% Cl uptake the pH would drop to 5.0. It can be seen that small differences in uptake can account for the pH changes observed and it is quite possible that anions and cations can be absorbed by plants about equally, particularly if H^+ and HCO_3^- absorption are considered. The role that CO_2-fixation into organic acids plays in compensating for less anion uptake than cation uptake is important in maintaining electrostatic balance in plants. This discussion does not mean that cations and anions are taken up as salts but that cation uptake need not be very different from anion uptake to cause large pH changes in the nutrient solution.

EFFECTS OF TEMPERATURE ON THE RATIO OF Ca TO K
ABSORBED BY BUSH BEANS IN SHORT-TIME STUDIES

With N. Hemaidan

Many investigators have placed considerable emphasis on the Ca-K ratios in plants as a criterion of adequacy of each and of responses to fertilizers or to liming. An example is that of Hunter et al. (1943). Very little is known of how the environment other than nutrient supply can influence the Ca-K ratio in plants. Wallace (1957) suggested that soil temperature caused a considerable difference in the Ca-K ratios in soybeans, barley, and citrus. If the accumulation of K by plants is dependent on temperature (page 29) and if uptake of Ca is not (page 143) then it is very apparent that soil temperature will cause a wide variation in the ratio. When the uptake of K is dependent on temperature the Q_{10} may be 2 and when the uptake of Ca is not necessarily dependent on temperature the Q_{10} may be 1.2. Then if the Ca to K ratio of uptake were 1.00 for a given plant at 5°C, it could be expected to be 0.60 at 15°C and 0.36 at 25°C. This is the type of variation that has been observed (Wallace, 1957). Some new studies with radioisotopes were undertaken to check this response.

Bush bean plants were pregrown in 1/10-strength nutrient solution for 10 days as described previously. They were then placed into 100 ml. solutions containing both KCl and $CaCl_2$. In one tube each salt was 10^{-4}M, in another 10^{-3}M, and in another 10^{-2}M. In one complete set K^{42} was used and Ca^{47} in another. There were 4 tubes for each treatment and 2 plants in each which were assayed separately to give 4 replications for each of the 2 root temperatures used.

The plants were exposed to these aerated solutions for 5 hours at pH 7 and at either 4 or 24°C. The tops were removed for counting and the roots were washed with 10^{-2}M $CaCl_2$ for one hour to remove the isotopes from free space.

The results on the whole-plant basis and for leaves are in table 1. The behavior of K and Ca was as expected. Low temperatures resulted in a higher Ca/K ratio than did the high temperature for leaves and for whole plants.

Table 1. Uptake (less free-space components) of K and Ca by bush beans at different temperatures.

K^+ and Ca^{++}	4°C			24°C		
	K	Ca	Ca/K	K	Ca	Ca/K
M	μmoles/g. dry wt.		ratio	μmoles/g. dry wt.		ratio
			whole plant basis			
10^{-4}	0.42	0.93	2.21	7.8	2.03	0.26
10^{-3}	2.19	15.2	6.94	25.4	15.14	0.60
10^{-2}	6.81	164.6	24.17	57.9	193.3	3.33
			leaves			
10^{-4}	0.002	0.002	1.00	0.099	0.014	0.14
10^{-3}	0.009	0.156	17.30	2.54	0.111	0.04
10^{-2}	0.048	0.326	6.79	5.26	0.464	0.09

Summary

The Ca/K ratio for Ca^{47} and K^{42} absorbed during a 5-hour period by bush beans decreased with increasing temperature (4°C vs. 24°C) at 3 different external concentrations of the salts.

SOME STUDIES OF TIME-COURSE OF UPTAKE OF SOME SOLUTES BY BUSH BEAN PLANTS

With S. M. Sufi and N. Hemaidan

Since Epstein et al. (1962) with studies of Rb uptake from 0 to 60 minutes has questioned that an absorption shoulder exists for uptake of some cations by plant tissues, this question has been briefly studied here. Several miscellaneous pieces of such data are presented in this report.

Epstein et al. observed a linear relationship between uptake and time in their 60-minute studies with barley roots and Rb[86]. They used an excess of Ca in the solution which because of the lyotropic series would supposedly saturate the root cation-exchange sites so that no exchangeable Rb would be present. The Rb then that could not be washed out of the roots with water would have been accumulated. In their studies the Rb uptake was not only linear for 60 minutes but was temperature dependent for the entire 60 minutes.

An experiment was made with intact bush beans previously grown in 1/4-strength nutrient solution. Uptake of K[42] from 10^{-5}M K[42]Cl in 10^{-3}M CaCl$_2$ was linear for the first hour only. After that the uptake leveled off. The roots were washed for 5 minutes in water before counting.

In a second experiment with 10^{-4}M KCl with 10^{-3}M CaCl$_2$, the results were essentially linear for 2 hours (figure 1). This would confirm the results of Epstein et al.

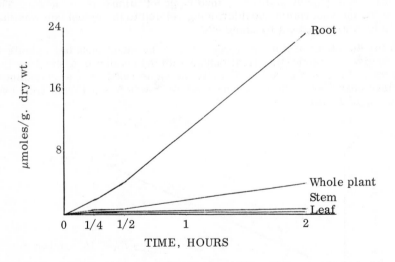

Figure 1.   K uptake from 10^{-4}M KCl + 10^{-3}M CaCl$_2$ (roots received post treatment of water washing for 5 minutes which assumes that the root cation-exchange sites were occupied by Ca).

When the uptake of K[42]Br (10^{-3}M) was studied in the presence of 10^{-4}M CaCl$_2$ at pH 7 and with post treatments of 1 hour with 10^{-2}M CaCl$_2$ to remove K[42] from the free space, a typical hyperbolic curve was obtained during 24 hours, (figure 2). There was linearity apparently for the first 2 hours.

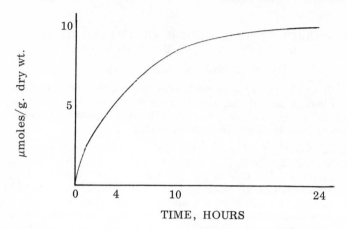

Figure 2.   Uptake of K^{42} at different time intervals by intact plants.

A differential effect of time on Q_{10} of uptake of K^{42} for different temperatures was described on page 28.

MacDonald and Laties (1963) after washing the Br^{82} from free space obtained typical two-phase uptake pattern with time with potato discs. They suggested that the first phase (or the absorption shoulder) which was pronounced for about an hour may be the filling of adsorption sites in the cytoplasm while the second phase (steady state) may involve penetration into the vacuole. Their evidence for the absorption shoulder being related to the cytoplasm was that the shoulder was wiped out by using $0^{o}C$.

Data for the effect of time on uptake of Br^{82} by intact bush bean plants appeared to give a straight-line relationship rather than that of a shoulder in studies up to 2 hours (figure 3).   Exactly the same result was also obtained for excised bean roots.   In these cases the Br^{82} was washed from free space for a period of 1 hour.

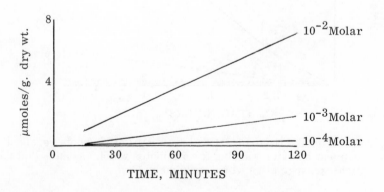

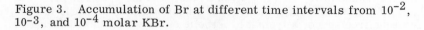

Figure 3.   Accumulation of Br at different time intervals from 10^{-2}, 10^{-3}, and 10^{-4} molar KBr.

Barley is a plant species that appears to translocate Na to its shoots.   Time-course for the uptake of Na $(10^{-2}\underline{M})$ in $10^{-4}\underline{M}$ $CaCl_2$ has been obtained (figure 4).   A linear relationship was obtained for both leaves and roots for a period of 4 hours.

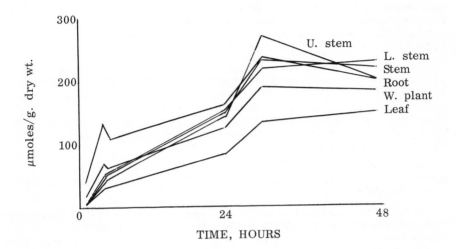

Figure 4.   Time-course uptake of Na by barley plants from $Na^{22}Cl$, $10^{-2}\underline{M}$ + $CaCl_2, 10^{-4}\underline{M}$ applied to the roots.

Summary

A limited number of studies of the time-course of uptake of some ions tend to confirm the data of Epstein et al. that the uptake of some cations is linear for one or more hours if the root cation-exchange sites are saturated with Ca. After 1-2 hours the curves tended to be hyperbolic.   Most of the present results were with intact plants.   Because of time-course differences in uptake at different temperatures, the Q_{10} of uptake for K varied with time. Br^{82} uptake was linear for at least 2 hours for intact bush beans and for excised bean roots. Na^{22} uptake by barley was linear for 4 hours as was also its content in the blades.

SOME EFFECTS OF BIOLOGICAL-PUMP AND OXIDATIVE-
PHOSPHORYLATION INHIBITORS ON K AND Na UPTAKE
BY BUSH BEAN PLANTS
With N. Hemaidan

Sodium and ATP are believed to be common requirements for all biological pumps (Csaky, 1963).   The enzyme, ATPase, which, at least in many animal systems, requires Na as an activator is considered to be the "motor" of biological pumps (Hokin and Hokin,   1960; Jarnefelt, 1961; Post and Albright, 1960; Skou, 1960; Taylor, 1962; Zerahn, 1960).   Sodium, of course, has never been demonstrated essential for the overwhelming majority of higher plants. This raises the question as to whether or not (a) biological pumps are absent in higher plants, (b) some other metal performs the function in higher plants, and (c) sodium is essential for higher plants for at least this function but the levels needed are too small to be detected even by the salt purification techniques now available.

An inhibitor which will eliminate either Na or the production of ATP will decrease activity of a Na-requiring biological pump. Ouabain, strophanthidin and other forms of digitalis are general pump inhibitors because they interfere with sodium utilization. Csaky (1963) reported that these steroid glucosides become attached to cellular membranes from which they are not easily removed. Their effect, consequently, is largely irreversible. Very low levels of digitalis, $10^{-5}-10^{-7}\underline{M}$, will inhibit Na-requiring systems.

Biological pumps may also be inhibited by uncouplers of oxidative phosphorylation such as 2,4-DNP (2,4-dinitrophenol) or CCP (carbonyl cyanide phenylhydrazone) (Heytler et al., 1962). In the present investigations it was wondered if these inhibitors were additive with digitalis (particularly ouabain) in their effects on K and Na uptake by bush bean plants. If ouabain does not inhibit K uptake or K transport in plants, then such is possibly not a Na-dependent coupled pump (Tosteson, 1960).

Ouabain should inhibit Na uptake if ouabain can be absorbed by plant roots and if Na is accumulated metabolically with the aid of the binding site with which ouabain will interfere.

Six of the experiments that were conducted on these general problems will be briefly described. For all, bush beans were used as in other experiments of this series. Generally they were pregrown in 1/10-strength nutrient solution for 8-10 days before the experiments were conducted. Where indicated no K was used in the pretreatment solutions. All test conditions were in the indicated solutions in 100 ml. culture tubes. An attempt was made to maintain the pH at 7.0 and all solutions were aerated. Each solution contained $10^{-4}\underline{M}$ $CaCl_2$ to preserve integrity of roots. Test periods were 5 hours. All plants received a post treatment of $10^{-2}\underline{M}$ $CaCl_2$ to remove radioisotopes from the free space. Stock solutions of $10^{-3}\underline{M}$ strophanthidin and ouabain were prepared by first dissolving the materials in a very small quantity of methanol.

Experiment 1: The effect of $10^{-4}\underline{M}$ strophanthidin or ouabain on uptake of Na^{22} from 10^{-4} and $10^{-3}\underline{M}$ NaCl was studied (table 1). The results indicate that under the conditions used and whether or not K was present in the pretreatment the Na uptake was inhibited very little if at all.

Table 1. Effect of strophanthidin and ouabain on Na^{22} uptake in 5 hours by intact bush beans (6 replications for each treatment).

Treatment	K in 12 day pretreatment		No K in 12 day pretreatment	
	$10^{-3}\underline{M}$ NaCl	$10^{-4}\underline{M}$ NaCl	$10^{-3}\underline{M}$ NaCl	$10^{-4}\underline{M}$ NaCl
$\underline{M}$	% Inhibition			
10^{-4} strophanthidin	15	14	2	6
10^{-4} ouabain	16	7	3	11

Experiment 2: An experiment similar to the first was conducted to determine if the forms of digitalis had an influence on K uptake. An inhibitory

effect perhaps could be interpreted as evidence for a coupled Na-K pump in the plant tissue and, hence, evidence of an Na requirement in the tissue. A very mild stimulation rather than inhibition was obtained (table 2).

Table 2. Effect of strophanthidin and ouabain on K uptake in 5 hours by intact bush beans.

Treatment	from $10^{-3}\underline{M}$ $K^{42}Cl$	from $10^{-4}\underline{M}$ $K^{42}Cl$
$\underline{M}$		
	% increase	
$10^{-4}\underline{M}$ strophanthidin	18	16
$10^{-4}\underline{M}$ ouabain	5	27

Experiment 3: To further explore the effect of ouabain on K uptake, plants were pregrown in dilute nutrient solutions from which K had been omitted (table 3). Addition of small quantities of Na had no effect on the K uptake and again ouabain inhibited it very mildly if at all.

Table 3. Effect of Na and ouabain on K uptake in 5 hours by K deficient bush bean plants. *

Treatment	Leaf	Stem	Root	Whole Plant	Inhibition
$\underline{M}$	μmoles/g. dry weight				%
Control	0.54	4.28	167.6	29.8	—
10^{-4} NaCl	0.54	4.65	182.2	31.3	+5
10^{-3} NaCl	0.33	4.29	157.4	28.0	5
10^{-4} ouabain	0.19	3.59	158.2	25.8	13
10^{-3} NaCl+10^{-4} ouabain	0.56	3.68	139.7	26.3	11

*All solutions contained $10^{-3}\underline{M}$ $K^{42}Cl$.

Experiment 4: The effect of the uncouplers of oxidative phosphorylation on K and Na uptake was studied (table 4). At $10^{-5}\underline{M}$, CCP inhibited the uptake of K somewhat more than Na although they were more nearly equal at lower concentrations. CCP at $10^{-5}\underline{M}$ particularly decreased K movement to leaves. So little Na moves to leaves of bush bean that there was no apparent effect of CCP on transport to leaves. Some workers prefer to think that Na in contrast to K is not moved into plant cells (only out of them) by a metabolic process and the results of this experiment may cast some doubt on a concept of metabolic uptake of Na because of the slight inhibition of Na uptake.

Experiment 5: Because some of the effect of CCP on cation uptake may be due to its drastic effect on transpiration and wilting (precautions to prevent wilting were taken), an experiment was made with excised whole roots to avoid the wilting problem (table 5). K^{42}, Na^{22}, and Ca^{47} were included. In all cases the inhibition of K uptake by both CCP and 2,4-DNP was greater than for Na or Ca. For Na and Ca the inhibition was somewhat similar.

Experiment 6: An experiment was conducted to determine if there was an additive effect of ouabain and CCP on the inhibition of K or of Na uptake. There was no indication that ouabain inhibited uptake of Na with or without the uncouplers of oxidative phosphorylation (table 6). For K the same slight

Table 4.　Effect of CCP on K^{42} or Na^{22} uptake in 5 hours from $10^{-3}\underline{M}$ $K^{42}Cl$ or $Na^{22}Cl$ by bush beans.

CCP	Leaf	Root	Whole Plant	Inhibition
$\underline{M}$	μmoles/g. dry weight			%
		K		
0	9.92	289	51.0	—
10^{-8}	9.55	285	48.7	5
10^{-7}	7.74	266	44.2	13
10^{-6}	4.89	256	42.0	18
10^{-5}*	0.05	113	15.8	69
		Na		
0	0.10	20.0	4.0	—
10^{-8}	0.00	20.2	3.6	10
10^{-7}	0.00	21.8	3.5	12
10^{-6}	0.18	20.4	3.4	15
10^{-5}*	0.06	18.2	2.7	33

*Plants tended to wilt.

Table 5.　Effect of CCP and 2,4-DNP on K, Na, and Ca uptake in 5 hours by excised bush bean roots. *

Treatment	K	Na	Ca	K	Na	Ca
$\underline{M}$	μmoles/g. dry wt.			% inhibition		
Control	455	16	110	—	—	—
10^{-5} CCP	88	13	110	81	20	0
10^{-4} CCP	60	12	55	87	27	50
10^{-5} 2,4-DNP	228	15	94	50	7	15
10^{-4} 2,4-DNP	71	13	87	84	19	21

*Each solution contained $10^{-4}\underline{M}$ $CaCl_2$ and $10^{-4}\underline{M}$ KCl or NaCl where appropriate. The cations were tagged with $K^{42},$ Na^{22}, or Ca^{47}.

Table 6.　Effect of $10^{-5}\underline{M}$ CCP and $10^{-5}\underline{M}$ 2,4-DNP with and without ouabain on K^{42} uptake and on Na^{22} uptake by intact bush bean plants in $10^{-3}\underline{M}$ $K^{42}Cl$.

Plant part	Without $10^{-4}\underline{M}$ ouabain			With $10^{-4}\underline{M}$ ouabain		
	Control	CCP	2,4-DNP	Control	CCP	2,4-DNP
	μmoles K/g. dry weight					
Leaf	0.31	0.10	0.27	0.26	0.19	0.53
Stem	4.32	2.40	4.48	4.81	2.26	3.94
Root	197.	116.	133.	150.	104.	159.
Whole Plant	25.7	14.0	19.1	21.3	14.5	18.5
% Inhibition	—	46	26	17	44	28
	μmoles Na/g. dry weight					
Leaf	0.08	0.04	0.10	0.08	0.22	0.02
Stem	0.29	0.10	0.33	0.82	0.38	0.39
Root	10.60	7.59	8.10	10.60	7.16	6.18
Whole Plant	1.97	1.24	1.49	1.96	1.20	1.31
% Inhibition	—	37	24	—	39	34

inhibition for ouabain was obtained but it was not additive with that of CCP or 2,4-DNP.

Summary

No evidence was found for a coupled Na-K pump in the bush bean material studied or for a Na requirement by the bush beans. A concentration of $10^{-4}\underline{M}$ ouabain and strophanthidin inhibited Na uptake very slightly if at all. K uptake was stimulated slightly. CCP, an uncoupler of oxidative phosphorylation, inhibited K uptake more than that of Na or Ca and it was more effective than 2,4-DNP in inhibiting uptake of both K and Na. CCP and ouabain combined inhibited uptake no more than CCP alone.

POSSIBLE EFFECTS OF ROOT CATION-EXCHANGE CAPACITY
ON THE RELATIVE AMOUNTS OF Ca AND K IN PLANTS

This subject was introduced on page 7. Laties (1959) has reviewed the problem of whether or not adsorption is the first step in accumulation. He cites the following to show that it probably is not: (a) accumulation rate is independent of the saturation state of the exchange sites, (b) carrier sites appear to be specific whereas exchange sites follow lyotropic series, (c) the apparent dissociation constant, K_s, differs for carrier-cation compared with exchange site-cation, (d) a very small quantity of anions enters the Donnan free space and this suggests no effect of exchange on accumulation of a salt, (e) exchange sites have been shown to be mostly in the cell wall, while the membranes that have to be penetrated for accumulation are other than cell walls, (f) temperature coefficients of reactions indicate no other than physical processes for adsorption-exchange in vivid contrast to accumulation, and (g) accumulation is a slower process than adsorption-exchange which is almost instantaneous.

Recent workers (Heintze, 1961; Mengel, 1961; Lagerwerff and Peech, 1961; Crooke and Knight, 1962) found no relationship of root cation-exchange capacity (CEC) with metabolic cation accumulation and also little evidence for inverse potassium relationships with root CEC. Heintze did get a barely significant relationship with some plant species from root CEC vs. the inverse K contents.

In spite of the fact that root CEC bears no direct relationship to the metabolic forces involved with ion uptake by plants it seems to be related to cation uptake. It may regulate the relative amounts of Ca vs. K taken up by plants (Wallace, 1960; Drake et al., 1951; Elgabaly and Wiklander, 1949; Huffaker and Wallace, 1958; Smith and Wallace, 1956a) or it may influence the total amounts of cations taken up by plants (Crooke and Knight, 1962; Morita and Aoki, 1960). The agricultural ramifications of these were outlined on page 10.

Cations are subject to movement into the Donnan free space of the cells (mostly walls?) of plant roots. Divalent and monovalent cations will be differentially distributed according to the relative amount of negative charge on the roots in obeying the laws of Donnan distribution. It can be expected that the greater the charge the greater will be the ratio of Ca/K in association with the root CEC when in the presence of dilute solutions of both Ca and K (Elgabaly and Wiklander, 1949; Huffaker and Wallace, 1958; Wallace, 1960). Since cations on the root CEC are available for movement inward (Mertz and Levitt, 1961) it can be expected that the root CEC would modify the Ca/K ratios in plants.

A problem that arises in this area is the relationship of root CEC to total cation content. In the general equations given on page 9 it was suggested that for different occasions either of the following is obtained:

$$\frac{CEC_1}{CEC_2} = \frac{K_2}{K_1} = \left(\frac{Ca_1}{Ca_2}\right)^{\frac{1}{2}} \tag{1}$$

or

$$\frac{CEC_1}{CEC_2} = \frac{K_1}{K_2} = \left(\frac{Ca_1}{Ca_2}\right)^{\frac{1}{2}} \tag{2}.$$

It is very apparent that if the second equation holds then the total cation content of plants would be positively correlated with root CEC as suggested by Crooke and Knight (1962) because an increase in root CEC would result in an increase of both K and Ca.

The following is reprinted from Wallace, 1962, page 18:

Chelating agents variously undergo isotopic exchange with metals as follows:

$$Zn*EDTA + Zn \longrightarrow ZnEDTA + Zn* \tag{A}$$

$$Zn*EDTA* + ZnEDTA \longrightarrow ZnEDTA* + Zn*EDTA \tag{B}$$

$$ZnEDTA + EDTA* \longrightarrow ZnEDTA* + EDTA \tag{C}$$

This is effected by overlapping orbitals and by reversible reactions.

This phenomenon can explain how cations which are adsorbed on cation-exchange sites of roots can be available to the metabolic accumulating sites in the root. That is, cation-exchange does not need to be a "dead-end street." If the root epidermis can be thought of as having cell walls with cation-exchange sites in tunnels or micropores then one of the above exchange systems can be operative (figure 1).

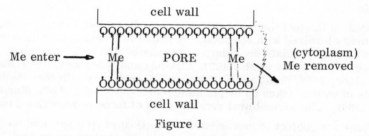

Figure 1

The carboxyl groups would radiate from all sides of the pore chelating the metal within it. The metal could move within the pore by isotopic exchange, analogous perhaps to reaction (C) above. A net movement "in" would be effected by the removal of the metal by the cytoplasm of the cell.

The model in figure 1 may be used to describe the availability of Ca and K to the plasmalemma of the root cells. It must be borne in mind that the cations on the root CEC are not static but in a state of rapid motion between sites or on and off sites of many thousand times a second. The following marked atoms or groups illustrate this effect:

Ca* Root CEC* + Ca Root CEC $\rightleftharpoons$ Ca* Root CEC + Ca Root CEC*.
A flow of cations can move through the pore if they are removed at one end by a mechanism (chelation) having greater affinity for them than does the root CEC.

It can be visualized that conditions can be varied to obtain either equation (1) or equation (2) above. From solution culture with different plant species the variable would involve relative concentrations of K and Ca. If both were in relatively high concentration a high density of charge on root CEC (in the pore in figure 1) may result in increase movement of both K and Ca to the metabolic sites. If K alone were in high concentration the K movement in the pore in figure 1 may be correlated directly with root CEC no matter what the Ca level. If the K concentration were low relative to Ca then it perhaps could be expected that K uptake or movement in the pore would be negatively correlated with root CEC. This inverse relationship is the condition that commonly obtains for field-grown crops. It is expected that as deficiency levels are approached the K contents of plants would be inversely related to the root CEC because Ca would dominate the sites. There are mathematical reasons for this: dilute solutions favor Ca over K in a Donnan system—concentrated ones do not.

Several attempts were made to experimentally verify the above suggestions. It appeared impossible to do so with radioactive isotopes and short-time studies. The correlations that have been observed between root CEC and cation contents have been for field-grown plants grown for periods of weeks, months or years (in the case of trees).

Summary

A hypothesis was proposed to explain how an increase in root cation-exchange capacity can in some cases result in an increased cation content of a plant while under other conditions it can result in an increased Ca and a decreased K content.

Ca STIMULATION OF K UPTAKE (VIETS EFFECT)

With N. Hemaidan

In previous studies in this laboratory (Wallace et al. , 1962, page 43; Wallace and Mueller, 1962b, page 98) EDTA (ethylenediaminetetraacetate) interferred with a Ca requirement for uptake of K and Rb but stimulated their uptake when Ca was not limiting. In those studies no direct effect of Ca was observed (only indirectly with EDTA) on Rb uptake and this was evidently due to the fact that the levels of Rb used (10^{-3} and 2.5 x 10^{-3}M) were too high. Tanada (1962) found the so-called Viets effect (Viets, 1944) with lower concentrations of Rb.

The Viets effect has been repeatedly demonstrated (Overstreet et al. , 1952; Tanada, 1955; Khan and Hanson, 1957; Epstein, 1960). This Viets effect supposedly is different from the apparent regulating effect Ca has on selectivity of monovalent cation uptake (Epstein, 1961; Jacobson, Moore and Hannapel, 1960; Jacobson, Hannapel, Schaedle, and Moore, 1961; Wadleigh and Bower, 1950). Jacobson, Hannapel, Schaedle, and Moore (1961) even found that Ca loss from roots in solution cultures was enough to cause great changes in uptake of other cations.

Several additional studies have been made in this laboratory to further explore the effect of EDTA and Ca levels on uptake of K^{42} (less the K^{42} in the free space in roots). The effects were examined at different pH values. In all cases the concentration of K used was 10^{-3}M as KCl. Just as in the case of Rb, this might have been too high.

The experimental techniques of the present studies with bush beans were identical to those used in previous studies. The K^{42} uptake periods were 2 hours or 4 hours and all plants received a 1 hour post treatment of 10^{-2}M $CaCl_2$ to remove the K^{42} from the free space of the roots. The pH was maintained as indicated in table 1. The results in table 1 indicate that the Viets effect was more pronounced at high pH than at low.

Table 1.   Effect of EDTA and Ca on K^{42} uptake from 10^{-3}M KCl or
KHCO$_3$ by bush bean plants.

Treatment *	Test A (2 hrs.)		Test B (4 hrs.)		
	pH 7	KHCO$_3$	pH 4	pH 7	KHCO$_3$
M		μmoles K/g. dry weight			
Control	18	32	55	64	87
10^{-4} EDTA	21	57	—	—	—
10^{-4} CaCl$_2$	24	49	55	49	102
10^{-4} CaCl$_2$+10^{-4} EDTA	22	77	55	91	150
10^{-3} CaCl$_2$	15	40	47	67	108
10^{-3} EDTA	9	17	25	40	43
10^{-2} CaCl$_2$	—	—	—	—	—

*Na$_2$ EDTA was used where indicated.

All values are means of 4.

The 10^{-4}M EDTA stimulated K^{42} uptake under some conditions. With an equimolar level of Ca with EDTA the uptake was still inconsistent indicating that chelation of Ca was not the reason for the EDTA stimulation. Perhaps the chelation of endogenous heavy metals that interfere with the K binding site may be the reason for the EDTA effect. At 10^{-3}M EDTA there was always considerable inhibition of K^{42} uptake. Separate studies indicated that the EDTA effects were not the result of the sodium supplied with it.

In an experiment which was designed to determine if EDTA had an effect of making roots leaky, 10^{-3}M EDTA in a 1 hour post treatment had no effect on the K^{42} content of bush bean roots. That is, the EDTA did not cause any previously absorbed K^{42} to be lost from the root. The K (from K^{42}) contents of roots were 117, 140, and 124 μmoles/g. dry weight for post treatments of 10^{-1} and 10^{-2}M CaCl$_2$ and 10^{-3}M EDTA respectively. The effect of 10^{-3}M EDTA on K^{42} uptake therefore very probably lies in the chelation of Ca rather than in making cells leaky although a slight chelation of K cannot be excluded.

In another study bean roots of intact plants were pretreated for 10 days with varying levels of CaCl$_2$ or KCl to determine if effects such as the Viets effect could be induced by pretreatments. The results in table 2 indicated no Viets effect from the pretreatments and no depressing effect of the pretreatments with K or Ca on uptake of Ca^{47} or K^{42}, respectively, in the tests. This may differ from the results of Nelson and Brady (1952) who found that adding K or Ca to the above ground parts of Ladino clover decreased Ca and K uptake, respectively, by roots.

Summary

A Viets effect was more pronounced at high pH than at low. EDTA at 10^{-4}M usually stimulated K uptake with or without equimolar $CaCl_2$. This effect was pH dependent, being pronounced at pH 6.5 or greater and absent below that pH. EDTA at 10^{-3}M always decreased K^{42} uptake supposedly because of Ca chelation. A post treatment with 10^{-3}M EDTA had no effect on previously accumulated K^{42}. Pretreatment of plants with $CaCl_2$ or KCl had little if any effect on subsequent uptake of K^{42} or Ca^{47} respectively.

Table 2.   Effect of 10 days pretreatment of bush bean roots with $CaCl_2$ solutions and KCl solutions on subsequent uptake of K^{42} and Ca^{47}, respectively.

K or Ca chlorides in pretreatment solution	Ca^{47} and K^{42} in intact bean plants after 4 hours.	
	Ca^{47}	K^{42}
$\underline{M}$	μmoles/g. dry weight	
0	20.1	4.8
10^{-5}	21.2	3.2
10^{-3}	20.2	5.7
10^{-1}	36.4	3.4

Means of 4.

EFFECT OF ROOT REMOVAL ON Na MOVEMENT TO LEAVES AND THROUGH STEMS OF PLANTS

With N. Hemaidan

In plants like bush beans and in perhaps the majority of vascular plants, Na is readily accumulated by the roots but is translocated extremely sluggishly to the shoots of those plants. Some apparently logical assumptions are that some mechanism in the roots prevents Na movement from the root cells or that the shoot has some mechanism that excludes Na or keeps it from entering. We surmised that it could be possible to determine whether or not the regulating factor was associated with the root by cutting off portions or all of the root to open the xylem so as to provide an open channel from the external solutions to the leaves.

In all cases the cuttings were made under water so that the channels would not fill with air. The plants had been pregrown for 10 days to 2 weeks with 1/10-strength nutrient solutions as in other experiments of this series. Test periods in this series were usually 24 hours. The pH of solutions which were aerated was maintained at 7. Test solutions contained 10^{-4}M $CaCl_2$ with 10^{-3}M $Na^{22}Cl$. Post treatments of plant parts exposed to test solutions were made for 1 hour with 10^{-2}M $CaCl_2$.

The results in table 1 indicate that Na applied through the stem of a plant from which the root had been removed did move into the stem but that it was essentially absent from the leaves just as it was when added to roots. The same type of treatment resulted in greatly enhanced movement of K into both stems and leaves.

In table 2 are results of an experiment which indicate that the removal of all roots is necessary to movement of increased quantities of Na into stems but that cutting of neither root nor stem increased Na movement into the leaves. An open channel, therefore, from the external solution to the leaves and coupled with a transpirational pull from the leaves does not provide the conditions necessary for Na movement to leaves. The root, consequently, apparently can be eliminated as the major barrier of Na transfer to leaves.

Table 1.   Effect of root removal on K^{42} and Na^{22} movement into leaves of bush bean in 5 hours.

	$10^{-3}\underline{M}\ K^{42}Cl$		$10^{-3}\underline{M}\ Na^{22}Cl$	
	Intact	No Root	Intact	No Root
		μmoles/g. dry wt.		
Leaf	0.58	10.57	0.0005	0.033
Stem	6.77	39.2	0.12	5.30
Root	254.	—	17.23	—

All solutions contained $10^{-4}\underline{M}$ $CaCl_2$.

Table 2.   Effect of partial and total root removal on Na^{22} distribution in bush bean from $10^{-3}\underline{M}\ Na^{22}Cl$ (with $10^{-4}\underline{M}$ $CaCl_2$).

Root removal treatments	Leaf	Stem	Root
		μmoles Na/g. dry weight	
Intact	0.04	2.48	58.63
$\frac{1}{2}$ root removed	0.04	3.82	55.14
3/4 root removed	0.04	2.60	64.59
All roots removed	0.08	21.42	—
All roots + 1 inch of stem removed	0.02	30.68	—

Since cyanide appears to enhance Na movement to the shoots of bush beans (page 64), cyanide was applied with Na^{22} solutions to cut stems (table 3). Just as in the intact plants the cyanide resulted in increased movement of Na^{22} at least into the stem. Most of the Na^{22} was retained in the lower stem. It would appear that the cells along the xylem have the ability to remove the Na^{22} from the xylem and prevent its further movement upward.

Table 3.   Effect of root removal and KCN on movement of Na^{22} through bush bean plants.

Plant Part	KCl		KCN	
	Intact	No Root	Intact	No Root
		μmoles/g. dry weight		
Leaf	0.014	0.030	0.009	0.022
Upper $\frac{1}{2}$ stem	0.01	0.03	0.04	0.10
Lower $\frac{1}{2}$ minus 1 inch of stem	0.01	0.35	0.02	3.11
Stem 1 inch above root	0.49	15.44	0.68	19.89
Root	6.22	—	5.54	—

Roots were removed from some other plant species to compare the results with those of bush beans (tables 4 and 5). Partial root removal with corn resulted in a slightly increased amount of Na^{22} transferred to leaves but no more than did complete removal. The latter resulted in considerable Na^{22} retained in stems. With intact barley plants considerable Na^{22} was translocated to the blades. This was increased somewhat when the roots were removed.

Table 4. Effect of partial and total root removal on Na^{22} distribution in corn from $10^{-3}\underline{M}$ $Na^{22}Cl$ (with $10^{-4}\underline{M}$ $CaCl_2$).

Root removal treatments	Leaf	Stem	Root
	μmoles Na/g. dry weight		
Intact	0.02	0.91	48.1
1/2 roots removed	0.23	3.84	20.1
3/4 roots removed	0.42	5.19	35.3
All roots removed	0.33	24.55	—
All roots + 1 inch stem removed	0.17	27.91	—

Table 5. Effect of root removal on Na^{22} distribution in barley from a $10^{-3}\underline{M}$ $Na^{22}Cl$ solution (with $10^{-4}\underline{M}$ $CaCl_2$).

	Intact plants	Roots removed
	μmoles Na/g. dry weight	
Leaf	6.94	11.11
Stem	37.02	46.14
Root	5.67	—

Summary

Removal under water of some of the roots from bush beans resulted in no increases of Na^{22} transfer from an external solution to the stems or leaves. Complete root removal resulted in some Na^{22} movement to the lower part of the stem but in no increases to the leaves. KCN increased that moving into stems after root removal. Root removal resulted in large increases of K^{42} being moved into stems and leaves in contrast to Na^{22}. The transfer of Na to blades was about doubled by root removal in barley in which Na does move to the blades ordinarily. Root removal resulted in increased Na^{22} movement into the stem (stalk) of corn but only slightly into the blades.

ABILITY OF FINELY DIVIDED METALLIC IRON TO OVERCOME IRON CHLOROSIS IN A CALCAREOUS SOIL

Insoluble iron salts and minerals are available to plants under some conditions (Salm-Horstman, 1849; Chapman, 1939; Wynd, 1950; Rhoads et al., 1956). Suggestions have been made that plant roots obtain iron from insoluble sources by means of some type of "contact exchange" (Charley and Jenny, 1961; Glauser and Jenny, 1960a; Glauser and Jenny, 1960b; Grunes and Jenny, 1960; Wallace, 1962a).

A commercial product* which contains finely divided metallic iron as at least part of its active principle (no chelating agents are present in it) has been made for supplying iron to plants. Preliminary studies with it indicate that when moderately high rates of it were incorporated into a calcareous soil (Hacienda loam containing 32% $CaCO_3$), PI 54619-5-1 soybeans grew satisfactorily. This particular soybean variety is extremely susceptible to iron chlorosis when grown in calcareous soils. The results of these pot tests are given in tables 1 and 2. Each of the weights is the mean of 4 individual plants.

Table 1. Fresh weights and plant condition of PI 54619-5-1 soybeans grown with metallic iron product in Hacienda loam soil which contains 32% $CaCO_3$.

Equivalent rates of product in pounds per acre*	Grams fresh weight per plant	Plant condition
0	3.20	Chlorotic
100	2.34	Chlorotic
200	3.50	Mildly chlorotic
400	4.72	No chlorosis
4,000	6.15	Healthy
20,000	3.54	Small
4,000 (filtrate part)	5.02	Healthy
4,000 (residual part)	4.53	Healthy

*Each pot contained 500 grams of soil. Nutrient solutions containing nitrogen and phosphorus were added so that these elements would not be limiting.

The 400-pound per acre rate prevented the symptoms of iron chlorosis but a higher rate (between 400 and 4000 pounds per acre) was necessary to give maximum yields. A rate equivalent to 20,000 pounds per acre produced no toxic symptoms but did decrease yields. When iron and other insoluble material was separated from the wetting agents and other soluble material in the product each fraction separately prevented symptoms of iron chlorosis but each gave less total plant yield than did the combination.

Table 2. Fresh weights and plant condition of soybeans grown as in table 1 but with all organic matter burned off the metallic iron product.

Equivalent rate of metallic iron in pounds per acre	Grams fresh weight per plant	Plant condition
0	2.2	Chlorotic
100	2.2	Chlorotic
200	3.0	Chlorotic
500	4.2	Mildly chlorotic
1000	4.0	No chlorosis

*Green Garde, a product of Nelsen Steel & Wire Company, Franklin Park, Ill., containing 25% metallic iron plus organic materials and surfactants none of which supposedly are chelating agents.

The fact that the insoluble material (filtered from the soluble) corrected the chlorosis indicates that the plants did obtain iron from the metallic source even in the calcareous soil. Since the product was not pure metallic iron this conclusion may not be definite, however. For this reason the organic matter was burned off a sample of the iron product so that metallic iron only was added to the soil. The results in table 2 indicate that the metallic iron did supply iron to the soybeans. The product does contain a small portion of iron oxide.

Summary

Evidence was presented which indicates that PI 54619-5-1 soybeans were able to obtain iron from finely divided metallic iron mixed into a calcareous soil.

pH VS. A BICARBONATE REQUIREMENT IN CATION ABSORPTION

With R. T. Mueller

There is nothing mysterious in the relationships of cation and anion uptake that results in the formation of loss of organic acids in roots. Bicarbonate when absorbed can be enzymatically combined with phosphoenolpyruvate to yield oxaloacetic acid which in turn is reduced to malic acid. Malate usually arises as an anion when bicarbonate salts are supplied to plant roots or when the absorption rate of metallic cations exceeds that of metallic anions. Either bicarbonate may be absorbed with those cations or bicarbonate may arise from internal respiration. Another factor of great importance in salt uptake is the role of H^+ in competing with other cations for uptake and the role of OH^- and/ or HCO_3^- in competing with other anions for uptake. Jacobson et al. (1957) have charted uptake of K vs. Br at varying pH and found that K uptake was inhibited more at low pH and that Br uptake was inhibited more at high pH consistent with concepts of H^+ and OH^- competition.

In table 1 are listed some of the effects that have been observed when salts are absorbed by plant roots. There has been considerable debate over such things as whether Ca is absorbed so that it can be combined with any oxalate in the plant as a means of oxalate inactivation or whether oxalate arises to inactivate Ca that has been absorbed. The information in table 1 implies that organic acids can arise or disappear as such as a consequence of the electrostatic differentials imposed by ion absorption and assimilation. The net effects are quite simple.

CO_2 and HCO_3^- are reported to inhibit salt uptake under some conditions (Sutcliffe, 1962, p. 52). The question as to whether or not dark fixation of CO_2 or of HCO_3^- promotes cation uptake and inhibits anion uptake has been reviewed by Walker (1962). Several workers have observed a relationship between CO_2 or HCO_3^- assimilation into organic acids and ion uptake (Jacobson, 1955; Poel and Graham, 1956; Jackson and Coleman, 1959a,b). Hurd (1958, 1959) has shown that K uptake is enhanced by HCO_3^- and that the HCO_3^- is assimilated into organic acids. Such assimilation in plant roots appears to be quite general (Bedri et al., 1960). Some work in this laboratory casts doubt on the concept of direct stimulation of cation uptake by the synthesis of organic acids from CO_2 or HCO_3^- (Bhan et al., 1960). The contention was that it is exceedingly difficult to separate the pH effect from the HCO_3^- effect. The ionic species HCO_3^- exists mostly at pH 7-9 and so wherever HCO_3^- exists there would be no H^+ competition for cation uptake. The separation of the two effects is difficult but certainly not impossible.

An experiment was devised after the pattern of Olson (1953) in which Chlo-

<u>rella</u> obtained as packed cells from the laboratory of Dr. David Appleman was added to the nutrient solutions in which the roots of intact bush bean plants were placed.   The bean plants had been prepared as in other studies of this series and the test solutions were $10^{-3}\underline{M}$ $K^{42}Cl$ with $10^{-4}\underline{M}$ $CaCl_2$.   The experimental period was 4 hours with 4 different pH levels and the plants were aerated with CO_2-free air.   The solutions were illuminated with incandescent lights so that the alga would use for photosynthesis any CO_2 present or arising in the system.   It was hoped in this experiment to have different pH values with HCO_3^- at an extremely low level.   The roots received a post treatment of $10^{-2}\underline{M}$ $CaCl_2$ for 1 hour to remove K^{42} from the free space.

Table 1.   Some of the changes that occur within roots from uptake of some specific salts. *

Salt in external solution	Result inside root after uptake and assimilation
$KHCO_3$	K malate** (pH rises)
KCl	KCl
KCl if K uptake $>$ Cl uptake	K malate + KCl
KCl if K uptake $<$ Cl uptake	HCl or organic acid disappears + KCl
KNO_3	K malate + amino acid or protein (pH rises)
$(NH_4)_2SO_4$	H_2SO_4 or organic acids disappear + amino acid or protein (pH decreases)
$Ca(NO_3)_2$	Ca oxalate + amino acids and proteins

*Information for this table comes from such works as Ulrich (1941), Hoagland and Broyer (1940), Poel and Graham (1956), and Jacobson and Ordin, (1954).
**The HCO_3^- used to make the malate can come either from the external source or from root respiration.

The results in table 2 do not follow the usual pH pattern when HCO_3^- is present at high pH.   There was an increased uptake between pH 5 and 6 as would be expected from an H^+ effect.   Since the uptake decreased at pH 7 and at pH 8 it can be suspected that the effect was due to the absence of bicarbonate.   An alternate explanation is that the alga may have taken up so much more K^{42} at high pH than at low that less was left available to the beans.   This was checked in separate studies (without bean plants) with $Rb^{86}Cl$ by assay of the algae.   The results also in table 2 indicate that the Rb uptake by the algae was extremely pH dependent even with HCO_3^- either absent or at low levels and that inclusion of HCO_3^- caused no further increase.

Since Voznesenskii (1959) reported that the illumination of plant leaves increased the absorption of CO_2 by plant roots by 15 times a study was made to determine if a similar treatment would increase K uptake by beans because of increased CO_2 uptake and assimilation by roots.   The results (table 3) indicate that there was no increase for the light treatment.   In all cases more K^{42} was taken up by plants completely in the dark for 4 hours than those for which the shoots were in the light.   This cannot be taken to mean that CO_2 absorption had no effect on K uptake but only that the technique did not indicate such.   The differential results are most likely due to other factors (see page 141).

A study was made of Na^{22} uptake with 3 different anions at different pH values to determine if the presence of HCO$_3^-$ made an appreciable difference on uptake. The treatment conditions with pre- and post-treatments were similar to other experiments. The results, table 4, indicate that the uptake was slightly greater for HCO$_3^-$ at the higher pH values. This was pronounced at pH 6.

Table 2.   Effect of pH on uptake of K^{42} from 10^{-3}M KCl by intact bush bean plants when Chlorella was present in illuminated nutrient solutions with the roots to decrease CO$_2$ and HCO$_3^-$ levels to an absolute minimum (aerated with CO$_2$-free air).

pH of solution	Leaf	Stem	Root	Whole Plant	Algae Alone*
		μmoles/g. dry weight			
5	0.6	1.8	35.9	4.8	3.0
6	0.2	1.1	45.6	6.3	4.5
7	0.1	0.8	29.2	3.6	5.4
8	0.2	0.9	22.1	2.9	5.6

*For pH 4 the uptake was 2.2 and for pH 8 with 10^{-4}M NaHCO$_3$ present it was 5.5 μmoles/g. dry weight. The studies for the alga were with Rb^{86}Cl.

Table 3.   Effect of pH of external solution vs. light and dark treatments on K^{42} uptake from 10^{-3}M KCl by intact bush bean when aerated with CO$_2$-free air.

pH	Light	Dark	Dark/Light
	μmoles K/g. dry weight		ratio
4.0	9.4	25.5	2.7
5.5	13.3	22.5	1.7
7.0	15.8	24.8	1.6
7.5	15.1	30.1	2.0
8.2	16.3	19.7	1.2

Table 4.   Effect of different anions on Na^{22} uptake from 10^{-3}N Na at different pH values by intact bush beans.

pH	Salt		
	NaCl	Na$_2$SO$_4$	NaHCO$_3$
	μmoles/g. dry weight		
3.0	1.07	1.68	—
4.5	1.11	1.71	—
6.0	1.72	1.96	2.55
7.5	2.40	2.64	2.88
9.0	2.24	2.41	2.46

Phosphoenolpyruvate carboxylase, the enzyme responsible for assimilation of HCO_3^-, is a sulfhydryl-containing enzyme and is very sensitive to poisoning by $HgCl_2$ and p-chloromercuribenzoate (pCMB). Rb^{86} uptake was drastically inhibited by these two agents. The inhibition by pCMB at pH 8 in the presence of HCO_3^-, however, was somewhat less than at pH 4 in the absence of HCO_3^-. For $10^{-5}M$ $HgCl_2$ there was no difference. Even though the results with pCMB may indicate a direct effect of HCO_3^- on Rb uptake, other explanations are possible.

An experiment was conducted to determine the extent of HCO_3^- inhibition of Br^{82} uptake (table 5). Several different levels of $NaHCO_3$ were applied to solutions containing bush bean plants with either $K^{42}Br$ or KBr^{82} with $10^{-4}M$ $CaCl_2$. The plants and treatment conditions were otherwise the same as in the above experiments. HCO_3^- uptake or assimilation greatly depressed the uptake of Br. The synthesis of the organic acid anions resulting from HCO_3^- assimilation would tend to depress the uptake of mineral anions (Walker, 1962). The depression in K uptake in this experiment was supposedly due to Na competition.

Table 5. Effect of $NaHCO_3$ on uptake of K^{42} and Br^{82} from KBr.

$NaHCO_3$ Treatment	K			Br		
	Leaf	Stem	Root	Leaf	Stem	Root
$\underline{M}$			μmoles g. dry weight			
0	1. 3	4. 4	192	1. 8	1. 3	11. 0
10^{-3}	0. 9	4. 0	169	1. 2	1. 1	7. 0
5×10^{-3}	0. 6	3. 3	155	1. 0	1. 2	3. 8
10^{-2}	0. 8	3. 5	131	0. 2	0. 6	3. 0
2×10^{-2}	0. 6	2. 2	100	0. 4	0. 2	1. 9

Summary

The role of dark fixation of CO_2 or of bicarbonate into organic acids as a means of balancing differences in cation and anion uptake by plants was discussed. High pH and therefore no competion from H^+ is just as likely an explanation for the apparent stimulating effect of bicarbonate on cation uptake as is the formation of organic acids in roots from assimilated bicarbonate. An alga was used in a nutrient solution to decrease CO_2 and HCO_3^- levels by photosynthesis so that the effect of pH on K^{42} uptake could be measured independently of an effect of HCO_3^-. Results with the alga alone were more consistant than with the beans and indicate that the effect of pH is more important than that of bicarbonate. The pH effect apparently is an H^+ inhibition of cation uptake. More K^{42} was taken up by intact plants in the dark during a 4-hour test than by those kept in light. Na^{22} uptake was slightly greater with HCO_3^- than without. HCO_3^- inhibited Br^{82} uptake considerably.

SALT UPTAKE AS A PROCESS OF ELECTRON FLOW

With R. T. Mueller

Lundegardh (1945, 1954) and Lundegardh and Burstrom (1933) have proposed and done considerable work on a theory of "anion respiration" in which salt uptake is considered as an electron flow. Lundegardh found a linear increase in the amount of CO_2 evolved with the amount of anion absorbed. Many objections have been raised concerning this theory (Sutcliffe, 1962, p. 80).

The Lundegardh hypothesis suggests that the transport of anions across a membrane is accompanied by an equivalent number of electrons and hydrogen ions moving in the opposite direction. It is well-known that an excess of anion uptake over cation uptake results in a pH increase of the external solution. This may not correspond with the hypothesis.

If the process of anion uptake is either a matter of oxidation in which an electron is released or a coupled anion-electron pump the following condition may obtain in which A^- is an anion:

(1) 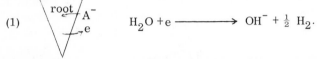 $H_2O + e \longrightarrow OH^- + \frac{1}{2} H_2.$

This model succeeds in producing the OH^- which would increase the pH of the external solution. The Lundegardh model may be different as follows:

(2) 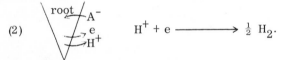 $H^+ + e \longrightarrow \frac{1}{2} H_2.$

An alternate model for anion transport across a membrane could be that of hydroxyl or bicarbonate exchange as follows:

(3)

This also would explain the increase in pH in the external solution for an excess of anion uptake. The appearance of HCO_3^- or CO_2, however, may not necessarily indicate a relationship of anion uptake to respiration. The model cannot correspond with the Lundegardh hypothesis if the HCO_3^- or CO_2 released represents the respiration because one anion is transported into the root for one CO_2 released instead of 4, as would be expected by Lundegardh's hypothesis.

If the process of cation transport across a membrane involves an opposite electron flow compared with that of anions or is a reduction process then the following model is possible:

(4) 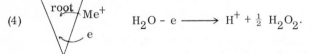 $H_2O - e \longrightarrow H^+ + \frac{1}{2} H_2O_2.$

An excess of cation uptake over anion uptake results in a decreased pH in the external solution and this is explained by the model. An alternate model could be by H^+ exchange or a coupled cation - H^+ pump as follows:

(5)

This also would explain the decrease of pH in the external solution which occurs for an excess of cation uptake over anion uptake. An elegant model for a coupled cation - H^+ biological pump was described by Rothstein (1960).

If the models are correct that suggest electron flow in and out of a root cell with salt uptake then electron donors may inhibit the uptake of anions more than of cations and electron acceptors may inhibit the uptake of cations more than of anions. Breazeale et al. (1951, 1953) have already suggested that the uptake of some cations can be stimulated with applied voltages such that a flow of electrons moves into roots with the cations. This does correspond with the model (4).

A preliminary experiment was made with ferricyanide as an electron acceptor to measure relative effects on K^{42} vs. Br^{82} uptake. The results for a 5-hour study at pH 7 on a whole-plant basis are in table 1. As expected the inhibition for Br^{82} was much less than for K^{42} (compare models 1 and 4).

Table 1. Effect of $Fe(CN)_6^=$ on K^{42} and Br^{82} uptake by intact bush beans.

Labeling	Without $Fe(CN)_6^=$	With $Fe(CN)_6^=$	Inhibition
	μmoles/g. dry weight		%
	with $10^{-2}M$ KBr		
$K^{42}Br$	46.5	12.9	72
KBr^{82}	11.3	9.2	18
	with $10^{-4}M$ KBr		
$K^{42}Br$	7.1	4.5	38
KBr^{82}	0.46	0.43	6

K^{42} uptake from $K^{42}Br$ and Br^{82} uptake from KBr^{82} were measured in the presence of different oxidizing-reducing agents (table 2). The bush bean plants had been pregrown as usual with 1/10-strength nutrient solution for 10 days. The test period was 4 hours at pH 7.0 in aerated solutions which also contained $10^{-4}M$ $CaCl_2$. The plants received a post-treatment of $10^{-2}M$ $CaCl_2$ for 1 hour to remove isotopes from the free space. H_2O_2 greatly inhibited Br^{82} uptake but had little effect on K^{42}. The effect was not due to pH changes. $KMnO_4$ ($10^{-4}M$) seemed to stimulate K^{42} uptake slightly and reduced Br^{82} uptake moderately. $Na_2S_2O_4$ seemed to depress uptake of both cation and anion. An oxidizing agent then seemed to increase K uptake and a reducing substance seemed to decrease it. Both decreased anion uptake although H_2O_2 decreased it by far the most. H_2O_2 can act as a reducing agent and as an oxidizing agent. The behavior of $KMnO_4$ does not correspond with predictions based on model (4). Part of the $Na_2S_2O_4$ effect was due to Na so actually there was little effect of the reducing agent on uptake of the cation K.

Some 1.5 volt batteries were attached to plants with similar treatments and similar pre-preparation as those in the above experiment. A small amount of current flowed through the plants. The results in table 3 indicate a greater effect on Br^{82} uptake than on K^{42}. These results suggest that anions will flow toward a postively charged center. Cation (K^{42}) uptake seemed to be decreased slightly in both cases.

Some studies have been made of K^{42} and Br^{82} uptake when plants were exposed to the isotopes in the dark vs. when the shoots (not roots) were exposed to light. These data are given here because they may have some bearing on the question of electron flow. The plants were handled just the same as in the previous experiments. Exposing the plants to darkness resulted in a moderately increased uptake of K^{42} but with little effect on Br^{82} (table 4). Larger differences in K^{42} uptake were obtained in a similar experiment (page 136). A possible explanation is that light resulted in greater reducing conditions in the plant (photoreduction of TPN some of which was transferred to roots). Such conditions of electron release could stimulate cation uptake according to model (4) or reduce anion uptake.

Table 2. Effect of some oxidizing-reducing agents on K and Br uptake by intact bush beans.

Treatment	K^{42} uptake	Br^{82} uptake	K^{42}/Br^{82}
$\underline{M}$	μmoles/g. dry weight		ratio
Control	29.3	4.5	6
10^{-4} H_2O_2	25.1	3.0	8
10^{-3} H_2O_2	26.4	0.5	53
10^{-2} H_2O_2	29.3	0.2	146
10^{-4} $KMnO_4$	35.0	1.3	27
10^{-4} $Na_2S_2O_4$	26.3	2.7	10
10^{-3} $Na_2S_2O_4$	16.0	1.2	13

Table 3. Effect of 1.5 volt storage batteries attached to bean plants on K^{42} and Br^{82} uptake.

Terminal in					
Plant	Solution	Leaf	Stem	Root	Whole Plant
		μmoles/g. dry weight			
			K^{42}		
+	−	0.14	1.5	86	10.0
−	+	0.03	1.7	72	9.4
Control		0.00	0.7	116	16.0
			Br^{82}		
+	−	0.48	0.4	1.10	0.54
−	+	0.02	0.1	0.76	0.14
Control		0.14	0.7	1.03	0.38

Table 4. Effect on uptake of K^{42} and Br^{82} of exposing intact bush bean plants to dark during exposure to K^{42} and Br^{82}.

Isotope	Solution	Light	Dark	Change for exposure in dark
		μmoles/g. dry weight		%
K^{42}	KCl, pH 6	27	34	+26
K^{42}	$KHCO_3$	35	42	+20
Br^{82}	KBr, pH 6	5.3	5.9	+12

Summary

Some models were constructed to suggest how electron flow may relate to cation and anion uptake. In presence of $Fe(CN)_6^=$, K uptake was inhibited more than that of Br. H_2O_2 had an opposite effect. Placing plants in dark resulted in increased uptake of K but not of Br. Possible explanations of these effects could be according to the models. Effects of attaching batteries to plants could not be explained by the models.

UPTAKE OF Ca^{47} BY BUSH BEAN PLANTS

With N. Hemaidan, C. Carmack, R. T. Mueller and G. A. Wallace

Calcium has been reported to be metabolically accumulated by some animal tissues (Vasington and Murphy, 1962) but passively taken up by some plant tissues (Moore et al., 1961) or metabolically by others (Winter, 1961). Since there is confusion concerning the mechanisms of Ca uptake by plants, various of the tests which were used for some of the ions in preceding reports of this series were used for Ca. It was hoped to characterize some aspects of Ca uptake by plants.

Ca^{47} was used in the present studies. The reason was that it is a gamma emitter and can easily be counted with the scintillation-well counter. One problem related to its use is that Sc^{47} is a daughter product and this has a gamma ray also. We concluded that this ray was too weak to cause much error in the results but it is apparent that there is some discrepancy with the present results and results obtained previously with Ca^{45}. It is apparent that Ca^{47} labeled Ca poorly and the present results indicate responses more to Ca^{47} than to Ca^{40}. The results reported are for Ca^{47} with no calculations for carrier Ca.

A recalculation of some previous data with Ca^{45} is given in table 1. The Q_{10} of those data averaged about 1 as found by Smith and Wallace (1956b). The concentration ratio (as previously defined for 10-fold increase in external concentration) was around 5. For the new data it was around 10, this being an example of the discrepancy between Ca^{47} and Ca^{40}. The Ca in table 1 appeared to be accumulated in the roots against a concentration gradient.

An experiment was conducted to find the effect of pH on calcium uptake. Bush beans were first germinated in sand. When the plants were 8 days old, they were transferred to 1/4-strength nutrient solution minus micronutrients and iron. Culture tubes (100 ml.) were used to contain the plants. Each tube contained 2 plants and the solutions were aerated. The temperature of the nutrient solutions was held at 25°C by means of a temperature bath. When the bush beans were 11 days old, the experiment was conducted.

$CaCl_2$ (10^{-3}M and 10^{-4}M) was used at pH levels of 3.5, 5.0, 6.5, 8.0, and 9.5. The calcium was tagged with 970 cpm. Ca^{47}/μmole Ca. The experiment lasted 2 hours and received a post treatment of 10^{-2}M $CaCl_2$ for 1 hour. The pH was checked twice during the experiment. The uptake of Ca^{47} appeared to be pH independent in contrast to K. The ratio for uptake for a 10-fold difference in concentration varied from 6 to 10 and averaged 8.6 (table 2).

Since so little Ca^{47} was translocated to leaves particularly at low concentrations, an uptake study was made with excised whole roots so that there would be no complications from differential transpiration. The plants were pregrown for 13 days in a 1/10-strength nutrient solution, then exposed for 5 hours at 25°C to different concentrations of $CaCl_2$ with constant specific activities of

Ca^{47} as in previous experiments and with a post treatment of $10^{-1}\underline{M}$ CaCl$_2$ for 1 hour. The results in table 3 indicate a concentration ratio of around 10 between 10^{-4} and $10^{-1}\underline{M}$ but understandably not between $10^{-1}\underline{M}$ and $1\underline{M}$.

Table 1.   Ca absorption (less free space) by bush beans in a 5 hour experiment with nutrient solutions.

CaCl$_2$	Leaf	Stem	Root	Whole Plant
$\underline{M}$		μmoles/g. dry weight		
		3°C		
10^{-2}	2.51	6.98	175.1	25.0
10^{-3}	0.16	0.61	38.8	5.0
10^{-4}	0.04	0.16	14.2	1.6
		33°C		
10^{-2}	2.25	6.79	304.2	38.7
10^{-3}	0.23	1.79	54.3	7.1
10^{-4}	0.04	0.44	15.5	1.9
		Concentration ratios		
		3°C		
$10^{-2}/10^{-3}$	15.6	11.4	4.5	4.9
$10^{-3}/10^{-4}$	4.0	3.8	2.7	3.0
		33°C		
$10^{-2}/10^{-3}$	9.8	3.8	5.6	5.4
$10^{-3}/10^{-4}$	5.8	4.1	3.5	3.6
		Q$_{10}$		
10^{-2}	0.96	0.99	1.20	1.15
10^{-3}	1.12	1.43	1.15	1.12
10^{-4}	1.00	1.40	1.03	1.05
	Concentration gradients, % of external solution			
		3°C		
10^{-2}			207	
10^{-3}			458	
10^{-4}			1680	
		33°C		
10^{-2}			359	
10^{-3}			642	
10^{-4}			1840	

The pH of the test solution was 7 and the roots received a post treatment of $10^{-2}\underline{M}$ CaCl$_2$ for 1 hour. Pretreatment was 1/4-strength solution for 7 days and solutions were aerated.

In table 4 are data for effects of some metabolic inhibitors on Ca^{47} uptake and distribution. The plants were handled as in the previous studies for intact plants. A respiratory inhibitor (KCN), a glycolitic inhibitor (arsenate), and an inhibitor of oxidative phosphorylation (2,4-DNP) all failed to inhibit Ca^{47} uptake but they all 3 markedly reduced translocation of Ca^{47} from roots to leaves. This effect was more pronounced after 48 hours than after 4 hours. In a similar type of study aeration with N_2 resulted in a slight inhibition only in Ca uptake (16%) but this type of treatment inhibits transpiration also and the slight inhibition may be the result of that factor. There was a 60% inhibition, however, for Ca^{47} movement into the stem as the result of bubbling N_2 into the nutrient solution.

Table 2. Ca^{47} uptake by bean plants at different pH.

pH	Leaf	Stem	Root	Whole Plant	Concentration ratios
			cpm./g. dry weight		
			$10^{-3}\underline{M}$ CaCl$_2$		
3.5	766	1,240	118,000	13,600	
5.0	299	3,490	36,400	7,340	
6.5	137	1,610	37,000	6,620	
8.0	148	2,900	39,200	7,100	
9.5	263	3,220	78,700	13,100	
			$10^{-4}\underline{M}$ CaCl$_2$		$10^{-3}/10^{-4}$
3.5	138	288	12,200	1,540	8.83
5.0	20	224	12,200	737	9.95
6.5	16	207	4,160	726	9.12
8.0	38	562	4,680	1,140	6.23
9.5	28	180	9,920	1,550	8.45

Each value is the mean of 4.

To further indicate that there was a major difference in mode of uptake of Ca and K, that of Ca^{47} was increased 21% when the test plants were kept in the dark for 2 days before the test while uptake of K^{42} was simultaneously decreased by 25%.

Table 3.   Effect of concentration of CaCl$_2$ on Ca^{47} uptake by excised whole roots (Ca^{47} was present at constant specific activity).

CaCl$_2$	Ca^{47} uptake
$\underline{M}$	cpm./g. dry weight
10^{-4}	160
10^{-3}	1,650
10^{-2}	15,380
10^{-1}	150,000
10^{0}	204,600

Barber and Koontz (1963) found that 2,4-DNP had little effect on calcium accumulation by roots but greatly decreased Ca movement into the shoot of barley seedlings when the studies were of short time duration. After 12 hours the 2,4-DNP resulted in large increases in Ca transferred to the shoot and this was dependent upon transpiration. This was evidence for a metabolic barrier to movement of Ca to the shoot which with time was destroyed by 2, 4-DNP so that Ca was free to move passively.

Table 4.   Uptake of Ca^{47} from 10^{-3}M CaCl$_2$ by bush bean plants as influenced by some metabolic inhibitors.

Treatment	Leaf	Stem	Root	Whole Plant
	per cent of inhibition (-) or stimulation (+)			
	uptake for 4 hours			
10^{-3}M KCN	-54	-16	-28	-24
10^{-3}M NaAsO$_4$	-66	-48	+115	+78
10^{-4}M 2,4-DNP	-93	-51	+33	+22
	uptake for 48 hours			
10^{-3}M KCN	-95	-33	+63	+30
10^{-4}M NaAsO$_4$	-98	-48	+98	+49
10^{-4}M 2,4-DNP	-98	-58	+15	-9

The pH of all solutions was 7.0. Each value is the mean of 4. Controls received K$^+$ or Na$^+$ wherever appropriate.

The uptake of Ca^{47} from 10^{-3}M CaCl$_2$ (2,000 cpm./μmole) was studied at time intervals from 0 - 180 minutes. Two washing procedures were used in the post treatment of 1 hour. The results were plotted in figure 1 for roots. Root data were used only because it was apparent that very little Ca^{47} had been translocated from roots. The roots apparently reached a saturation stage at 1 hour. The difference between water wash and HCl was constant and apparently represented exchangeable Ca^{47} on the roots.

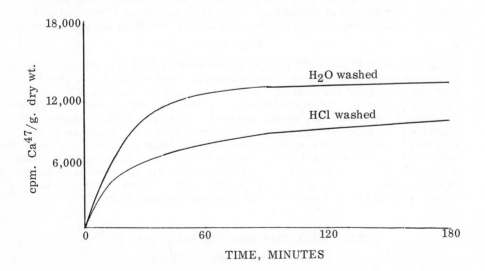

Figure 1.   Uptake of Ca^{47} by bean roots at different time intervals with different washing procedures.

LeCann and Heller (1961) reported that chelation of Ca did not inhibit its absorption by plant roots. In a 5-hour study conducted similar to other studies EDTA curtailed considerably the uptake of the Ca^{47} (table 5). The chelated Ca^{47} was not available and the EDTA might even have had other effects on the uptake. In an additional study it was learned that a post treatment with $10^{-4}M$ EDTA for 1 hour relative to a 1 hour post treatment with $10^{-1}M$ $CaCl_2$ after removal of excised roots from treatment solutions decreased $\overline{Ca}^{47}$ content of roots by 66%, 55%, 50%, and 28% respectively for 10^{-1}, 10^{-2}, 10^{-3}, and 10^{-4} M $CaCl_2$ test solutions. This would indicate that EDTA could remove Ca^{47} from roots that was not exchangeable and not in the apparent free space. EDTA in the external solution evidently removed Ca^{47} either from within the cytoplasmic compartment or from cell walls.

Table 5. Effect of EDTA on uptake of Ca^{47} from $10^{-3}M$ $CaCl_2$

	EDTA level, M		
	10^{-4}	10^{-3}	10^{-2}
	per cent inhibition		
Leaf	50	65	73
Stem	33	85	99
Root	98	99	99
Whole Plant	96	98	99

Control had $2 \times 10^{-3}M$ NaCl.
One hour $10^{-2}M$ $CaCl_2$ post treatment.

The technique of $10^{-2}M$ EDTA in the post treatment to remove this type of removable Ca^{47} was used to determine if 2,4-DNP during Ca^{47} uptake had any effect on Ca^{47} remaining in roots (after the EDTA post treatment). The reason was to determine if there was a component of Ca^{47} taken up by the root that had been subject to metabolism. The Ca^{47} remaining in the root after EDTA treatment was the same with and without 2,4-DNP in the test solutions.

Summary

The use of Ca^{47} and Ca^{45} to label Ca resulted in the following observations: Ca uptake was neither pH nor temperature dependent as was K. A 10-fold increase in external concentration of Ca resulted in an increase of 5 - 10 times in Ca uptake. Metabolic inhibitors or aeration with N_2 did not decrease Ca uptake by roots but they greatly decreased transfer of Ca to shoots. Ca appeared to be absorbed against a concentration gradient. Chelation of Ca with EDTA greatly decreased its uptake by bean plants and EDTA in post treatment solutions removed more Ca than supposedly was exchangeable or in the water-free space. The inhibitor, 2,4-DNP, had little influence on Ca uptake with or without post treatments of $10^{-2}M$ EDTA. Most of these results should be considered as valid for Ca^{47} and not necessarily for Ca^{40}.

NITRATE AND CHLORIDE INHIBITION OF $HC^{14}O_3^-$

UPTAKE BY BEAN ROOTS

Huffaker et al. (1960) showed that C^{14} from $HC^{14}O_3^-$ was absorbed by plant roots as HCO_3^- rather than as CO_2. The anions, chloride and nitrate, perhaps can be expected to compete with HCO$_3^-$ for uptake by plant roots even though the mechanism of phosphoenolpyruvate (PEP) carboxylase by which HCO$_3^-$ is assimilated does not use chloride or nitrate as substrates. Nitrate has been shown to inhibit considerably the PEP carboxylase reaction while chloride does not (Biely et al., 1961). For this reason it was wondered if nitrate would inhibit the uptake of HCO$_3^-$ more than does chloride. If such an inhibition pattern occurs it may indicate either that the HCO$_3^-$ uptake is limited if not mediated by PEP carboxylase or that HCO$_3^-$ is subject to both influx and efflux in cells with its assimilation being the rate-limiting step to HCO$_3^-$ retention.

Excised whole roots of bush bean plants were exposed for 4 hours to 100 ml. of a 10^{-3}M KHC^{14}O$_3$ solution with 10^{-5}M CaCl$_2$. KNO$_3$ and KCl each were superimposed on these solutions at 0, 10^{-3}, 10^{-2}, and 10^{-1}M. The solutions were aerated and at the conclusion of the test period the solutions were replaced with 10^{-2}M CaCl$_2$ for 1 hour to remove C^{14} from the free space. The samples were prepared and assayed for C^{14} as in studies described on page 41.

The results in table 1 indicate that nitrate inhibited HC^{14}O$_3^-$ uptake more than did chloride. Since nitrate might have been absorbed faster than chloride, the results obtained could be due to competition of nitrate with HCO$_3^-$ for uptake. The possibility exists, however, that nitrate may inhibit HCO$_3^-$ uptake through an inhibition of the PEP carboxylase reaction.

Table 1. Per cent inhibition by nitrate and chloride of HC^{14}O$_3^-$ uptake from 10^{-3}M KHCO$_3$ by excised whole bush bean roots.

KNO$_3$ or KCl	Per cent inhibition	
M	By KNO$_3$	By KCl
10^{-3}	36	16
10^{-2}	56	23
10^{-1}	63	35

ETHYLENEDIAMINE DI(o-HYDROXYPHENYL ACETATE) INFLUENCE
ON Fe UPTAKE AND TRANSLOCATION IN BUSH BEANS
With C. Carmack and G. A. Wallace

A large amount of information is available on the influence of chelating agents on the availability of iron in soils and of their effects on iron uptake and distribution in plants. The subject was recently reviewed in some detail (Wallace, 1962). Some aspects of the subject, however, remain unanswered and additional studies are being made in this laboratory concerning some of these problems.

It is now generally accepted that synthetic chelating agents are, to a slight extent at least, absorbed by plant roots and translocated to leaves of plants. Even though Fe and chelating agents generally may not be absorbed in equivalent amounts, chelating agents do facilitate translocation of Fe from roots to leaves in at least some plant species.

An excess of chelating agents tends to compete with plant roots for iron depending on plant species or variety and on stability constants of the respective iron chelates. Some unanswered questions relate to the nature of plant species differences. Previous findings indicated that the relative absorption of Fe vs.

the chelating agent appeared to be very pH dependent. Much more Fe was absorbed from FeEDDHA (ethylenediamine di(o-hydroxyphenyl acetate)) at pH 4 than at pH 8 and the ratio of Fe absorbed to EDDHA absorbed was much more narrow at pH 8 than at pH 4. A major difference in the present studies was washing of roots with EDDHA to remove Fe adhering to the outside of them (Jeffreys, 1962).

The uptake of iron at pH 4 and at pH 6 by bush bean plants was measured at low and at high temperatures to test the possibility of a relationship with metabolism. One experiment was made in which the post treatment was 10^{-2}M $CaCl_2$ for 1 hour but this was repeated with a different set of plants with 10^{-2} M K_2EDDHA for 22 hours as the post treatment.

In both experiments, bean plants, about 2 weeks old and having received dilute pretreatment nutrient solution for several days, were subjected for 5 hours to the treatments briefly outlined in table 1. The specific activity of Fe was 3150 cpm./μmole.

Table 1.   Effect of pH and temperature on uptake of Fe by bush beans
from FeEDDHA.

Temperature	Leaves	Stems	Roots	Whole Plants
	μmoles Fe/g. dry weight			
	Post treatment of 10^{-2}M $CaCl_2$			
	pH 4			
3°C	0.07	0.20	88.4	11.3
23°C	1.31	0.92	100.9	12.9
Q_{10}	4.3	2.2	1.1	1.1
	pH 6			
3°C	0.07	0.12	26.8	4.3
23°C	0.79	0.53	71.7	9.3
Q_{10}	3.4	2.1	1.6	1.5
	Post treatment of 10^{-2}M EDDHA			
	pH4			
3°C	0.02	0.03	13.1	2.0
23°C	0.08	0.03	31.4	4.7
Q_{10}	2.0	1.0	1.5	1.5
	pH 6			
3°C	0.05	0.02	9.1	1.4
23°C	0.13	0.10	37.5	5.3
Q_{10}	1.6	2.2	2.0	1.9

Each value is the mean of 4.

The results for both experiments are in table 1. It appeared that the 10^{-2}M EDDHA was able to remove much Fe from roots that either had not been accumulated or that had been passively moved into roots. If this argument is correct then this removable component is the main portion of increased Fe uptake at low pH. In all cases in table 1 the transfer of Fe to leaves appeared to be temperature dependent.   Branton and Jacobson (1962a) reported that Fe transfer from roots to shoots was dependent upon metabolic energy.   The necessity for using an agent like EDDHA to wash roots in Fe uptake studies as mentioned was discussed recently by Jeffreys (1962).   Branton and Jacobson (1962b) similarly showed with microautoradiographs that roots become coated with iron particles when placed in Fe solutions.

Another experiment was made of the effect of washing procedures on both Fe and EDDHA uptake and this is described in table 2.   The plants which had been pregrown for 3 days in 1/4-strength nutrient solution were exposed for 6 hours either to 10^{-3}M Fe^{59}EDDHA (1550 cpm./ml.) or to 10^{-3}M FeC^{14}EDDHA (500 cpm./ml.) each in 2 x 10^{-3}M CaCl$_2$.   The pH was maintained between 5. 0 and 5. 5.   At the end of the 6 hours, the plants were rinsed for 2. 5 minutes in distilled water then subjected to the aerated post treatments outlined in table 2.   The controls were not subjected to additional post treatments.   The results indicate the importance of a post treatment with the chelating agent to remove from roots the Fe that had not been accumulated.   With this technique Fe^{59} and C^{14} remained in the plants in close to equal amounts.   With C^{14}EDDHA the washing treatment seemed to have little effect.   Any EDDHA that could be washed from the free space seemed to be removed with the $2\frac{1}{2}$ -minute water wash.

Table 2.   Fe and EDDHA uptake less free-space components by bush
            bean plants measured after different post treatment wash-
            ing procedures.

Method of washing	Leaves	Stems	Roots	Whole Plant
		μmoles/g. dry weight		
		Fe from 10^{-3}M Fe^{59}EDDHA		
Control*	0. 38	0. 52	49. 19	9. 62
1 hr. 10^{-2}M CaCl$_2$	0. 45	0. 34	51. 69	8. 51
1 hr. Distilled H$_2$O	0. 19	0. 40	49. 42	9. 28
1 hr. 10^{-2}M EDDHA	0. 54	0. 12	25. 43	4. 80
24 hrs. Distilled H$_2$O	2. 03	0. 71	50. 26	9. 47
24 hrs. 10^{-2}M EDDHA	0. 42	0. 21	13. 51	2. 73
		C^{14} from 10^{-3}M FeC^{14}EDDHA		
Control*	1. 67	0. 70	9. 44	2. 82
1 hr. 10^{-2}M CaCl$_2$	1. 24	0. 59	10. 94	2. 62
1 hr. Distilled H$_2$O	1. 00	0. 64	10. 78	2. 53
1 hr. 10^{-2}M EDDHA	1. 33	0. 62	16. 66	3. 52
24 hrs. Distilled H$_2$O	1. 42	0. 66	12. 44	3. 06
24 hrs. 10^{-2}M EDDHA	1. 28	0. 68	13. 18	3. 54

*Control = $2\frac{1}{2}$ minutes running water after the 6-hour treatment.

An experiment was conducted to find the effect of EDDHA on the distribution of previously absorbed iron in bush beans.   The bush beans were first germinated in sand for 7 days.   After the bush beans were germinated they were transferred to 100 ml. culture tubes.   These culture tubes contained 1/4-strength nutrient solution minus micronutrients and iron.   Each culture tube contained 2 plants and was aerated.   The temperature of the nutrient solutions was maintained at 25°C by a water bath.   When the plants were 10 days old, they were put into 1/4-strength nutrient solution minus micronutrients and containing

$10^{-4}\underline{M}$ $Fe^{59}EDDHA$. The iron was labeled with 100,000 cpm. of Fe^{59} per 100 ml. of solution. When the plants were 12 days old, they were placed in 1/4-strength nutrient solution minus micronutrients and iron. A control was counted when this last solution was added. After 24 hours the plants were transferred back to 1/4-nutrient solution minus micronutrients and iron. These solutions also contained 0, $10^{-4}\underline{M}$, $10^{-3}\underline{M}$, and $10^{-2}\underline{M}$ EDDHA. Another control was counted when the solutions were changed this time. After 24 additional hours, the experiment was ended. All bush beans were given a 5-minute water wash before counting. The results of this experiment in table 3 indicate that some Fe* associated with the roots could be transferred to shoots during the post treatments under the influence of low levels of EDDHA (10^{-4} and $10^{-3}\underline{M}$). With a very high level of EDDHA in the post treatment, the Fe* content of leaves was similar to that of the control. It would appear that Fe that could not be washed from roots by water but could be washed from them by EDDHA was still available for transfer to shoots if not washed off.

Table 3.   Effect of EDDHA post treatments on distribution of Fe^{59} previously absorbed by bush beans.

Post treatments	Leaves	Stems	Roots	Whole Plants
	μmoles/g. dry weight			
1st Control	0.177	0.0784	6.84	1.48
2nd Control	0.214	0.0787	5.98	1.31
0 EDDHA	0.359	0.126	4.97	1.29
$10^{-4}\underline{M}$ EDDHA	1.10	0.194	1.88	0.93
$10^{-3}\underline{M}$ EDDHA	0.431	0.122	1.27	0.51
$10^{-2}\underline{M}$ EDDHA	0.164	0.062	0.97	0.32

Means of 4 plants.

Since the use of EDDHA proved to be a good technique for removing non-absorbed Fe from roots, an experiment was conducted to further evaluate the effect of pH on Fe uptake. The iron chlorosis susceptible PI 54619-5-1 soybean and iron chlorosis resistant Hawkeye soybean were used. The plants had been pregrown in the usual dilute nutrient solutions and then they were subjected to $10^{-4}\underline{M}$ $Fe^{59}EDDHA$ (12,000 cpm./μmole) in $10^{-3}\underline{M}$ $CaCl_2$ for 5 hours at pH 4.0, 5.5, 7.0, or 8.5. They all then received a post treatment for 1 hour of $10^{-2}\underline{M}$ K_2EDDHA. They were then divided into plant parts and counted for Fe^{59} as usual. The results (table 4) indicate that the Fe^{59} contents of the roots of PI 54619-5-1 actually increased with pH in contrast to findings without the EDDHA post treatment. The same increase with pH also obtained for the Hawkeye soybeans but it was less pronounced. The Fe^{59} content in leaves with both varieties tended to decrease with pH, the values for PI 54619-5-1 being much smaller than for Hawkeye. These results indicate that the susceptibility of PI 54619-5-1 soybean to iron chlorosis is due to failure of transport from roots to shoots and that this transport is depressed by high pH of the external rooting medium.

Since the previous experiment indicated that transfer of Fe from root to shoot may be a problem with the PI 54619-5-1 soybean, Fe^{59} uptake was measured by both soybean varieties in the presence of some metabolic inhibitors (table 5) (see page 30 for a description of classes of inhibitors). The general techniques were similar to the previous experiment and a post treatment for 1 hour with 10^{-2}M K$_2$EDDHA was used.   The results were very complex. Zn depressed the uptake of Fe by the roots of both species at both pH 4 and pH 7.   It drastically depressed Fe^{59} transfer to leaves in the Hawkeye soybean at pH 4.   This may be similar to the data of Lingle et al. (1963).   At pH 7 and at both pH values with PI 54619-5-1, Zn had less effect but the transfer to shoots in these cases was low without the Zn.   Fe^{59} uptake by roots might have been reduced by KCN and azide in the PI 54619-5-1 soybeans at pH 4 but not at pH 7 or in Hawkeye.   Azide, but not KCN, decreased transport of Fe^{59} to shoots of the Hawkeye soybean.   There was little evidence that indicated a different type of metabolically controlled iron transport mechanism in the 2 soybean varieties. The mild amount of inhibition obtained for some of the metabolic inhibitors was somewhat similar to that observed earlier (Jeffreys et al., 1961).   These do not strongly indicate the involvement of metabolism in Fe uptake form FeEDDHA at least by roots.   Similar results were obtained with the same inhibitors for Fe^{59} uptake from Fe^{59}EDDHA by bush beans.

Table 4.   Effect of pH on Fe uptake and distribution in PI 54619-5-1 and Hawkeye soybeans when roots received post treatments of 10^{-2}M K$_2$EDDHA to remove adsorbed Fe.

pH (maintained)	Leaves	Stems	Roots	Whole Plants
		μmoles/g. dry weight		
		PI 54619-5-1 soybean		
4.0	0.08	0.02	1.04	0.27
5.5	0.05	0.04	1.38	0.31
7.0	0.01	0.00	2.24	0.46
8.5	0.00	0.01	2.18	0.47
		Hawkeye soybean		
4.0	0.46	0.32	1.39	0.72
5.5	0.52	0.19	1.54	0.71
7.0	0.14	0.07	2.54	0.77
8.5	0.13	0.18	2.40	0.80

Means of 4.   The pH of the post treatment solutions was constant and about 7.

An experiment was made to determine, if possible, whether or not the inhibiting effect of chelating agents on Fe uptake by plants was due to Fe chelation or to Ca chelation.   Wallace and Mueller (1962) indicated that Ca may stimulate uptake of Fe from EDDHA.   Since excesses of chelating agents were present in the test solutions, a post treatment of 10^{-2}M CaCl$_2$ was used.   The results in table 6 further demonstrate that chelating agents either remove Fe from roots or prevent its uptake.   If Fe is taken up as the free ion then the effects of the chelating agents are obviously due to lowering the level of free Fe.   If Fe is taken up as FeEDDHA then the chelating agent has other effects such as Ca chelation.   With an abundance of available Ca, 10^{-4}M EDDHA greatly suppressed Fe uptake by roots although this may be merely the prevention of Fe adhering to the outside of the root.   In an experiment where Fe^{59} uptake was measured at different levels of Ca and in which the post treatment was 10^{-2}M K$_2$EDDHA to remove non-absorbed Fe^{59} from roots, Ca appeared to actually increase the Fe^{59} absorbed by the roots (table 7).   At least the

Table 5.   Effect of metabolic inhibitors on Fe uptake and distribution by two different soybean varieties.

Treatments	PI 54619-5-1				Hawkeye			
	Leaf	Stem	Root	Whole Plant	Leaf	Stem	Root	Whole Plant
	μmoles/g. dry weight							
	pH 4							
Control	0.08	0.02	1.05	0.26	0.27	0.10	1.37	0.52
CCP	0.11	0.01	1.09	0.28	0.16	0.08	1.96	0.64
2,4-DNP	0.25	0.02	1.89	0.47	0.24	0.12	1.91	0.59
KCN	0.05	0.02	0.75	0.17	0.28	0.11	1.04	0.45
Azide	0.07	0.02	0.75	0.17	0.05	0.05	1.35	0.41
Zn	0.03	0.01	0.81	0.15	0.03	0.03	1.06	0.30
pCMB	0.17	0.02	1.12	0.28	0.33	0.04	2.25	0.69
Fluoroacetate	0.05	0.03	1.05	0.24	0.10	0.05	2.40	0.48
	pH 7							
Control	0.03	0.04	1.99	0.43	0.05	0.15	2.41	0.68
CCP	0.03	0.01	1.88	0.38	0.04	0.05	1.71	0.47
2,4-DNP	0.04	0.02	1.26	0.26	0.03	0.04	1.12	0.30
KCN	0.01	0.02	2.20	0.47	0.03	0.05	2.35	0.69
Azide	0.03	0.01	1.55	0.34	0.01	0.02	1.90	0.52
Zn	0.04	0.02	0.79	0.18	0.03	0.02	0.83	0.22
pCMB	0.01	0.01	1.46	0.28	0.01	0.01	1.72	0.47
Fluoroacetate	0.01	0.02	0.94	0.20	0.04	0.06	1.86	0.58

Table 6.   Effect of levels of chelating agents less than and equal to the Ca level on the uptake of Fe by bush bean plants.

Treatment* (extra levels of chelating agent)	Leaves	Stems	Roots	Whole Plants **
	μmoles Fe/g. dry weight			
	pH 4.0			
Control	0.005	0.012	3.72	0.701
10^{-4}M EDDHA	0.011	0.003	0.56	0.090
10^{-4}M EDTA	0.008	0.000	0.20	0.036
10^{-3}M EDTA	0.018	0.001	0.12	0.022
10^{-2}M EDTA	0.010	0.004	0.05	0.010
	pH 8.0			
Control	0.007	0.006	3.29	0.442
10^{-4}M EDDHA	0.010	0.004	0.38	0.065
10^{-4}M EDTA	0.008	0.012	2.85	0.425
10^{-3}M EDTA	0.002	0.009	1.84	0.284
10^{-2}M EDTA	0.004	0.002	0.12	0.017

*All treatments received 10^{-4}M Fe^{59}EDDHA and 5 x 10^{-3}N Ca(NO$_3$)$_2$.
**Since roots were not further washed with EDDHA, the Fe in roots of control plants would include that adhering to root surfaces.

EDDHA wash did not remove the extra Fe^{59} associated with roots due to the presence of Ca.

Table 7. Effect of $CaCl_2$ on Fe uptake from $10^{-4}M$ Fe^{59}EDDHA when roots received a post treatment of $10^{-2}\underline{M}$ K_2EDDHA to remove non-absorbed Fe^{59}.

Treatment	Leaves	Stems	Roots	Whole Plants
		μmoles Fe/g. dry weight		
Control	0.015	0.01	0.44	0.10
$10^{-3}M$ $CaCl_2$	0.005	0.01	1.05	0.22
$10^{-2}\underline{M}$ $CaCl_2$	0.010	0.01	1.23	0.26

Since the technique of washing roots with EDDHA to remove Fe not absorbed may be useful in clarifying some of the problems of Fe uptake, the conclusions of Brown and Jones (1962) were checked to verify that chlorotic Hawkeye soybeans took up more Fe than green Hawkeye or green or chlorotic PI 54619-5-1 soybeans. These were verified for roots at pH 4 and for leaves at pH 4 and pH 7 (table 8). Results for bush beans were slightly different (page 103).

Table 8. Effect of iron deficiency on Fe^{59} uptake from $10^{-4}\underline{M}$ FeEDDHA by 2 soybean varieties when roots received a post treatment of $10^{-2}\underline{M}$ EDDHA to remove Fe^{59} from root surfaces.

Variety and pH	Leaves	Stems	Roots	Whole Plant
		μmoles Fe/g. dry weight		
		Iron sufficient		
Hawkeye, pH 4	0.14	0.07	1.83	0.56
Hawkeye, pH 7	0.02	0.02	2.61	0.70
PI 54619-5-1, pH 4	0.20	0.09	1.64	0.52
PI 54619-5-1, pH 7	0.03	0.02	1.93	0.41
		Iron deficient		
Hawkeye, pH 4	0.35	0.30	2.70	1.03
Hawkeye, pH 7	0.10	0.12	2.38	0.73
PI 54619-5-1, pH 4	0.10	0.08	1.60	0.41
PI 54619-5-1, pH 7	0.02	0.03	1.76	0.47

Since Guinn and Joham (1962) have shown that metals such as Zn and Mn can displace Fe from FeEDTA, an experiment was made to determine the relative amounts of Fe, Mn, and Zn absorbed by plants when present together and with different combinations of chelating agents. Bush beans were used in this experiment. They were first germinated in sand. When the plants were 17 days old, they were transferred to 1/4-strength nutrient solution minus micronutrients and iron. The bush beans were grown in 100-ml. culture tubes. Each tube held 2 plants and the solution was aerated. The temperature of the culture tubes was kept constant at $25^{\circ}C$. When the bush beans were 20 days old, the experiment was conducted. Fe, Zn, and Mn ($10^{-4}M$) were used in all culture solutions. The treatments consisted of a control, $10^{-4}\underline{M}$ EDDHA, $10^{-4}M$ EDTA, $10^{-4}\underline{M}$ EDDHA + $10^{-4}\underline{M}$ EDTA, and $10^{-4}\underline{M}$ EDDHA + 2 x $10^{-4}\underline{M}$ EDTA. Each treatment had $10^{-3}M$ $CaCl_2$ in it. The treatments were done in triplicate and in each case a different metal was tagged with either Fe^{59}, Zn^{65}, or Mn^{54} at an activity of 100,000 cpm./100 ml. The experiment lasted 5 hours and all plants received a post treatment of $10^{-2}M$ $CaCl_2$ + $10^{-4}M$ EDDHA for 1 hour. The pH values were all between 7.0 and 7.5.

Table 9.   Simultaneous uptake of Fe, Zn, and Mn as influenced by chelating agents.

Metal Measured	Leaves	Stems	Roots	Whole Plants
	μmoles/g. dry weight			
(A) Control*				
Fe	0.113	0.576	17.6	2.92
Zn	0.120	0.421	6.51	1.34
Mn	0.152	0.900	3.61	0.966
(B) $10^{-4}M$ EDDHA				
Fe	0.0618	0.124	5.26	0.817
Zn	0.0913	0.202	4.52	0.442
Mn	0.0527	0.531	1.67	0.519
(C) $10^{-4}M$ EDTA				
Fe	0.247	0.540	32.4	5.88
Zn	0.0398	0.0532	2.03	0.310
Mn	0.147	0.797	4.05	0.993
(D) $10^{-4}M$ EDTA + EDTA				
Fe	0.115	0.225	4.04	0.724
Zn	0.0305	0.0713	0.798	0.149
Mn	0.237	1.05	2.51	0.917
(E) $2\times10^{-4}M$ EDTA + $10^{-4}M$ EDDHA				
Fe	0.060	0.0624	1.74	0.302
Zn	0.0184	0.0374	0.225	0.074
Mn	0.109	0.249	1.49	0.422

Means of 4 plants.

*The sources of salts for the control were — $FeSO_4$, $ZnSO_4$, and $MnSO_4$. Every solution contained $10^{-4}M$ of each.

The results are in table 9. In these solution cultures even if there were a tendency for Zn or Mn to displace Fe when it was chelated there was no indication of the Fe being less available to plants. This replacement of chelated Fe by Zn or Mn might have made Fe more available (treatment C). Had the plants been in soil the effect might have been different because Fe released from the chelating agent could be fixed in the soil. Chelated Fe especially with EDDHA had less tendency to become tied up on roots than non-chelated Fe. Chelation tended to decrease the uptake of Zn and Mn. In treatment (A) it would be expected that some Fe would precipitate in solution because of no chelation, that in (B) Fe mostly would be chelated, that in (C) mostly Zn would be chelated, that in (D) Fe and Zn mostly would be chelated, and that in (E) Fe, Zn, and Mn all would be mostly chelated. Most Mn was translocated to leaves in treatment

(D), most Zn in (A), and most Fe in (C). The least Fe in plants was in (B) and (E), least Zn in (E), and least Mn in (B). The tendency for chelating agents to decrease uptake and translocation was more pronounced than was metal competion with metals.

Summary

Several aspects of the uptake of Fe by bush bean plants were re-evaluated using the technique of a post treatment of EDDHA to remove Fe adhering to root surfaces. Transfer of Fe from roots to shoots appeared to be temperature dependent. After roots were washed with a high concentration of EDDHA following uptake of Fe^{59}, the amount of Fe remaining in the root appeared to be more temperature dependent at a high pH than at a low. $C^{14}EDDHA$ was not removed from roots in post treatments with EDDHA. Low levels of EDDHA in post treatments stimulated transfer to shoots of Fe previously taken up by or adsorbed on roots. The post treatment of $10^{-2}M$ EDDHA made it possible to show that the Fe uptake increased with pH in roots but decreased in leaves. Metabolic inhibitors sometimes decreased Fe uptake in roots but only mildly. Some decreased the transfer to shoots. Ca did not increase Fe transfer to shoots but did increase that absorbed by roots. When post treatments contained $10^{-2}M$ EDDHA green and chlorotic Hawkeye soybeans took up more iron than PI 54619-5-1 and translocated more of it to leaves. The PI 54619-5-1 soybean appeared to have a deficient Fe transport mechanism between root and leaves especially when grown in a medium with high pH. Chlorotic Hawkeye took up more Fe than green Hawkeye. Roots of both species contained more Fe^{59} at high pH than at low in contrast to previous reports where EDDHA post treatments were not used. Chelating agents decreased uptake by bush beans of Fe, Zn, and Mn from solution and removal of Fe from FeEDTA by Zn appeared to increase Fe translocation to the leaves. With the EDDHA post treatment it appeared that Fe^{59} and C^{14} from $Fe^{59}C^{14}EDDHA$ had been absorbed in close to equal quantities. Azide decreased Fe^{59} transfer to leaves in Hawkeye but not in PI 54619-5-1.

EFFECT OF SUBSTRATE CONCENTRATION ON ENZYMATIC
HCO_3^- FIXATION

Several of the studies of this series were made on the effect of concentration on the uptake of several different solutes by bush bean plants (see pages 19, 41, 62, and 142). With several solutes studied, the uptake appeared to be, under some conditions at least, proportional to the term, $c^{\ln 2}$, where c is the concentration of the solute in the external solution. If the uptake of a specific solute is reversible, i. e. , subject to both influx and efflux, then the effect of concentration would be subject to considerable variability. For this reason it was thought that an in vitro enzyme system with a homogenate may give more consistent results for the effect of substrate concentration on activity of enzyme than does solute uptake by roots because the substrate with the homogenate would not be free to move through membranes away from the site of fixation. Studies with two enzyme systems accordingly were made.

If the activity of an enzyme is plotted against substrate concentration, an exponential type of curve is obtained. When the activity is plotted, therefore, against a log function of the substrate concentration, a straight line is obtained. The line, however, will probably cease to be straight somewhere above the saturation point of the enzyme for one or more reasons. In the straight-line portion of the curve, comparisons between different concentrations should be a valid index of the effect of substrate concentration on enzyme activity.

The two systems used both involve fixation of carbon dioxide or HCO_3^-. The phosphoenolpyruvate (PEP) carboxylase system as partially purified by the method of Bandurski (1955) was used. The substrates for this enzyme are PEP and supposedly bicarbonate as suggested by Maruyama and Lane (1962). The carboxylation enzyme sequence involves a 3-enzyme system and uses ribose-5-phosphate (R5P), ATP, and carbon dioxide (not bicarbonate) as substrates (Weissbach et al., 1956). Sweet orange leaves were used in the present studies and the methods of preparation and assay have been reported in detail (Wallace, Mueller, and van Noort, 1962).

Results for two systems at different concentrations of the two substrates are summarized in figure 1 and in table 1. Sometimes the uptake of solutes by plant roots is directly proportional to the external concentration such as for urea (page 48). Such a curve in figure 1 indicates that none of the substrates for the enzyme systems gave that result. This may further imply that when a ratio of 10 is obtained for uptake of a solute when the external concentrations differ by 10-fold, the process must be passive rather than metabolic, i.e., nonenzymatic.

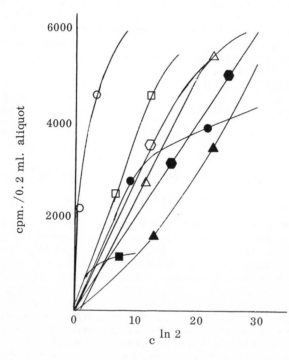

Figure 1. $C^{14}O_2$ fixation by different in vitro fixing systems with different substrates plotted against $c^{\ln 2}$ where c is substrate concentration. The first-named substrate identifies the system and the second identifies the substrate which was varied as follows: R5P-ATP, $\bigcirc$; R5P-R5P, $\square$; R5P-HCO_3^- uncorrected, $\triangle$; R5P-HCO_3^- corrected for CO_2 from the air, $\lozenge$; PEP-HCO_3^-, $\bullet$; PEP-PEP, $\blacksquare$; fixation directly proportional to concentration, $\blacktriangle$; a theoretically perfect C^{14}-fixation $-c^{\ln 2}$ relationship, $\hexagon$.

Table 1.   Ratios of $HC^{14}O_3^-$ fixation at different concentrations (c) of substrates for two different in vitro fixing systems in relationship to values expected if the function, $c^{\ln 2}$, holds as a measure of substrate concentration on activity*.

System, and the substrate that was varied	Ratios of $HC^{14}O_3^-$ fixation for 10-fold differences in substrate concentration			
	μmole concentrations			
	$^{.1}/_{.01}$	$^{1}/_{0.1}$	$^{2}/_{0.2}$	$^{5}/_{0.5}$
	(4.93 expected)			
R5P-R5P	—	5.21	2.39	—
-HCO$_3^-$	—	5.78	6.13	4.68
-ATP	4.82	3.43	3.10	—
PEP-PEP	3.70	1.43	1.64	—
-HCO$_3^-$	—	5.04	4.06	3.65

System	Ratios of $HC^{14}O_3^-$ fixation for 5-fold differences in substrate concentration			
	μmole concentrations			
	$^{.05}/_{.01}$	$^{.5}/_{.1}$	$^{1.0}/_{.2}$	$^{5}/_{1}$
	(3.05 expected)			
R5P-R5P	—	3.16	2.64	—
-HCO$_3^-$	—	3.16	3.65	2.54
-ATP	2.85	2.50	2.40	—
PEP-PEP	2.67	1.67	1.41	—
-HCO$_3^-$	—	3.33	3.32	1.83

System	Ratios of $HC^{14}O_3^-$ fixation for 2-fold differences in substrate concentration			
	μmole concentrations			
	$^{0.1}/_{.05}$	$^{0.2}/_{0.1}$	$^{1.0}/_{.5}$	$^{2.0}/_{1.0}$
	(1.62 expected)			
R5P-R5P	—	1.87	1.64	1.49
-HCO$_3^-$	—	1.59	1.83	1.66
-ATP	1.70	1.43	1.37	1.29
PEP-PEP	1.46	1.30	1.19	1.46
-HCO$_3^-$	—	1.72	1.72	1.22

*Zero substrate values for the $HC^{14}O_3^-$ fixation were subtracted from the actual values where appropriate when R5P was used with varying levels of HCO$_3^-$.
Corrections were made for CO_2 from the air where appropriate.

The expression, $c^{\ln 2}$, suggests that a 10-fold difference in substrate concentration should give a 4.93-fold difference in activity. A 5-fold difference in concentration should give a 3.05-fold difference in activity and a 2-fold difference should give a 1.62-fold difference. These values would be more likely to be obtained at the low substrate concentrations where the enzyme would not be saturated and in the straight line portion of the plots. The system with ratios most closely approaching the expected values was for the PEP system with the concentration of HCO_3^- varied (table 1). For the PEP system with PEP varied the values were close to the expected at the low concentrations.

With the R5P system, varying R5P and also ATP by a factor of 10 resulted in about a 5-fold increase in fixation at the more dilute concentrations (table 1). When HCO_3^- was varied the curve did not pass through the origin (figure 1) until the HCO_3^- levels supplied were corrected for CO_2 supplied from the air (see page 51). When this correction was made the ratios of fixation (table 1) were very close, particularly at the lower levels used, to the theoretical values necessary to correspond with $c^{\ln 2}$. This correction was not necessary for PEP when HCO_3^- was varied possibly because HCO_3^- rather than CO_2 is believed to be the substrate with PEP.

As mentioned, the factor $c^{\ln 2}$ suggests that doubling the substrate concentration should result in a 1.62-fold increase in enzyme activity. In table 1 are included comparisons of activity for the substrate ratios of 0.1/0.05, 0.2/0.1, 1.0/0.5, and 2.0/1.0 μmoles where appropriate. The values were all closer to 1.62 than to 2.0 with the possible exception of one value with the R5P system. A comparison of values when concentrations differed by 5 times is also given in table 1. The expected ratios of activity on the basis of $c^{\ln 2}$ is 3.05. At the lowest levels compared the values appeared to be reasonably close to this value. In general these data do suggest that the expression $c^{\ln 2}$ may be valid for all the systems and substrates.

The expression, $c^{\ln 2}$, in no way challenges anything in the Michaelis-Menton equation which is

$$\frac{1}{v} = \frac{Km}{V} \times \frac{1}{S} + \frac{1}{V}$$

where Km is the Michaelis-Menton constant, v is velocity, V is maximum velocity and S is the substrate concentration.

Summary

In vitro carbon dioxide and bicarbonate fixation with two different enzyme systems tended to vary with substrate concentration at low levels of substrate according to the expression $c^{\ln 2}$ where c is the concentration of the substrate. A saturation point was reached above which the relationship no longer held. This same relation often holds for ion uptake by plant roots. The plots of both ion uptake by plants and anzyme activity vs. $c^{\ln 2}$ indicate that when solute uptake is directly proportional to its external concentration, the uptake is passive.

REFERENCES

Arisz, W. H. 1953 Active uptake, vacuole secretion and plasmatic transport of chloride ions in leaves of Vallisneria spiralis. Acta bot. Neerl. 1:506-515.

Arisz, W. H. 1954 Transport of chloride in the "symplasm" of Vallisneria leaves. Nature 174:223-224.

Arisz, W. H. 1956 Significance of the symplasm theory for transport across the root. Protoplasma 46:5-62.

Arisz, W. H. , Helder, R. J. and van Nie, R. 1951 Analysis of the exudation process in tomato plants. J. Expt. Bot. 2:257-297.

Arnon, D. I. , Fratzke, W. E. and Johnson, C. M. 1942 Hydrogen ion concentration in relation to absorption of inorganic nutrients by higher plants. Plant Physiol. 17:515-524.

Atkins, W. R. G. 1916 Some Recent Researches in Plant Physiology. Whittaker & Co. , London.

Bandurski, R. S. 1955 Further studies on the enzymatic synthesis of oxalacetate from phosphorylenopyruvate and carbon dioxide. J. Biol. Chem. 217: 137-150.

Bandurski, R. S. and Greiner, Claire M. 1953 The enzymatic synthesis of oxalacetate from phosphoryl-enolpyruvate and carbon dioxide. J. Biol. Chem. 204:781-786.

Bange, G. G. J. 1959 Interactions in the potassium and sodium absorption by intact maize seedlings. Plant and Soil 11:17-29.

Bange, G. G. J. 1962 The carrier theory of ion transport. Acta bot. Neer. 11:139-146.

Bange, G. G. J. and van Vliet, E. 1961 Translocation of potassium and sodium in intact maize seedlings. Plant and Soil 15:312-328.

Barber, D. A. and Koontz, H. V. 1963 Uptake of dinitrophenol and its effect on transpiration and calcium accumulation in barley seedlings. Plant Physiol. 38:60-65.

Barbier, G. and Chabannes, J. 1951 Accumulation du sodium dans les racines des plants. Ann. Agron. Ser. A. 2:545-546.

Bear, F. E. 1950 Cation and anion relationships in plants and their bearing on crop quality. Agron. J. 42:176-178.

Bear, F. E. and Prince, A. L. 1945 Cation-equivalent constancy in alfalfa. J. Amer. Soc. Agron. 37:217-222.

Bedri, A. A. , Wallace, A. and Rhoads, W. A. 1960 Assimilation of bicarbonate by roots of different plant species. Soil Sci. 89:257-263.

Beeson, K. C. 1946 The effect of mineral supply on the mineral concentration and nutritional quality of plants. Bot. Rev. 12:424-455.

Bergquist, P. L. 1958 Evidence of separate mechanisms for sodium and potassium regulation in Hormosira banksii. Physiol. Plant. 11:760-770.

Bernstein, L. and Gardner, W. R. 1961 Perspective on function of free space in ion uptake by roots. Sci. 133:1482-1483.

Bernstein, L. and Nieman, R. H. 1960 Apparent free space of plant roots. Plant Physiol. 35:589-598.

Bhan, K. C. 1959 The effect of ammonium and nitrate nitrogen and bicarbonate on cation accumulation by plant roots. Ph. D. Dissertation, U. C. L. A., Los Angeles, California.

Bhan, K. C. , Huffaker, R. C. , Bedri, A. A. , Mueller, R. T. , Jeffreys, R. A. , Carmack, R. M. , Biely, M. I. and Wallace, A. 1960 Possible relationships of bicarbonate or CO_2 assimilation to cation accumulation by plant roots. Soil Sci. 89:276-284.

Bhide, S. V. and Brachet, J. 1960 Study of the uptake of ribonuclease by onion root-tip cells. Exptl. Cell Research 21:303-315.

Biddulph, O. 1959 Translocation of inorganic solutes. In: Plant Physiology,

II. Plants in relation to water and solutes. F. C. Steward, Editor, Academic Press, New York, pp. 553-603.

Biddulph, S. and Biddulph, O. 1959 The circulatory system of plants. Scientific American, February, 1959.

Bidwell, R. G. S. and Ghosh, N. R. 1962 Photosynthesis and metabolism in marine algae. IV. The fate of mannitol-C^{14} Fucus vesiculosus. Can. J. Bot. 40:803-807. cf. Chem. Absts. 57:8911b (1962).

Biely, M. I. , Wallace, A. and Mueller, R. T. 1961 Effects of salts on $C^{14}O_2$ fixation with ribose-5-phosphate and phosphoenolpyruvate as substrates in cell-free preparations from sweet orange leaves. Proc. Amer. Soc. Hort. Sci. 77:219-224.

Bollard, E. G. 1959 Urease, urea and ureides in plants. In: Symposia of the Society for Experimental Biology. No. XIII. Utilization of Nitrogen and Its Compounds by Plants. pp. 304-329.

Bollard, E. G. 1960 Transport in the xylem. Ann. Rev. Plant Physiol. 11: 141-166.

Bonner, W. and Bonner, J. 1948 The role of carbon dioxide in acid formation by succulent plants. Amer. J. Bot. 35:113-117.

Bosemark, N. O. 1954 The influence of nitrogen on root development. Physiol. Plant. 7:497-502.

Bould, C. 1962 Leaf analysis in relation to raspberry (Rubus idaeus) nutrition. XVIth International Horticultural Congress 1:439.

Boynton, D. , Margolis, D. and Gross, C. R. 1953 Exploratory studies on nitrogen metabolism by McIntosh apple leaves sprayed with urea. Proc. Amer. Soc. Hort. Sci. 62:135-146.

Branton, D. and Jacobson, L. 1962a Iron transport in pea plants. Plant Physiol. 37:539-545.

Branton, D. and Jacobson, L. 1962b Iron localization in pea plants. Plant Physiol. 37:546-551.

Breazeale, E. L. and McGeorge, W. T. 1953 Cation uptake by plants as affected by applied potential. Soil Sci. 75:443-448.

Breazeale, E. L. , McGeorge, W. T. and Breazeale, J. F. 1951 Nutrition of plants considered as an electrical phenomenon, a new approach. Soil Sci. 71:371-375.

Briggs, G. E. , Hope, A. B. and Robertson, R. N. 1961 Electrolytes and Plant Cells. W. O. James, Editor, Botanical Monographs, Blackwell Scientific Publications, Oxford, England.

Brouwer, R. 1953 Water absorption by the roots of Vicia Faba plants at various transpiration strengths. I. Analysis of the uptake and the factors determining it. Proc. Kon. Ak. Wet. C 56:105-115. II. Causal relations between suction tension, resistance and uptake. Proc. Kon. Ak. Wet. C 56: 129-136. III. Changes in water conductivity artificially obtained. Proc. Kon. Ak. Wet. C 57:68-80.

Brouwer, R. 1954 The regulating influence of transpiration and suction tension on the water and salt uptake by the roots of intact Vicia faba plants. Acta bot. Neer. 3:264-312.

Brown, J. C. 1956 Iron chlorosis. Ann. Rev. Plant Physiol. 7:171-190.

Brown, J. C. and Jones, W. E. 1962 Absorption of Fe, Mn, Zn, Ca, Rb, and phosphate ions by soybean roots that differ in their reductive capacity. Soil Sci. 94:173-179.

Brown, J. C. and Tiffin, L. O. 1960 Iron chlorosis in soybeans as related to the genotype of rootstock: 2. A relationship between susceptibility to chlorosis and capacity to absorb iron from iron chelate. Soil Sci. 89:8-15.

Broyer, T. C. 1950 Further observations on the absorption and translocation of inorganic solutes using radioactive isotopes with plants. Plant

Physiol. 25:367-376.

Broyer, T. C. 1951 Exudation studies on the water relations of plants. Amer. J. Bot. 38:157-162.

Burström, H. and Krogh, A. 1947 Bleeding and bud development in Carpinus. Svensk. Bot. Tidskr. 41:17-44. cf. Biol. Absts. 22:2169 (1948).

Cameron, S. H., Mueller, R. T., Wallace, A. and Sartori, E. 1952 Influence of age of leaf, season of growth, and fruit production on the inorganic composition of Valencia orange leaves. Proc. Amer. Soc. Hort. Sci. 60: 42-50.

Case, E. M. and McIlwain, H. 1951 Respiration and phosphorylation in preparations from mammalian brain. Biochem. J. 48:1-11.

Chaberek, S. and Martell, A. E. 1959 Organic Sequestering Agents. John Wiley & Sons, Inc., New York.

Chance B., Williams, G. R., Holmes, W. F. and Higgins, J. 1955 Respiratory enzymes in oxidative phosphorylation. V. A mechanism for oxidative phosphorylation. J. Biol. Chem. 217:439-451.

Chapman, H. D. 1939 Absorption of iron from finely ground magnetite by citrus seedlings. Soil Sci. 48:309-317.

Charley, J. L. and Jenny, H. 1961 Two-phase studies on availability of iron in calcareous soils. IV. Decomposition of iron oxide by roots and iron diffusion in roots. Agrochimica 5:99-107.

Chasson, R. and Levitt, J. 1956 Stimulation of calcium uptake by potato tuber in response to 2,4-dinitrophenol. Plant Physiol. 31 (Suppli.): vi.

Clark, H. E. 1936 Effect of ammonium and nitrate nitrogen on the composition of the tomato plant. Plant Physiol. 11:5-24.

Clark, R. B. and Wallace, A. 1961 C^{14}-biuret accumulation and translocation by bush beans. Proc. Amer. Soc. Hort. Sci. 77:393-400.

Collander, R. 1941 Selective absorption of cations by higher plants. Plant Physiol. 16:691-720.

Collander, R. 1954 The permeability of Nitella cells to non-electrolytes. Physiol. Plant. 7:420-445.

Collander, R. 1959 Cell Membranes: Their resistance to penetration and their capacity for transport. In: Plant Physiology, Vol. II, F. C. Steward, Editor, Academic Press, New York, pp. 3-102.

Collander, R. and Barlund, H. 1930 Permeability studies with Chara ceratophylla. II Permeability to nonelectrolytes. Acta Bot. Fenn. 11:1-114. cf. Chem. Absts. 27:4828 (1933).

Conway, E. J. 1951 The biological performance of osmotic work. A redox pump. Sci. 113:270-273.

Conway, E. J. 1953 A redox pump for the biological performance of osmotic work, and its relation to the kinetics of free ion diffusion across membranes. Int. Rev. Cytol. 2:419-445.

Cooper, W. C. and Peynado, A. 1954 The chemical composition of papaya plants grown in saline soils. Texas Avacado Society Yearbook, pp. 43-48.

Crafts, A. S. and Broyer, T. C. 1938 Migration of salts and water into xylem of the roots of higher plants. Amer. J. Bot. 25:529-535.

Crooke, W. M. and Knight, A. H. 1962 An evaluation of published data on the mineral composition of plants in the light of the cation-exchange capacities of their roots. Soil Sci. 93:365-373.

Csaky, T. Z. 1963 Biological transport mechanisms: Action of digitalis on cellular transport. (Physiol. Seminar, Jan. 18, 1963 at U.C.L.A.)

Dainty, J. 1962 Ion transport and electrical potentials in plant cells. Ann. Rev. Plant Physiol. 13:379-402.

Dalev, D., Danchev, D. and Lidzhi, L. 1957 The dynamics of accumulation of alginic acid, mannitol, and halogenides in the Black Sea seaweed, Cystoseira barbata. Izvest. Khim. Inst. Bulgar. Akad. Nauk 5:135-141.

cf. Chem. Absts. 55:16694e (1961).

Davies, R. E. and Keynes, R. D. 1960 A coupled sodium-potassium pump. In: Membrane Transport and Metabolism. A. Kleinzeller and A. Kotyk, Editors, Academic Press, New York, pp. 336-340.

De Turk, W. E. 1956 The adaptive formation of urease by washed suspensions of Pseudomonas aeruginosa. J. Bact. 70:187-191.

Dilley, O. R. and Walker, D. R. 1961 Assimilation of C^{14}, N^{15} labeled urea by excised apple and peach leaves. Plant Physiol. 36:757-761.

Drake, M., Vengris, J. and Colby, W. G. 1951 Cation-exchange capacity of plant roots. Soil Sci. 72:139-147.

Drosdoff, M., Barrows, H. L., Lagasse, F. S. and Shear, C. B. 1955 Interrelations of source of nitrogen with levels of nitrogen, calcium, and magnesium in tung nutrition. Proc. Amer. Soc. Hort. Sci. 65:32-40.

Dunham, C. W., Hamner, C. L. and Asen, S. 1956 Cation-exchange properties of the roots of some ornamental plant species. Proc. Amer. Soc. Hort. Sci. 68:556-563.

Eaton, F. M. 1943 The osmotic and vitalistic interpretations of exudation. Amer. J. Bot. 30:663-674.

Elgabaly, M. M. and Wiklander, L. 1949 Effects of exchange capacity of clay mineral and acidoid content of plant on uptake of sodium and calcium by excised barley and pea roots. Soil Sci. 67:419-424.

El Kholi, A. F. 1961 Influence of the trace elements on the uptake of macro elements (by plants). Verslag. Landbouwk. Onderzoek. 67:78. cf. Chem. Absts. 55:20287g (1961).

Emmert, F. H. 1960 Quantitative measurement of phosphorus-32 passage from the root milieu to the xylem. Plant Physiol. 35 (Suppli.): v.

Emmert, F. H. 1961a Volume determination of xylem conduits in stem and petioles of Phaseolus vulgaris using radiophosphorus. Physiol. Plant. 14: 470-477.

Emmert, F. H. 1961b Evidence of a barrier to lateral penetration of P-32 across roots of intact transpiring plants, based on measurements of xylem stream composition. Physiol. Plant. 14:478-487.

Emmert, F. H. 1962 Components of phosphorus buildup in stems of Phaseolus vulgaris with particular reference to the employment of xylem stream composition as a quantitative guide in root penetration studies. Physiol. Plant. 15:293-303.

Eppley, R. W. 1958 Sodium exclusion and potassium retention by the red marine alga, Porphyra perforata. J. Gen. Physiol. 41:901-911.

Epstein, E. 1956a Mineral nutrition of plants: Mechanisms of uptake and transport. Ann. Rev. Plant Physiol. 7:1-24.

Epstein, E. 1956b Passive passage and active transport of ions in plant roots. U. S. Atomic Energy Comm. TID-7512, 297-301. cf. Chem. Absts. 51:8211h (1957).

Epstein, E. 1956c Ion transport in plants. Sci. 124:937.

Epstein, E. 1960 Calcium-lithium competition in absorption by plant roots. Nature 185:705-706.

Epstein, E. 1961 The essential role of calcium in selective cation transport by plant cells. Plant Physiol 36:437-444.

Epstein, E., Rains, D. W. and Schmid, W. E. 1962 Course of cation absorption by plant tissue. Sci. 136:1051-1052.

Esterman, E. F. and McLaren, A. D. 1961 Contribution of rhizoplane organisms to the total capacity of plants to utilize organic nutrients. Plant and Soil 15:243-260.

Etherton, B. 1961 The use of microelectrode measurements of cellular potentials in the study of active transport in plants. Plant Physiol. 36 (Suppli.): xxxvi.

Etherton, B. ,and Higinbotham, N. 1960 Transmembrane potential measurements of cells of higher plants as related to salt uptake. Sci. 131:409-410.

Foulkes, E. C. 1956 Cation transport in yeast. J. Gen. Physiol. 39:687-704 cf. Biol. Absts. 31:2526 (1957).

Freeland, R. O. 1936 Effect of transpiration upon the absorption and distribution of mineral salts in plants. Amer. J. Bot. 23:355-362.

Freiberg, S. R. , Bollard, E. G. and Hegarty, M. P. 1957 The natural occurrence of urea and ureides in the soluble nitrogen of banana plant. Plant Physiol. 32 (Suppli.): lii.

Frey-Wyssling, A. 1929 Theorie des Blutens. Ber. Deutsch. Bot. Ges. 47: 434-450.

Fried, M. , Oberlander, H. E. and Noggle, J. C. 1961 Kinetics of rubidium absorption and translocation by barley. Plant Physiol. 36:183-191.

Fried, M. and Shapiro, R. E. 1961 Soil-plant relationships in ion uptake. Ann. Rev. Plant Physiol. 12:91-112.

Gardos, G. 1960 The function of calcium in the regulation of ion transport. In: Membrane Transport and Metabolism, A. Kleinzeller and A. Kotyk, Editors, Academic Press, New York, pp. 553-558.

Geisler, G. 1963 Morphogenetic influence of $(CO_2 + HCO_3^-)$ on roots. Plant Physiol. 38:77-80.

Glauser, R. and Jenny, H. 1960a Two-phase studies on availability of iron in calcareous soils. I. Alfalfa. Agrochimica 4:263-278.

Glauser, R. and Jenny, H. 1960b Two-phase studies on availability of iron in calcareous soils. III. Contact and exchange diffusion in ionic membranes. Agrochimica 5:1-9.

Goodall, D. W. and Gregory, F. G. 1947 Chemical composition of plants as an index of their nutrient status. Tech. Commun. 17, Imperial Bureau of Horticulture and Plantation Crops.

Goring, C. A. I. 1956 The nitrogen nutrition of plants. Down to Earth 11: 7-9.

Goss, J. A. and Romney, E. M. 1957 Effects of bicarbonate and some other anions on the shoot content of P^{32}, Ca^{45}, Fe^{59}, Rb^{86}, Sr^{90}, Ru^{106}, Cs^{137}, and Ce^{144} in bean and barley plants. Plant and Soil 10:233-241.

Gray, B. , Drake, M. and Colby, W. G. 1953 Potassium competition in grass-legume associations as a function of root cation exchange capacity. Soil Sci. Soc. Amer. Proc. 17:235-239.

Groenewegen, H. and Mills, J. A. 1960 Uptake of mannitol into the shoots of intact barley plants. Aust. J. Biol. Sci. 13:1-4.

Grossenbacher, K. A. 1938 Diurnal fluctuation in root pressure. Plant Physiol. 13:669-676.

Grossenbacher, K. A. 1939 Autonomic cycle of rate of exudation of plants. Amer. J. Bot. 26:107-109.

Grunes, D. L. and Jenny, H. 1960 Two-phase studies on availability of iron in calcareous soils. II. Decomposition of colloidal iron hydroxide by ion exchangers. Agrochimica 4:279-287.

Guinn, G. and Joham, H. E. 1962 Effects of two chelating agents on absorption and translocation of Fe, Cu, Mn, and Zn by the cotton plant. Soil Sci. 94:220-223.

Hagan, R. M. 1949 Autonomic diurnal cycles in the water relations of non-exuding detopped root systems. Plant Physiol. 24:441-454.

Hagen, C. E. , Leggett, J. E. and Jackson, Patricia C. 1957 The sites of orthophosphate uptake by barley roots. Proc. Nat'l Acad. Sci. U. S. 43: 496-506.

Hale, V. Q. and Wallace, A. 1962a Uptake by plants of Fe^{59} vs. C^{14}-chelating agents at different temperatures. In: A Decade of Synthetic Chelating

Agents in Inorganic Plant Nutrition. A. Wallace, Editor, Los Angeles 64, California, pp. 53-57.

Hale, V. Q. and Wallace, A. 1962b Effect of chelating agents and iron chelates on absorption of manganese by bush beans. In: A Decade of Synthetic Chelating Agents in Inorganic Plant Nutrition. A. Wallace, Editor, Los Angeles 64, California, pp. 21-25.

Hale, V. Q. , Wallace, A. and Jeffreys, R. A. 1962 Some metabolic inhibitor studies on uptake of FeEDDHA by plants. Ibid. pp. 41-43.

Harris, E. J. 1960 Transport and Accumulation in Biological Systems. Academic Press, New York, New York.

Harris, J. E. , Gruber, Louise and Hoskinson, Gertrude 1959 The effect of methylene blue and certain other dyes on cation transport and hydration of the rabbit lens. Amer. J. Ophthalmol. 47 (pt. 2): 387-395. cf. Chem. Absts. , 54:16489d (1960).

Hattori, A. 1958 Studies on the metabolism of urea and other nitrogenous compounds in Chlorella ellipsoidea. II. Changes on levels of amino acids and amides during the assimilation of ammonia and urea by nitrogen-starved cells. J. Biochem. (Japan) 45:57-64.

Hayes, A. D. and Rothstein, A. 1962 The metabolism of inhaled mercury vapor in rat studied by isotope techniques. J. Pharmacology Experimental Therapeutics 138:1-10.

Heintze, S. G. 1961 Studies of cation-exchange capacities of roots. Plant and Soil 13:365-383.

Helder, R. J. 1957 Influence of pretreating young barley plants with water and various solutions on subsequent absorption of labeled ribudium. I. , II. Koninkl. Ned. Akad. Wetenschap. Proc. , Ser. C. , 60:603-614, 615-629. cf. Chem. Absts. 52:8299c (1958).

Hemaidan, N. 1961 Unpublished data.

Hendler, R. W. 1959 Self-absorption correction for carbon-14. Sci. 130: 772-777.

Hewitt, E. J. 1952 Sand and water culture methods used in the study of plant nutrition. Commonwealth Agricultural Bureaux, East Malling, Maidstone, Kent, England, pp. 93-98.

Heytler, P. G. , Prichard, W. W. and Goldsby, R. A. 1962 Carbonyl cyanide phenylhydrazones — a new class of uncouplers of oxidative phosphorylation. Fed. Proc. 21:54.

Higinbotham, N. and Hanson, J. 1955 The relation of external rubidium concentration to amounts and rates of uptake by excised potato tuber tissue. Plant Physiol. 30:105-112.

Hinsvark, O. N. , Wittwer, S. H. and Tukey, H. B. 1953 The metabolism of foliar-applied urea. I. Relative rates of $C^{14}O_2$ production by certain vegetable plants treated with labeled urea. Plant Physiol. 28:70-76.

Hoagland, D. R. 1944 Inorganic Nutrition of Plants. Chronica Botanica Co. , Waltham, Mass. p. 129.

Hoagland, D. R. and Broyer, T. C. 1940 Hydrogen-ion effects and the accumulation of salt by barley roots as influenced by metabolism. Amer. J. Bot. 27:173-185.

Hoagland, D. R. and Broyer, T. C. 1942 Accumulation of salt and permeability in plant cells. J. Gen. Physiol. 25:865-880.

Hodges, T. K. ,and Vaadia, Y. 1962 Uptake and movement of chloride in plant roots. Plant Physiol. 37 (Suppli.): xi.

Hokin, L. E. and Hokin, M. R. 1960 Studies on the enzymatic mechanism of the sodium pump. In: Membrane Transport and Metabolism. A. Kleinzeller and A. Kotyk, Editors, Academic Press, New York, pp. 204-218.

Honda, S. I. and Robertson, R. N. 1956 Studies on the metabolism of plant

cells. XI. The Donnan equilibration and the ionic relations of plant mitochondria. Austr. J. Biol. Sci. 9:305-320.

Hopkins, H. T. 1956 Absorption of ionic species of orthophosphate by barley
roots: Effects of 2,4-dinitrophenol and oxygen tension. Plant Physiol. 31:
155-161.

Horie, K. 1957 Contribution to the foliar spray of urea. III. Absorption of
urea by radish leaves immersed in urea solution. Hyogo Noka Daigaku
Kenkyu Hokoku 3:50-54. cf. Chem Absts. 52:20831c (1958).

Huffaker, R. C. 1960 Dark fixation of CO_2 by cell-free homogenates from
bush bean roots. Ph. D. Thesis, University of California, Los Angeles.

Huffaker, R. C., Clark, R. B., Mueller, R. T. and Wallace, A. 1960 Relative importance of bicarbonate vs. carbon dioxide in reactions, including
$KHCO_3$ accumulation by bush beans. Soil Sci. 89:264-268.

Huffaker, R. C., Hall, D. O., Shannon, L. M., Wallace, A. and Rhoads, W.
A. 1959 Effects of iron and chelating agents on dark carboxylation reactions in plant homogenates. Plant Physiol. 34:446-449.

Huffaker, R. C. and Wallace, A. 1958 Possible relationships of cation-exchange capacity of plant roots to cation uptake. Soil Sci. Soc. Amer.
Proc. 22:392-394.

Huffaker, R. C. and Wallace, A. 1959a Sodium absorption by different plant
species at different potassium levels. Soil Sci. 87:130-134.

Huffaker, R. C. and Wallace, A. 1959b Effect of potassium and sodium levels
on sodium distribution in some plant species. Soil Sci. 88:80-82.

Huffaker, R. C. and Wallace, A. 1959c Variation in root cation-exchange
capacity within plant species. Agron. J. 51:120.

Humphries, E. C. 1951 The absorption of ions by excised root systems. II.
Observations on roots of barley grown in solutions deficient in phosphorus,
nitrogen or potassium. J. Expt. Bot. 2:344-379.

Humphries, E. C. 1952 The absorption of ions by excised root systems. III.
Observations on roots of pea plants grown in solutions deficient in phosphorus, nitrogen, or potassium. J. Expt. Bot. 3:291-309.

Hunter, A. S., Toth, S. J. and Bear, F. E. 1943 Calcium-potassium ratios
for alfalfa. Soil Sci. 55:61-72.

Hurd, R. G. 1958 The effect of pH and bicarbonate ions on the uptake of salts
by disks of red beet. J. Expt. Bot. 9:159-174.

Hurd, R. G. 1959 An effect of pH and bicarbonate on salt accumulation by
disks of storage tissue. J. Expt. Bot. 10:345-358.

Hylmo, Bertil 1953 Transpiration and ion absorption. Physiol. Plant. 6:333-
405.

Hylmo, Bertil 1955 Passive components in the ion absorption of the plant.
I. The zonal ion and water absorption in Brouwer's experiments. Physiol.
Plant. 8:433-449.

Hylmo, Bertil 1958 Passive components in the ion absorption of the plant.
II. The zonal water flow, ion passage and pore size in roots of Vicia faba.
Physiol. Plant. 11:382-400.

Iljin, W. S. 1951 Metabolism of plants affected with lime-induced chlorosis
(calciose). II. Organic acids and carbohydrates. Plant and Soil 3:339-351.

Impey, R. L. 1959 Studies on the foliar absorption of urea and the metabolism of biuret and urea in citrus. Ph. D. Thesis, University of California,
Los Angeles.

Ingold, C. T. 1935 Note on exudation and exudation pressures in birch. New
Phytol. 34:437-441.

Jackson, Patricia C. and Hagen, C. E. 1960 Products of orthophosphate
absorption by barley roots. Plant Physiol. 35:326-332.

Jackson, Patricia C., Hendricks, S. B. and Vasta, B. M. 1962 Phosphorylation by barley root mitochondria and phosphate absorption by barley roots. Plant Physiol. 37:8–17.

Jackson, W. A. 1957 Carbon dioxide fixation by plant roots and its influence on cation absorption. Ph. D. Thesis, North Carolina State College.

Jackson, W. A. and Coleman, N. T. 1959a Ion absorption by bean roots and organic acid changes brought about through CO_2 fixation. Soil Sci. 87:311–319.

Jackson, W. A. and Coleman, N. T. 1959b Fixation of carbon dioxide by plant roots through phosphoenolpyruvate carboxylase. Plant and Soil 11:1–16.

Jackson, W. A. and Evans, H. J. 1962 Effect of Ca supply on the development and composition of soybean seedlings. Soil Sci. 94:180–186.

Jacobs, M. H. 1924 Permeability of the cell to diffusing substances. In: General Cytology, E. V. Cowdry, Editor, University Chicago Press, Chicago, Illinois, pp. 97–164.

Jacobson, L. 1955 Carbon dioxide fixation and ion absorption in barley roots. Plant Physiol. 30:264–269.

Jacobson, L., Hannapel, R. J., Moore, D. P. and Schaedle, M. 1961 Influence of calcium on selectivity of ion absorption process. Plant Physiol. 36:58–61.

Jacobson, L., Hannapel, R. J., Schaedle, M. and Moore, D. P. 1961 Effect of root to solution ratio in ion absorption experiments. Plant Physiol. 36:62–65.

Jacobson, L., Moore, D. P. and Hannapel, R. J. 1960 Role of calcium in absorption of monovalent cations. Plant Physiol. 35:352–358.

Jacobson, L. and Ordin, L. 1954 Organic acid metabolism and ion absorption in roots. Plant Physiol. 29:70–75.

Jacobson, L., Overstreet, R., Carlson, R. M. and Chastain, J. A. 1957 The effect of pH and temperature on the absorption of potassium and bromide by barley roots. Plant Physiol. 32:658–662.

James, W. O. 1953 The use of respiratory inhibitors. Ann. Rev. Plant Physiol. 4:59–90.

James, W. O. and Baker, H. 1933 Sap pressure and the movements of sap. New Phytol. 32:317–343.

Jamison, V. C. 1942 Adsorption and fixation of copper in some sandy soils of Central Florida. Soil Sci. 53:287–297.

Jarnefelt, J. 1961 ATP-dependent binding of sodium by microsomes from brain. Biochem. Biophys. Res. Comm. 6:285–288.

Jeffreys, R. A. 1962 The absorption of Fe^{59} by potato discs—A preliminary discussion. In: A Decade of Synthetic Chelating Agents in Inorganic Plant Nutrition, A. Wallace, Editor, Los Angeles 64, California, pp. 92–98.

Jeffreys, R. A., Hale, V. Q. and Wallace, A. 1961 Uptake and translocation in plants of labeled iron and labeled chelating agents. Soil Sci. 92:268–273.

Jenny, H. and Grossenbacher, K. 1962 Root-soil boundary zones as seen by the electron microscope. Calif. Agric. 16:7.

Jensen, W. A. and McLaren, A. D. 1960 Uptake of proteins by plant cells—The possible occurrence of pinocytosis in plants. Exptl. Cell Res. 19:414–417.

Kahn, J. S. and Hanson, J. B. 1957 The effect of calcium on potassium accumulation in corn and soybean roots. Plant Physiol. 32:312–316.

Kihlman-Falk, Eva. 1961 Components in the uptake and transport of high accumulative ions in wheat. Physiol. Plant. 14:417–438.

Kleinzeller, A. and Kotyk, A., Editors 1960 Membrane Transport and Metabolism. Academic Press, New York.

Knauss, H. J. and Porter, J. W. 1954 The absorption of inorganic ions by Chlorella pyrenoidosa. Plant Physiol. 29:229–234.

Kramer, P. J. 1940 Root resistance as a cause of decreased water absorption by plants at low temperatures. Plant Physiol. 15:63-79.

Kramer, P. J. 1941 Soil moisture as a limiting factor for active absorption and root pressure. Amer. J. Bot. 28:446-451.

Kramer, P. J. 1949 Plant and Soil Water Relationships. McGraw-Hill Book Co. , Inc. , New York.

Kramer, P. J. 1956 The uptake of salts by plant cells. Encyclopedia Plant Physiol. 2:290-318. Ruhland, W. , Editor, Springer-verlag. , Berlin.

Kramer, P. J. 1957 Outer space in plants. Sci. 125:633-635.

Kroll, H. and Gordon, Maria 1960 The effect of structural modifications on polyamineacetic acid chelating agents. N. Y. Acad. Sci. 88:341-352.

Kuykendall, J. R. and Wallace, A. 1954 Absorption and hydrolysis of urea by detached citrus leaves immersed in urea solutions. Proc. Amer. Soc. Hort. Sci. 64:117-127.

Kylin, A. and Hylmo, B. 1957 Uptake and transport of sulphate in wheat. Active and passive components. Physiol. Plant. 10:467-484.

Lagerwerff, J. V. and Peech, M. 1961 Relation between exchange adsorption and accumulation of calcium and rubidium by excised barley roots. Soil Sci. 91:84-93.

Laine, T. 1934 On the absorption of electrolytes by the cut roots of plants and the chemistry of plant exudation sap. Acta Bot. Fennica 16.

Laties, G. G. 1949 The oxidative formation of succinate in higher plants. Arch. Biochem. 22:8-15.

Laties, G. G. 1959 Active transport of salt into plant tissue. Ann. Rev. Plant Physiol. 10:87-112.

LeCann, F. and Heller, R. 1961 Chelated calcium adsorption by roots. Compt. rend. 253:3038-3040.

Leggett, J. E. 1961 Entry of phosphate into yeast cell. Plant Physiol. 36: 277-284.

Letey, J. , Lunt, O. R. , Stolzy, L. H. and Szuszkiewicz, T. E. 1961 Plant growth, water use, and nutritional response to rhizosphere differentials of oxygen concentration. Soil Sci. Soc. Amer. Proc. 25:183-186.

Lineweaver, H. and Burk, D. 1934 The determination of enzyme dissociation constants. J. Amer. Chem. Soc. 56:658-666.

Lingle, J. C. , Tiffin, L. O. and Brown, J. C. 1963 Iron uptake-transport of soybeans as influenced by other cations. Plant Physiol. 38:71-76.

Lister, A. J. 1956 The kinetics of urease activity in Corynebacterium renale. J. Gen. Microbiol. 14:478-484.

Litvinov, L. S. and Gebhardt, A. G. 1928 Bleeding of steppe plants. Bull. Inst. Rech. Biol. Univ. Perm. 6:91-111. In Russian. cf. Biol. Absts. 3: 17877 (1929).

Litvinov, L. S. 1932 The criterion of estimation of soil moisture. J. Bot. URSS 17:451-473. cf. Biol. Absts. 11:6767 (1937).

Loomis, W. F. and Lipman, F. 1948 Reversible inhibition of the coupling between phosphorylation and oxidation. J. Biol. Chem. 173:807-808.

Lowry, M. W. and Tabor, P. 1931 Sap for analysis by bleeding corn plants. Sci. 73:453.

Lundegardh, H. 1944 Bleeding and sap movement. Arkiv För Bot. 31A:1-56.

Lundegardh, H. 1945 Absorption, transport and exudation of inorganic ions by the roots. Arkiv För Bot. 32A:1-139.

Lundegardh, H. 1949 Growth, bleeding, and salt absorption of wheat roots as influenced by substances which interfere with glycolosis and aerobic respiration. Ann. Agric. Coll. Sweden 16:339-371.

Lundegardh, H. 1950 The translocation of salts and water through wheat roots.

Physiol. Plant. 3:103-151.

Lundegardh, H. 1951 Leaf Analysis. (Translated from German by R. L. Mitchell.) Hilger and Watts, Ltd., London, p. 8.

Lundegardh, H. 1954 Anion respiration: The experimental basis of a theory of absorption, transport, and exudation of electrolytes by living cells and tissue. Symp. Soc. Expt. Biol. 8:262-296.

Lundegardh, H. 1955 Mechanisms of absorption, transport, accumulation, and secretion of ions. Ann. Rev. Plant Physiol. 6:1-24.

Lundegardh, H. 1958 Investigations on the mechanism of absorption and accumulation of salts 1. Initial absorption and continued accumulation of potassium chloride by wheat roots. Physiol. Plant. 11:332-346.

Lundegardh, H. and Burström, H. 1933 Untersuchungen über die Salzaufnahme der Phlanzen. III. Quantitative Beziehungen zwischen Atmung und Anionenaufnahme. Biochem. Z. 261:235-251.

Lunt, O. R., Oertli, J. J. and Kohl, H. C., Jr. 1960 Influence of environmental conditions on the salinity tolerance of several plant species. Proc. 7th International Congress of Soil Sci. 6:560-570.

MacDonald, I. R. and Laties, G. G. 1963 Kinetic studies of anion absorption by potato slices at $0^{\circ}C$. Plant Physiol. 38:38-44.

Martin, P. 1956 Qualitative and quantitative investigations on the excretion of organic compounds by the radicle of oats (Avena sativa). Naturwissenchaften 43:227-228. cf. Chem. Absts. 53:18190g (1959).

Maruyama, H. and Lane, M. D. 1962 Investigation of the mechanism of enzymatic carboxylation of phosphoenolpyruvate. Biochem. Biophys. Res. Comm. 9:461-465.

Mattson, S. 1948 Laws of ionic exchange: III. Donnan equilibria in plant nutrition. Ann. Agr. Royal Col. Sweden 15:308-316.

McDermott, J. J. 1945 The effect of the moisture content of the soil upon the rate of exudation. Amer. J. Bot. 32:570-574.

McLean, E. O. 1956 Uptake of sodium and other cations by five crop species. Soil Sci. 82:21-28.

McLean, E. O. 1957 Plant growth and uptake of nutrients as influenced by levels of nitrogen. Soil Sci. Soc. Amer. Proc. 21:219-222.

McLean, E. O., Adams, D. and Franklin, R. E., Jr. 1956 Cation exchange capacities of plant roots as related to their nitrogen contents. Soil Sci. Soc. Amer. Proc. 20:345-347.

Mengel, K. 1961 The Donnan distribution of cations in the free space of the plant root and its importance for active cation uptake. Z. Pflanzenernachr. Bueng. Bodenk. 95:240-253. cf. Chem. Absts. 57:17081i (1962).

Mertz, D. and Levitt, J. 1961 The relation between ion adsorption on the cell wall and active uptake. Physiol. Plant. 14:57-61.

Miller, E. C. 1938 Plant Physiology. McGraw-Hill Book Co., Inc., New York, pp. 642-653.

Miller, G. W. 1960 Carbon dioxide-bicarbonate absorption, accumulation, effects on various plant metabolic reactions, and possible relations to lime-induced chlorosis. Soil Sci. 89:241-245.

Minshall, W. H. 1961 The effect of nitrogen on root pressure and uptake of nutrient ions by tomato roots. Plant Physiol. 36 (Suppli.): xvi.

Mitsui, S. and Kurihara, K. 1957 The intake and utilization of carbon by plant roots from carbon-14-labeled urea. I. The determination of radioactive carbon of plant material and a preliminary seedling experiment utilizing carbon-14-labeled urea. Soil and Plant Food (Tokyo) 3:59-64. cf. Chem. Absts. 52:8301h (1958).

Mitsui, S. and Kurihara, K. 1959 Uptake and utilization of carbon by plant roots from urea-C^{14}. II. Comparison of the uptake of carbon from urea with that from carbonate by plant roots. Nippon Dojo-Hiryogaku Zasshi 30: 405-410. cf. Chem. Absts. 55:23897e (1961).

Mitsui, S. , Kumazawa, K. and Maesawa, T. 1962 Absorption, translocation and redistribution of chloride and sulfate ions in the bean plant. Nippon Dojo-Hiryogaku Zasshi 32:121-124. cf. Chem. Absts. 57:10229a (1961).

Moore, D. P. , Jacobson, L. and Overstreet, R. 1961 Uptake of calcium by excised barley roots. Plant Physiol. 36:53-57.

Morita, S. and Oaki, A. 1960 Nutrient uptake by the roots of fruit trees. I. Cation-exchange capacity of root and its cation adsorption from solution. Nippon Dojo-Hiryogaku Zasshi 31:234-236. cf. Chem.Absts. 57:6335h (1962).

Mueller, E. 1961 The physiology and biochemistry of urea in plants. Nova Acta Leopoldina 24:74. cf. Chem. Absts. 58:755e (1963).

Nelson, L. E. and Brady, N. C. 1953 Some greenhouse studies of cation interactions of Ladino clover using split root techniques. Soil Sci. Soc. Amer. Proc. 17:274-278.

Niel, James 1962 Personal communication, (U. C. L. A.).

Nightingale, G. T. 1948 The nitrogen nutrition of green plants. II. Bot. Rev. 14:185-221.

North, C. P. and Wallace, A. 1955 Soil temperature and citrus. Calif. Agric. 9:13.

Olsen, C. 1950 The significance of concentration for the rate of ion absorption by higher plants in water culture. Physiol.Plant. 3:152-164.

Olsen, C. 1953 The significance of concentration for the rate of ion absorption by higher plants in water culture. IV. The influence of hydrogen ion concentration. Physiol.Plant. 6:848-858.

Ordin, L. , Applewhite, T. H. and Bonner, J. 1951 Auxin-induced water uptake by Avena coleoptile sections. Plant Physiol. 31:44-53.

Ordin, L. and Jacobson, L. 1955 Inhibition of ion absorption and respiration in barley roots. Plant Physiol. 30:21-27.

Overstreet, R. and Jacobson, L. 1952 Mechanisms of ion absorption by roots. Ann. Rev. Plant Physiol. 3:189-206.

Overstreet, R. , Jacobson, L. and Handley, R. 1952 The effect of calcium on the absorption of potassium by barley roots. Plant Physiol. 27:583-590.

Overstreet, R. , Ruben, S. and Broyer, T. C. 1940 The absorption of bicarbonate ion by barley plants as indicated by studies with radioactive carbon. Proc. Nat'l Acad. Sci. , U. S. 26:688-695.

Parker, F. W. and Truog, E. 1920 The relation between the nitrogen content of plants and the function of calcium. Soil Sci. 10:49-56.

Pavlinova, E. 1926 Physiological significance of guttation. Bull. Inst. Rech. Biol. Univ. Perm. 4:471-478. cf. Biol. Absts. 3:5170 (1929).

Pearson, G. A. 1962 Sodium absorption and translocation by beans, peas, and cotton. Plant Physiol. 37 (Suppli.): x.

Peech, M. 1941 Availability of ions in light sandy soils as affected by soil reaction. Soil Sci. 51:473-486.

Poel, L. W. 1953 Carbon dioxide fixation by barley roots. J. Expt. Bot. 4:157-163.

Poel, L. W. and Graham, Janet S. D. 1956 Carbon dioxide fixation and mineral absorption in barley roots. Bull. des Fermentations, 4:1-3.

Post, R. L. and Albright, C. D. 1960 Membrane adenosine triphosphatase system as a part of a system for active sodium and potassium transport. In: Membrane Transport and Metabolism. A. Kleinzeller and A. Kotyk, Editors, Academic Press, New York, pp. 219-227.

Prevot, P. and Ollagnier, M. 1961 Diagnostic foliaire: relations reciproques de certains elements mineraux (arachide-palmier a huile-cocotier). Advances in Horticultural Science and their Applications 1:217-228.

Priestley, J. H. 1920 The mechanism of root pressure. New Phytol. 19: 189-200.

Priestley, J. H. and Armstead, Dorothy 1922 Physiological studies in plant anatomy. II. The physiological relation of the surrounding tissue to the xylem and its contents. New Phytol. 21:62-80.

Reifer, I. and Melville, J. 1949 The source of ammonia in plant tissue extracts. II. The influence of urea. J. Biol. Chem. 178:715-726.

Robertson, R. N. 1944 Studies in the metabolism of plant cells. 2. Effects of temperature on accumulation of potassium chloride and on respiration. Austral. J. Expt. Biol. Med. Sci. 22:237-245.

Robertson, R. N. 1951 Mechanism of absorption and transport of inorganic nutrients in plants. Ann. Rev. Plant Physiol. 2:1-24.

Robertson, R. N., Wilkins, M. J. and Weeks, D. C. 1951 Studies in the metabolism of plant cells. IX. The effects of 2,4-dinitrophenol on salt accumulation and salt respiration. Aust. J. Sci. Res. B. 4:248-264.

Rodney, D. R. 1952 The entrance of nitrogen compounds through the epidermis of apple leaves. Proc. Amer. Soc. Hort. Sci. 59:99-102.

Rothstein, A. 1960 Interrelationships between the ion transporting systems of the yeast cell. In: Membrane Transport and Metabolism, A. Kleinzeller and A. Kotyk, Editors, Academic Press, New York, pp. 270-284.

Rufelt, H. 1956 Influence of the root pressure on transpiration of wheat plants. Physiol. Plant. 9:154-164.

Russell, R. S. 1954 The relationship between metabolism and the accumulation of ions by plants. Symp. Soc. Expt. Biol. 8:343-366.

Russell, R. S. and Barber, D. A. 1960 The relationship between salt uptake and the absorption of water by intact plants. Ann. Rev. Plant Physiol. 11: 127-140.

Russell, R. S., Martin, R. P. and Bishop, O. N. 1953 A study of the absorption and utilization of phosphate by young barley plant. II. The effect of phosphate status and root metabolism on the distribution of absorbed phosphate between roots and shoots. J. Expt. Bot. 4:136-156.

Russell, R. S. and Shorrocks, V. M. 1959 The relationship between transpiration and the absorption of inorganic ions by intact plants. J. Expt. Bot. 10:301-316.

Salm-Horstmar, F. 1849 Versuche über die nothwendigen Aschenbestandtheile einer Pflanzen-Species. J. prakt. Chem. 1:2, 26, 102.

Sandström, B. 1950 The ion absorption in roots lacking epidermis. Physiol. Plant. 3:496-505.

Scott, Lorna I. and Priestley, J. H. 1928 The root as an absorbing organ. I. A reconsideration of the entry of water and salts into the absorbing region. New Phytol. 27:125-140.

Scofield, C. S. 1927 The effect of absorption by plants on the concentration of the soil solution. J. Agric. Res. 35:745-756.

Serry, A. and Eid, M. T. 1959 The effect of the hydrogen-ion concentration and mineral deficiency on the growth and chemical composition of Egyptian clover and wheat. Egypt, Min. Agr., Bull., 1959, p. 14. cf. Chem. Absts. 57:11573g.

Shardakov, V. S. 1928 The physiological significance of guttation. Bull. Inst. Rech. Biol. et Sta. Biol. Univ. Perm. 6:193-208. cf. Biol. Absts. 5: 10715 (1931).

Shear, C. B., Crane, H. L. and Myers, A. T. 1946 Nutrient-element balance: A fundamental concept in plant nutrition. Proc. Amer. Soc. Hort. Sci. 47:239-248.

Shear, C. B., Crane, H. L. and Myers, A. T. 1948 Nutrient-element balance: Application of the concept to the interpretation of foliar analysis.

Proc. Amer. Soc. Hort. Sci. 51:319-326.

Skou, F. C. 1960 The relationship of a (Mg^{2+} and Na^+)—activated, K^+ stimulated enzyme or enzyme system to the active, linked transport of Na^+ and K^+ across the cell membrane. In: Membrane Transport and Metabolism. A. Kleinzeller and A. Kotyk, Editors, Academic Press, New York, pp. 228-236.

Smith, P. F. 1962 Mineral analysis of plant tissues. Ann. Rev. Plant Physiol. 13:81-108.

Smith, P. F. , Rasmussen, G. K. and Hrnciar, G. 1962 Leaching studies with metal sulfates in light sandy citrus soil in Florida. Soil Sci. 94:235-238.

Smith, R. L. 1955 Factors influencing absorption and translocation of calcium and potassium by citrus and some other plant species. Ph. D. Dissertation, University of California, Los Angeles.

Smith, R. L. and Wallace, A. 1956a Cation-exchange capacity of roots and its relation to calcium and potassium contents of plants. Soil Sci. 81:97-109.

Smith, R. L. and Wallace, A. 1956b Influence of cation ratio, temperature, and time on adsorption and absorption of calcium and potassium by citrus and other plant species. Soil Sci. 82:9-19.

Smith, R. L. and Wallace, A. 1956c Influence of nitrogen fertilization, cation concentration, and root cation-exchange capacity on calcium and potassium uptake by plants. Soil Sci. 82:165-172.

Steward, F. C. and Pollard, J. K. 1956 A symposium of inorganic nitrogen metabolism. Johns Hopkins Press, Baltimore, Md. , pp. 377-407.

Steward, F. C. , Prevot, P. and Harrison, J. A. 1942 Absorption and accumulation of rubidium bromide by barley plants. Localization in the root of cation accumulation and of transfer to the shoot. Plant Physiol. 17:411-421.

Steward, F. C. and Sutcliffe, J. F. 1959 Plants in relation to inorganic salts. In: Plant Physiology II. Plants in Relation to Water and Solutes. F. C. Steward, Editor, Academic Press, New York, pp. 253-478.

Stewart, G. R. 1918 Effect of season and crop growth in modifying the soil extract. J. Agric. Res. 12:311-368.

Stocking, C. R. 1956 Guttation and bleeding. Encyclopedia Plant Physiol. Rutland, W. , Editor, Springer Verlag. , Berlin, 3:489-502.

Stoev, K. D. , Mamarov, P. T. and Benchev, I. B. 1959 The effect of fertilizer on the composition of the ascending stream in grape vines. Doklady Akad. Nauk S. S. S. R. (Bot. Sci. Sect.) Transl. 125(1/60):115-118 (1959). cf. Biol. Absts. 35:27517 (1960).

Stolwijk, J. A. J. and Thimann, K. V. 1957 On the uptake of carbon dioxide and bicarbonate by roots and its influences on growth. Plant Physiol. 32:513-520.

Sutcliffe, J. F. 1954 The exchangeability of potassium and bromide ions in cells of red beetroot tissue. J. Expt. Bot. 5:313-326.

Sutcliffe, J. F. 1959 Salt uptake in plants. Biol. Rev. 34:159-220.

Sutcliffe, J. F. 1962 Mineral Salts Absorption in Plants, Pergamon Press, New York.

Tanada, T. 1955 Effects of ultraviolet radiation and calcium and their interaction on salt absorption by excised mung bean roots. Plant Physiol. 30:221-225.

Tanada, T. 1961 Non-steady state kinetics of rubidium absorption by barley roots. Plant Physiol. 36(Suppli.): xxxv.

Tanada, T. 1962 Localization and mechanism of calcium stimulation of rubidium absorption in the mung bean root. Amer. J. Bot. 49:1068-1072.

Taylor, C. B. 1962 Cation-stimulation of an ATPase system from the intestinal mucosa of the guinea pig. Biochim. Biophys. Acta 60:437-440.

Thimann, K. V. , Loos, G. M. and Samuel, E. W.   1960 Penetration of mannitol in potato discs. Plant Physiol. 35:848-853.

Thomas, W. H. and Krauss, R. W.   1955 Nitrogen metabolism in Scenedesmus as affected by environmental changes. Plant Physiol. 30:113-122.

Tiffin, L. O. and Brown, J. C.   1959 Absorption of iron from chelate by sunflower roots. Sci. 130:274-275.

Tiffin, L. O. and Brown, J. C.   1961a Selective absorption of iron from iron
chelates by soybean plants. Plant Physiol. 36:710-714.

Tiffin, L. O. and Brown, J. C.   1961b Iron chelates in plant exudate. Plant
Physiol. 36(Suppli.): xiv.

Tosteson, D. C. and Hoffman, J. F.   1960 Regulation of cell volume by active cation transport in high and low potassium sheep red cells. J. Gen.
Physiol. 44:169-194.

Toth, S. J. , Prince, A. L. , Wallace, A. and Mikkelsen, D. S.   1948 Rapid
quantitative determination of eight mineral elements in plant tissue by a
systematic procedure involving use of a flame photometer. Soil Sci. 66:
459-466.

Trelease, S. F. and Trelease, Helen M.   1935 Changes in hydrogen-ion concentration of culture solutions containing nitrate and ammonium nitrogen.
Amer. J. Bot. 22:520-542.

Truog, E. , Goates, R. J. , Gerloff, G. C. and Berger, K. C.   1947 Magnesium-phosphorus relationships in plant nutrition. Soil Sci. 63:19-25.

Tukey, H. B. , Ticknor, R. L. , Hinsvark, O. N. and Wittwer, S. H.   1952
Absorption of nutrients by stems and branches of woody plants. Sci. 116:
167-168.

Ulrich, A.   1941 Metabolism of non-volatile organic acids in excised barley
roots as related to cation-anion balance during salt accumulation. Amer.
J. Bot. 28:526-537.

Ussing, H. H.   1949 The distinction by means of tracers between active
transport and diffusion. Acta Physiol. Scand. 19:43.

Ussing, H. H.   1957 General principles and theories of membrane transport .
In: Metabolic Aspects of Transport Across Cell Membranes, Q. R. Murphy,
Editor, University of Wisconsin Press, Madison.

Vaadia, Y.   1960 Autonomic diurnal fluctuations in rate of exudation and root
pressure of decapitated sunflower plants. Physiol. Plant. 13:701-717.

Vaadia, Y, , Raney, F. C. and Hodges, T. K.   1961 Dispersion of H^3 and
transport of Cl^{36} in topped sunflower and grapevine plants. Plant Physiol.
36 (Suppli.): xvi.

van Andel, O. M.   1952 Determinations of the osmotic value of exudation sap
by means of the thermo-electric method of Baldes and Johnson. K. Nederland, Akad. Wetenschap, Amsterdam. Proc. 55:40-48. cf. Biol. Absts.
28:11932 (1954).

Van der Merwe, A. J.   1952-1953 Nitrogen nutrition of citrus in the nitrate
and ammonium form. Union So. Africa Sci. Bull. No. 299.

van Die, J.   1959 Synthesis of carboxylic and amino acids in the roots and
their transport to aerial parts of the tomato plant. Koninkl. Ned. Akad.
Wetenschap. Proc. 62c:505-517. cf. Chem. Absts. 54:11159e (1960).

Van Itallie, T. B.   1938 Cation equlibria in plants in relation to the soil.
Soil Sci. 48:175-186.

van Nie, R., Helder, K. J. and Arisz, W. H.   1950 Ion-secretion into the xylem
and osmotic regulation of exudation. Proc. K. Nederland. Akad. Wetenschap, Amsterdam 53:567-575. cf. Biol. Absts. 25:2912 (1951).

van Overbeek, J.   1942 Water uptake by excised root systems of the tomato
due to non-osmotic forces. Amer. J. Bot. 29:677-683.

Vasington, F. D. and Murphy, J. V. 1962 Ca^{++} uptake by rat kidney mito-
    chondria and its dependence on respiration and phosphorylation. J. Biol.
    Chem. 237:2670-2677.

Vennesland, Birgit, Ceithaml, J. and Collub, Miriam 1947 The fixation of
    carbon dioxide in a plant tricarboxylic acid system. J. Biol. Chem. 171:
    445-446.

Viets, F. G. , Jr. 1944 Calcium and other polyvalent cations as accelerators
    of ion accumulation by excised barley roots. Plant Physiol. 19:466-480.

Voznesenskii, V. L. 1959 The absorption of carbon dioxide by plant roots.
    Plant Physiol. (Fiziologia Rastenii) 5:325-332.

Wadleigh, C. H. and Bower, C. A. 1950 The influence of calcium ion activ-
    ity in water cultures on the intake of cations by bean plants. Plant Physiol.
    25:1-12.

Walker, D. A. 1962 Pyruvate carboxylation and plant metabolism. Biol.
    Rev. 37:215-256.

Walker, J. B. 1952 Arginosuccinic acid from Chlorella. Proc. Nat'l Acad.
    Sci. , U.S. 38:561-566.

Wallace, A. 1949 A study of factors limiting yields and longevity of alfalfa
    in New Jersey. Ph. D. Thesis, Rutgers University, New Brunswick.

Wallace, A. 1951 Does potash fertilizer reduce protein content of alfalfa?
    Better Crops 33:20-22, 38-41.

Wallace, A. 1952 Influence of nutrient concentration on the growth and chem-
    ical composition of alfalfa. Agron. J. 44:57-60.

Wallace, A. 1953a General rules concerning plant nutrients. Better Crops
    37:21-24, 45-48.

Wallace, A. 1953b Nitrogen absorption and translocation by citrus cuttings
    at different root temperatures. Proc. Amer. Soc. Hort. Sci. 61:89-94.

Wallace, A. 1954 Ammonium and nitrate nitrogen absorption by citrus. Soil
    Sci. 78:89-94.

Wallace, A. 1957 Influence of soil temperature on cation uptake in barley and
    soybeans. Soil Sci. 83:407-411.

Wallace, A. 1960 Cation exchange and its possible effects in plant nutrition.
    Tree Physiology Studies at U. C. L A. , Special Report No. 2, A. Wallace,
    Editor, pp. 15-23.

Wallace, A. 1962 A Decade of Synthetic Chelating Agents in Inorganic Plant
    Nutrition. A. Wallace, Editor, Los Angeles 64, California.

Wallace, A. 1962a Chelate-metal-chelate binding of importance in soil-plant
    relationships. Ibid. pp. 14-20.

Wallace, A. 1962b Chelation in heavy-metal induced iron chlorosis. Ibid.
    pp. 25-28.

Wallace, A. 1962c Growth effects of chelating agents. Ibid. pp. 117-119.

Wallace, A. 1963 Review of chelation in plant nutrition. J. Agric. and Food
    Chem. 11:103-107.

Wallace, A. and Ashcroft, R. T. 1956a Correlation of phosphorus and mag-
    nesium contents of plants grown in synthetic ion-exchange resins. Agron.
    J. 48:219-222.

Wallace, A. and Ashcroft, R. T. 1956b Preliminary comparisons of the
    effects of urea and other nitrogen sources on the mineral composition of
    rough lemon and bean plants. Proc. Amer. Soc. Hort. Sci. 68:227-233.

Wallace, A. and Bear, F. E. 1949 Influence of potassium and boron on nutri-
    ent-element balance in and growth of Ranger alfalfa. Plant Physiol. 24:
    664-680.

Wallace, A. and Bhan, K. C. 1962 Plants that do poorly in acid soils. In:
    A Decade of Synthetic Chelating Agents in Inorganic Plant Nutrition. A.
    Wallace, Editor, Los Angeles 64, California, pp. 36-38.

Wallace, A. and Hale, V. Q. 1962a A hypothesis of the cause of lime-induced chlorosis. In: A Decade of Synthetic Chelating Agents in Inorganic Plant Nutrition. A. Wallace, Editor, Los Angeles 64, California, pp. 28-35.

Wallace, A. and Hale, V. Q. 1962b Do chelating agents penetrate plant cells? Ibid. pp. 57-62.

Wallace, A., Hale, V. Q., Krohn, E. J. and Wallace, G. A. 1962 Effect of chelating agents on cation accumulation by bush bean. Ibid. pp. 43-50.

Wallace, A. and Jeffreys, R. A. 1962 Preliminary studies on the effect of concentration of FeEDDHA on iron uptake by potato discs. Ibid. pp. 50-53.

Wallace, A., Kimball, M. H., Mueller, R. T. and Welch, H. V., Jr. 1952 Influence of nitrogen fertilizers on orange trees and on the soil in the coastal zone of Southern California. Proc. Amer. Soc. Hort. Sci. 59:22-30.

Wallace, A. and Mueller, R. T. 1957 Ammonium and nitrate nitrogen absorption from sand culture by rough lemon cuttings. Proc. Amer. Soc. Hort. Sci. 69:183-188.

Wallace, A. and Mueller, R. T. 1958 Further studies concerning girdling and cutting the xylem on absorption and translocation of nitrogen in small citrus trees. In: Tree Physiology Studies at U. C. L. A., Special Report No. 1, A. Wallace, Editor, pp. 139-143.

Wallace, A. and Mueller, R. T. 1962a Effect of calcium level on uptake of Fe^{59} from FeEDDHA by bush beans. In: A Decade of Synthetic Chelating Agents in Inorganic Plant Nutrition, A. Wallace, Editor, Los Angeles 64, California, pp. 87-88.

Wallace, A. and Mueller, R. T. 1962b Influence of EDTA and calcium on rubidium accumulation. Ibid. pp. 98-99.

Wallace, A., Mueller, R. T. and van Noort, D. 1962 Effect of chelating agents on in vitro CO_2-fixing enzyme systems. Ibid. pp. 75-82.

Wallace, A., Naude, C. J., Mueller, R. T. and Zidan, Z. I. 1952 The rootstock-scion indluence on the inorganic composition of citrus. Proc. Amer. Soc. Hort. Sci. 59:133-142.

Wallace, A., Sufi, S. M. and Jeffreys, R. A. 1962 The stem-exudate as an index of solute uptake by plants. Plant Physiol. 37(Suppli.): xlvii.

Wallace, A., Toth, S. J. and Bear, F. E. 1948a Further evidence supporting cation-equivalent constancy in alfalfa. J. Amer. Soc. Agron. 40:80-87.

Wallace, A., Toth, S. J. and Bear, F. E. 1948b Sodium content of some New Jersey plants. Soil Sci. 65:249-258.

Wallace, A., Toth, S. J. and Bear, F. E. 1948c Influence of sodium on growth and composition of Ranger alfalfa. Soil Sci. 65:477-486.

Wallace, A., Toth, S. J. and Bear, F. E. 1949 Cation and anion relationships in plants with special reference to seasonal variations in the mineral content of alfalfa. Agron. J. 41:66-71.

Wallace, A., Zidan, Z. I., Mueller, R. T. and North C. P. 1954 Translocation of nitrogen in citrus trees. Proc. Amer. Soc. Hort. Sci. 64:87-104.

Wanner, H. 1948a Untersuchungen uber die temperaturabhangigkeit der salzsufnahme durch pflanzenwurzeln: I. Die relative grosse der tempersturkoeffizienten (Q_{10}) von kationen-und anionen-aufnahme. Ber. Schweiz. Botan. Ges. 58:123-130.

Wanner, H. 1948b Untersuchungen uber die temperaturabhangigkeit der salzsufnahme durch pflanzenwurzeln: II. Die temperaturkoeffizienten von kationenund anionen-aufnahme in abhangigkeit von der salzkonzentration. Ibid. pp. 383-390.

Webster, G. C. 1959 Nitrogen Metabolism in Plants. Row-Peterson Biological Monographs, Evanston, Ill.

Webster, G. C., Varner, J. E. and Gansa, A. N. 1955 Conversion of carbon-14-labeled urea into amino acids in leaves. Plant Physiol. 30:372-374.

Weeks, D. C. and Robertson, R. N. 1950 Studies in the metabolism of plant cells. VIII. Dependence of salt accumulation and salt respiration upon the cytochrome system. Austral. J. Sci. Res. B. 3:487.

Weissbach, A., Horecker, B. L. and Hurwitz, J. 1956 The enzymatic formation of phosphoglyceric acid from ribulose diphosphate and carbon dioxide. J. Biol. Chem. 218:795-810.

Weissman, G. S. 1950 Growth and nitrogen absorption of wheat seedlings as influenced by the ammonium: nitrate ratio and the hydrogen-ion concentration. Amer. J. Bot. 37:725-738.

Welch, H. V., Jr., Wallace, A. and Mueller, R. T. 1954 Influence of factorially combined levels of cations and nitrate ions adsorbed on ion-exchange resins on the nutrient absorption by plants. Soil Sci. Soc. Amer. Proc. 18:137-140.

Went, F. W. 1944 Plant growth under controlled conditions. III. Correlation between various physiological processes and growth in the tomato plant. Amer. J. Bot. 31:597-618.

White, P. R. 1938 "Root Pressure" — An unappreciated force in sap movement. Amer. J. Bot. 25:223-227.

Wiebe, H. H. and Kramer, P. J. 1954 Translocation of radioactive isotopes from various regions of barley seedlings. Plant Physiol. 29:342-348.

Wilbrandt, W. and Rosenberg, T. 1961 The concept of carrier transport and its corollaries in pharmacology. Pharmacol. Rev. 13:109-183.

Winter, H. 1961 The uptake of cations by Vallisneria leaves. Acta Bot. Neer. 10:341-393.

Woodham, R. C. 1956 The chloride status of the irrigated Sultana vine and its relation to vine health. Austral. J. Agric. Res. 7:414-427.

Wynd, F. L. 1950 The use of iron-containing frit as a new medium for hydroponic cultures. Mich. Agr. Expt. Sta. Quart. Bull. 33:52-53.

Zerahn, K. 1960 Active sodium transport across the isolated frog skin in relation to metabolism. In: Membrane Transport and Metabolism. A. Kleinzeller and A. Kotyk, Editors, Academic Press, New York, pp. 237-246.

After this report was completed the following reviews and papers of various aspects of the subject of inorganic plant nutrition were seen:

Bange, G. G. J. and Van Gemerden, H. 1963 The initial phase of ion uptake by plant roots. Plant and Soil 18:85-98.

Epstein, E. 1962 Mutual effects of ions in their absorption by plants. Agrochimica 6:293-322.

Jackson, P. C. and Adams, H. R. 1963 Cation-anion balance during potassium and sodium absorption by barley roots. J. Gen. Physiol. 46:369-386.

Leggett, J. E., Olsen, R. A. and Spanlger, B. D. 1962 Cation absorption by bakers' yeast as a passive process. Proc. Nat'l Acad. Sci. U. S. 48: 1949-1956.

Russell, R. S. 1962 Some aspects of plant nutrition. IV Simposio Internazionale di Agrochimica, Pisa-Firenze 9-14 Aprile 1962, pp. 27-50.

Waisel, Y. 1962 Effect of calcium on the uptake of monovalent ions by excised barley roots. Physiol. Plant. 15:709-724.

Handley, R. and Overstreet, R. 1963 Uptake of strontium by roots of Zea Mays. Plant Physiol. 38:180-184.